THE
POX

THE LIFE AND NEAR DEATH
OF A VERY SOCIAL DISEASE

KEVIN BROWN

SUTTON PUBLISHING

To Jackie and Iain Grace

First published in the United Kingdom in 2006 by
Sutton Publishing Limited · Phoenix Mill
Thrupp · Stroud · Gloucestershire · GL5 2BU

British Library Cataloguing in Publication Data
A catalogue record for this book is available from the British Library.

ISBN 0-7509-4041-7

Typeset in 11/14.5pt Sabon.
Typesetting and origination by
Sutton Publishing Limited.
Printed and bound in England by
J.H. Haynes & Co. Ltd, Sparkford.

Contents

List of Illustrations

Preface and Acknowledgements

'Know syphilis in all its manifestations and relations, and all other things clinical will be added unto you,' wrote William Osler, the doyen of medical humanism.[1] It might equally be claimed that to know something of the history of syphilis, popularly referred to as 'the pox', since it first burst with all its horror on the consciousness of Western Europe in the late fifteenth century is to learn something about the history of modern medicine. This book is the history, covering over five centuries, of a disease that evokes in most people a certain frisson of fascinated horror. No disease is pleasant, but those that are sexually transmitted are also generally seen as shameful and smutty, not to be talked about in polite society but rather the subject of a furtive, almost forbidden, interest. Sex, violent death and toilets always arouse a prurient interest from school students upwards, and the story of the pox certainly contains all these elements to grab the attention. Even in an age that sees itself as liberated from the sexual prudishness of years gone by, there is still a notion of sinfulness about syphilis. In that lies a great deal of the fascination of a subject that tells us as much about shifting notions of social and individual virtue and the interaction between disease and morality as it does about the history of medicine. Its story is grounded in the social history of its times and in the varied responses of mankind to the unknown, to changing moral certainties and to the darker side of sexuality. Syphilis is a disease that has certainly had a dramatic impact upon mankind, and the story of how sufferers have come to terms with it and how doctors and reformers have fought against it is a gripping one.

What can often be forgotten when syphilis and other sexually transmitted diseases are regarded from a moralistic standpoint is

v

that these are bacterial infections like any others. The difference lies in the way that they are transmitted and it is this that colours perceptions of them. The fact that they are so unpleasant in their symptoms also evokes a fascinated horror, with which such infections can be perceived as somehow worse than other illnesses.

Syphilis was commonly known as 'the pox'. This has led to popular confusion with other 'poxes' with which it has no connection, other than that all the infections are noted for nasty skin eruptions. It is in no way related to smallpox, chickenpox or cowpox. All these infections got their names from the pustules or 'pocks' that marked the skin of their sufferers. By far the most dreaded of these infections, syphilis, was often referred to as 'the great pox' (though popularly shortened to 'the pox') to distinguish it from other skin eruptions and diseases. It may not have been the first disease to inflict pock marks on its victims, but it was the most feared and thus the 'great' one.

The anti-hero or villain of this book, whichever way it may have been regarded throughout its long history, is syphilis, but a supporting role is played by gonorrhoea, popularly known as the clap, the dose or strain. For a long time, it was believed that this very different infection was merely the first stage of syphilis, and that it might or might not develop into a full-blown pox, depending on the luck of the sufferer. It was not until 1879 that the bacterium that causes it, *Neisseria gonorrhoea*, was first identified and only then was it realised that they were two distinct diseases. Inevitably, their stories must be told together.

It is almost a given that any history of sexually transmitted infections should have some contemporary relevance and resonance. For the late twentieth century, AIDS was the new syphilis, a frightening disease when it first appeared. The story of HIV and AIDS, though recent, is a big one, and any full treatment of it is outside the scope of this book, which concentrates on syphilis from its first appearance in Western Europe to the present day when it has enjoyed a resurgence.

It is all too easy to look for and find victims of syphilis in historical figures. A whole industry seems to have developed in outing such victims and diagnosing them from their medical symptoms and their behaviour.[2] However, the situation is not as simple as that. Until the development of a reliable test, the Wassermann reaction, in 1905, there was no sure way of diagnosing syphilis. Depending merely on recorded medical symptoms could be misleading, as they could be equally applicable to syphilis or to some other disease. Before the twentieth century, it was 'almost impossible to describe its clinical symptoms without mentioning almost every symptom of every disease known'.[3] Perhaps more important is people's attitude to the loathesome disease when they believed that they or others had it. Identifying people diagnosed with syphilis once there was an accurate test for it also had its difficulties, since the stigma still attached to the disease meant that it was often hushed up both by the victims and by their families. The confidentiality of medical records also means that the evidence will invariably remain elusive as to whether any prominent figure has actually suffered from the disease. It does not stop people speculating, but that may be as far as such surmises can ever go.

It has also been argued that a history of syphilis covering more than half a millennium is impossible because what is understood by the disease has changed over time. Also, the terminology for it has altered radically; all we can be sure of is that we are studying the cultural connotations and construction of an illness at any one time.[4] Such an approach has some validity in encouraging the questioning of what an illness is and in challenging the idea of any absolute certainties, but important in the study of history is an appreciation of change. Syphilis has changed in its manifestations over time and the bacteria causing it have evolved, just as surely as perceptions of the disease have altered. Both its changing character and how it has been perceived are the proper objects of this study. It is often difficult to be absolutely certain that the same disease is meant by sixteenth-century terminology and descriptions compared with our understanding of them in the twenty-first century. However, it is possible to make an educated and informed retrospective diagnosis that equates the French Disease, the Italian Disease and the pox with each other and with modern syphilis, especially when the symptoms are so similar and the textual evidence can be supplemented with that from ancient bones that show the marks of something similar to the modern effects of syphilis.

My own interest in the history of syphilis and the issues it raises began when I was asked to give a special Christmas lecture in 1999 to staff of the Jefferiss Wing at St Mary's Hospital, Paddington, on the history of the treatment of sexually transmissible diseases (STD) in their department. Like most STD clinics, the Jefferiss Wing is a Cinderella service within the National Health Service serving a large clientele close to a mainline London railway station. In the years since then, I have been invited back to give regular lectures to new staff on the history of the speciality in which they are working. This gives them a context that they might not otherwise get in the midst of their busy workload. I am grateful to them for their patience in listening to my views, and to those members of staff who have come back and heard me speak many years running. By their very nature, these talks were intended to be more entertaining than most clinical presentations, but also to give insights into current issues. In return I have been grateful for the insights that these current practitioners, whether doctors, nurses, social workers or administrative staff, have given me into their work. Their dedication, enthusiasm and cheerfulness stand out, though they do not always get the appreciation they deserve. Among them I must particularly single out Sarah Gill, who gave up her time to discuss with me the current resurgence in sexually transmissible infections and the issues facing specialists in that area today.

As always, I owe a debt of gratitude to a number of other friends and colleagues for their interest, support and suggestions. Tudor Allen, Neil Handley, Katy Goff and Tony Rippon have been assiduous 'pox hunters' of eminent syphilitics, drawing my attention to people who may have had the disease. Visits to museums and art galleries with friends have certainly been enlivened by the search for signs of syphilis in portraits. Other visitors must have wondered at the nature of some of the conversations they may have overheard. Maria Lorentzon has again happily offered her translation skills over a bottle of wine or two. Bill Frankland shared his memories of working as a newly qualified doctor in a special clinic in the 1930s. Michael Wolach passed on anecdotes of doctors he knew in his youth in pre-war Poland, though socially, not as their patient. Per Lundqvist drew my attention to Swedish references. I am grateful to Simon Chaplin, senior curator at the Royal College of Surgeons and an expert on John Hunter, who suggested some sources for the study of Hunter's probable self-inoculation with syphilis. Briony Hudson and Peter Homan of the Museum of the Royal Pharmaceutical Society of Great Britain have been of great assistance with the sourcing of pharmaceutical material.

There are a number of people in Frankfurt I wish to thank for their help and hospitality during my research trip there. At the Paul Ehrlich Institut at Langen, just outside Frankfurt, I wish to thank Suzanne Stöcker, head of press and public relations, for giving me access to the Paul Ehrlich Museum and allowing me the freedom to explore its wonderful resources. I am grateful to Dr Bernd Groner, director of the Georg-Speyer Haus, for allowing me access to the laboratory in which Ehrlich developed salvarsan, the first effective modern treatment for syphilis, and to its archives, as well as for the time he spent discussing my project with me during my visit. My thanks also go to Christine Kost of the Georg-Speyer Haus for facilitating my visit. At the Städel art gallery, I must thank Michael Maeck-Gerard, curator of baroque art, for allowing me to see Luca Giordano's *Allegory of Youth Tempted by the Vices*, with its figure of syphilis, and for supplying me with some references to it in art journals. The massive Giordano painting was in storage and I will not forget the search through the basement storerooms of the Städel for it, nor squeezing between it and other canvases to view it intimately and closer up than I might have done had it been on display.

I am grateful to Craig Hendrix of Johns Hopkins University Medical School, Baltimore, for inviting me to lecture there and introducing me to a number of his colleagues with an interest in the history of sexually transmitted diseases, particularly Jonathan Zenilman and John Ticehurst, who in turn recommended to me other useful leads. On the same visit to the United States, after lecturing at the Lyceum, Alexandria, on Alexander Fleming and Scotland at a National Tartan Day event, I was sent some references on the history of syphilis and AIDS by one of the audience, Lesli Rothwell of Massachusetts, in one of those serendipitous occasions when someone offered unexpected information at the unlikeliest of events.

It would be pleasant if all the necessary information could be gleaned from social interaction, but much of the research for this book has been conducted in dusty archives and libraries, although there was something magical about reading Fracastoro's poem on syphilis in Verona and Padua, and at Lake Garda, the places that inspired him. As for scholarly institutions, I would like to thank the helpful staff of the Wellcome Institute, the British Library, The National Archives, Kew (formerly the Public Records Office), the Bodleian Library, the Library of Congress, the National Academy of Sciences in Washington DC, the National Library of Medicine at the National Institute of Health, Bethesda, Maryland, and the National Archives and Records Service of the United States.

I am grateful to staff at the Museo La Specola in Florence, especially front-of-house attendants, for admitting an insistent latecomer to see the wax anatomical models when they clearly would have preferred to close; in particular, they must have been a bit alarmed at his avowed interest in seeing Gaetano Zumbo's *Morbus Gallicus*, which is reproduced in this book with the kind permission of photographer Saulo Bambi. They must have wondered even more when I eagerly returned to see that wax tableau on syphilis a second time the following day. I am sure that they and other curators of medical museums accepted that my interest was professional rather than stemming from some weird and morbid curiosity about diseased sexuality.

Finally, at Sutton Publishing, I wish to thank, as ever, Jaqueline Mitchell and her team: Hilary Walford, Jane Entrican and Elizabeth Teague.

London
December 2005

ONE

The Wrath of Apollo

It was an age in turmoil, a time when the excitement of the new was such that it seemed to those living through it to be a time of fundamental change for mankind. In Renaissance Italy there was a brilliant burst of achievement in scholarship, literature, architecture, sculpture and painting that accompanied a rediscovery of the splendours of classical antiquity and the appreciation of the capabilities of the individual. In the quest for the fabled wealth of the Indies, a New World had been discovered and an era of exploration initiated that was to expand the horizons of the Old World, albeit at the expense of older, if previously unknown cultures. Knowledge was opened up and resources and diseases exchanged. Yet, even as a golden age seemingly dawned, there were troubles ahead. Italy, cradle of the rebirth of the arts, became a battleground for foreign powers seeking supremacy, and from the smoke of battle came a fearful new disease destined to wreak havoc, cause great personal suffering and upturn long-established ideas in medicine and society.[1]

The invasion of Italy by Charles VIII of France in 1494 in pursuit of his claims to the throne of Naples initiated thirty-six fruitless years of campaigning for supremacy in the Italian peninsula that changed very little politically except for the acquisition by Spain of the Duchy of Milan and the Kingdom of Naples and Sicily. For Italy, these were indeed years of woe, heralded by a succession of natural disasters such as floods, severe snowstorms, famine and outbreaks of pestilent disease.[2] Foremost among these disasters was a new and frightening disease that was to be the scourge not only of Italy for an age but of the entire world for centuries to come. The earliest written reports of it followed the battle of Fornovo on 6 July 1495.

1

Marcello Cumano, a military doctor serving with the Venetian troops, wrote:

> Several men-at-arms or foot soldiers, owing to the ferment of the humours, had pustules on their faces and all over their bodies. These looked rather like grains of millet and usually appeared on the outer surface of the foreskin or on the glans, accompanied by a mild pruritis. Sometimes the first sign would be a single pustule looking like a painless cyst, but the scratching provoked by the pruritis subsequently produced a gnawing ulceration. Some days later, the sufferers were driven to distraction by the pains they experienced in their arms, legs and feet, and by an eruption of enormous pustules which lasted . . . for a year and more if left untreated.[3]

This new disease among the soldiers fighting at Fornovo was also observed by another doctor from the Veneto serving as chief surgeon to the Italian armies massed against Charles VIII. Alessandro Benedetti, 45-year-old Professor of Medicine at the University of Padua, was a humanist physician and epidemiologist convinced of the importance of naturalistic observation as the basis of all medical progress.[4] He was quick not only to record the repulsive symptoms but also to establish how this new disease was transmitted from person to person:

> Through sexual contact, an ailment which is new, or at least unknown to previous doctors, the French sickness, has worked its way in from the West to this spot as I write. The entire body is so repulsive to look at and the suffering so great, especially at night, that this sickness is even more horrifying than incurable leprosy or elephantiasis, and it can be fatal.

It is remarkable that the sexual nature of the disease should have been apparent so early after it first caught the attention of the medical profession. However, it was not only in soldiers that Benedetti had investigated the effects of the disease. He had also performed an autopsy on a woman suffering from it and observed that her bones were tumorous and suppurated to the very marrow, even though the membrane covering her bone was still intact.[6] Moreover, licentiousness and marauding soldiers went hand in hand; the disease had first been observed the previous year among French troops at the siege of Naples, where they had come into intimate contact not only with their own camp-followers but also with the Neapolitan prostitutes who had plied their trade with mercenaries from all over Europe recruited for defence against the invaders. Former Florentine ambassador to Spain and adviser to three popes, Francesco Guicciardini wrote in 1537 in his magisterial history of Italy in his own lifetime that at 'those very times when it seemed destined that the woes of Italy should have begun with the passage of the French . . . was the same period when there first appeared that malady which the French called the Neapolitan disease and the Italians commonly called either the boils or the French disease'.[7]

This new disease was what we now know as venereal syphilis. It is caused by the corkscrew-shaped spirochaete *Treponema pallidum*, a bacterium not discovered until 1905.[8] It is passed on primarily by sexual intercourse, but can also be transferred by infected mothers to foetuses during pregnancy. As a disease, it has three very distinct stages: primary, secondary and tertiary syphilis, separated by latent periods with no visible symptoms. Primary syphilis usually appears between a fortnight and a month after infection. It is characterised by the development of a chancre, a small, firm, hard-edged but painless ulcer, on the genitals where it has entered the body. If it is left untreated this primary lesion will usually heal spontaneously within a few weeks. Buboes, swellings of the lymph glands, can also appear. In women, this primary stage may go undetected if the chancre has formed inside the body, and the disease is revealed only in the secondary stage. However, syphilis is at its most infectious during the primary stage.[9]

If early syphilis has been left untreated, most sufferers will go on to the secondary stage after the spirochaete has spread through the body. Extensive but painless skin rashes develop all over the body, often accompanied by fever, headaches, a general exhaustion and aching bones. There may also be patchy hair loss or alopecia, resulting in an almost moth-eaten appearance to the scalp. Then, after a few weeks these secondary lesions and symptoms disappear in their turn. Sometimes these symptoms will recur after a latent period. Both the latent and secondary periods remain infectious.

Tertiary syphilis develops only in roughly one-third of untreated cases after a further latent period of anywhere between 12 months and 20 years. It progressively destroys the skin, mucous membranes, bones and internal organs, inflicting the greatest horrors on its victims. Gumma, a small rubbery, benign tumour, can develop anywhere in the body. The attack on the bones can cause small depressions where the tumours have been or eat away the bone entirely, producing especially horrific mutilations when the nasal and palate bones have been destroyed. Meanwhile, late syphilis can also attack the cardiovascular and central nervous system. Cardiovascular syphilis may weaken the walls of the aorta, causing aneurysms (balloon-like swellings of the artery wall), which may sooner or later burst, with fatal results. Neurosyphilis can take a number of forms. With *tabes dorsalis* (a form of neurosyphilis that progressively destroys the sensory nerves), the destruction of the nerve cells in the spinal cord produces a stumbling gait and very poor coordination in its victims. Paresis or general paralysis of the insane is caused by a general softening of the brain resulting in a form of insanity often linked with a form of creative genius but actually more destructive in its effects. Such an array of symptoms led the physician and medical humanist William Osler to dub it 'the great imitator' in the early twentieth century and explains why deaths from tertiary syphilis might be ascribed variously to heart disease, insanity or meningitis.[10] Since the introduction of antibiotics, tertiary syphilis has virtually disappeared, but it was once a great killer. Yet, even if they correctly diagnosed the cause of death, doctors often put on the death certificate the more socially acceptable disease that the symptoms resembled, prompting Osler to comment wryly that 'men do not die of the diseases that afflict them'.[11]

One manifestation of syphilis that has all but disappeared in the Western world since the 1960s is congenital syphilis, although it can still be found in underdeveloped countries. This is transmitted to the foetus during pregnancy by an infected mother. Children unfortunate enough to be born with the affliction bore the stigmata of shame. Often they would be small in stature because their skeletons were underdeveloped. Generally they could be recognised by their 'family appearance' of flat faces with saddle-noses. Sometimes the septum (partition) of their noses and their palates would be eaten away by gumma. Linear scars radiated from their noses and mouths, and the wrinkling of their skin gave an 'old-man look', whatever age they may actually have been. Patchy hair loss and a skin discoloration that gave them a 'café-au-lait' tinge were further signs of the disease. Most characteristic of all were notched and peg-shaped Hutchinson's teeth.[12] Such were the manifestations of syphilis that now struck Europe with terrible effect.

The pox may have first erupted into public consciousness in Naples, but it had its origins elsewhere. It had been noticed that some of the Spanish soldiers defending Naples against the French had accompanied Columbus on his second voyage. The Spanish mercenaries had withdrawn before the arrival of the French, but not before they had had the opportunity to sleep with local prostitutes. That this was the origin of the pox was proposed by Fernandez de Oviedo in 1525, and the theory was supported in 1539 by Ruy Diaz de Isla, who had attended Columbus's crew in March 1493 when he reported his discoveries in the New World to Ferdinand and Isabella, the Catholic Kings, at Barcelona. These pox-stricken sailors had originally thought that their disease was merely the effect of the hardships of their voyage, but had then spread it among the inhabitants of Barcelona, who responded with prayers and fasting in an attempt to avert the malady. The mercenaries had subsequently taken it to Naples. Diaz de Isla identified it with the Serpent in the Eden of the newly discovered demi-paradise of Hispaniola, now better known as Haiti, and named it the serpentine disease because, 'as the serpent is abominable, terrifying and horrible, so is this disease'.[13] Although other sixteenth-century physicians denied that the disease was new to Europe and tried to link it with elephantiasis and leprosy in the classical writings of Hippocrates and Galen, the idea that the disease had been imported from the Americas became dominant, especially as it could be depicted as evidence of a decay or weakness in the New World that might justify its conquest and colonisation by the European powers. The theory depended on the coincidence of the date of Columbus's return from his second voyage with the first great European epidemic of syphilis. Spanish sailors had undoubtedly raped Indian women, and there were frequent allusions to sickness and exhaustion of his sailors in Columbus's own accounts of his voyages, but no conclusive evidence as to the nature of that illness.[14] In the twentieth century, this explanation of the origin of syphilis was given new prominence with the idea of the Columban Exchange: syphilis was the only serious disease to be transmitted from the New to the Old World, whereas the Europeans had brought with them to the Americas many pathogens to which the indigenous population had no immunity. By contrast, the Amerindians experienced much milder cases of syphilis than the Europeans, since they had immunity to that disease.[15]

Indeed, the medical lore of the indigenous cultures of Central and South America was well aware of syphilis-like diseases. Mayan medical texts had terms for gonorrhoea (*kazay*), syphilitic sores (*yaah*) and buboes (*zali*). Meanwhile the Aztecs had several gods concerned with venereal diseases. Titlacahuan, Tezcatlipoca, Macullxochital (god of pleasure) and Xochiquetzal (goddess of love) all punished any breach of vows or unchaste behaviour with an infliction of nasty diseases affecting the genitals of their victims.[16] This would suggest that the disease was already familiar in these parts of the New World when the conquistadores arrived.

There was a certain symmetry and indeed justice to the idea of the Columban Exchange, but the notion has not gone unchallenged. Some European skeletons from before 1493 have been excavated that showed such signs of syphilitic infection as star-shaped scars on the skull and traces of inflammation in the bones.[17] If syphilis was already present in Europe, its apparently sudden appearance in the 1490s could be accounted for only by a great increase in the virulence of the infection by a mutation of the bacterium, *Treponema pallidum*, causing it. This theory was based on the idea that a non-venereal syphilitic infection known as yaws may have originated in Central Africa. It had spread east and north from the earliest times, its dispersal encouraged by slave trading, reaching first Egypt and then Mesopotamia, where it was called *bejel*. It had then spread into Europe by the eighth century, when the Crusades had encouraged travel and made the slave trade from Africa more popular. The discovery in the nineteenth century of a number of yaws-like diseases in poor, remote, backward rural areas on the fringes of Europe, such as spirocolon in Greece and Bosnia, button scurvy in Ireland, radesgye in Norway and sibbens in Scotland, showed that yaws-like infections were indeed present in Europe, transmitted by social contact and commonest in children. If such relatively benign treponemal diseases were already present in Europe, their survival was threatened from the fourteenth century onwards by greater attention to personal hygiene and the use of soap. The theory is that, in order to survive, the bacteria mutated into a more infectious and lethal organism spread by sexual contact rather than by touch.[18] Another plausible explanation was that treponemal infections native to Europe had combined with others imported from overseas, such as non-venereal yaws, which the Portuguese may have brought from Africa as a result of their voyages of discovery in the half-century before Columbus set out on his voyages, and that this combination proved more potent and devastating than the two infections had ever been singly.[19] Thomas Sydenham, a seventeenth-century physician, actually blamed the slave trade, 'that barbarous custom of changing men for ware', for the introduction into Europe of what he called 'the contagion of the Blacks bought in Africa'.[20] However, the evidence still remains strongest for an American origin for syphilis. The indications of the presence of the disease in medieval Europe remain inconclusive, because signs of syphilis in skeletons are difficult to distinguish from damage caused by other diseases such as leprosy. Moreover, relatively few European skeletons show signs of syphilis before 1492 compared with later, although many more indications are found in skeletons in the Americas from the pre-Columban era.[21]

Although the pox in the form it took in the late fifteenth century was new in Europe, sexually transmitted diseases were nothing unusual. Gonorrhoea, which was believed by many people before the nineteenth century to be the first stage of syphilis, had been a problem since antiquity. Like the bacterium that causes syphilis, the gonococcus is primarily spread through sexual contact. In men, its most common symptom is white or yellowish milky pus discharging from the penis, accompanied by pain when urinating. However, some men may be infected and show no symptoms, although asymptomatic infection is more common in women, who otherwise suffer from vaginal discharges and infection of the uterine cervix. In the past, because fewer women than men displayed any symptoms, it was commonly believed to be a less serious disease for women. In fact, it can destroy the female reproductive organs.[22] William Osler described it as 'not a great destroyer of life' but 'the greatest known preventer of life'.[23]

In Egypt the Ebers papyrus of *c.* 1550 BC mentioned herbal extracts as treatment to soothe painful urination, the result of what may possibly have been gonorrhoeal infections. Another medical text from ancient Egypt, the Kahun papyrus, describes what may be a gonococcal infection that had caused a woman to suffer a discharge from her vagina and given her problems with her eyes.[24] The biblical book of Leviticus advised the children of Israel to avoid contact with any man or woman who 'hath a running issue' and to cleanse themselves by bathing and washing their clothes if they came in to contact with anyone 'unclean'.[25] Hippocrates and Galen, the prime authorities of classical medicine, recognised the venereal nature of the disease.[26] In medieval England, gonorrhoea was referred to as 'the brennynge' or 'the burning', a name reflecting the symptom of painful and sometimes bloody urination that afflicted sufferers. The French term for the disease, *chaude pisse* ('hot piss'), was just as descriptive. Polite society in England preferred to call the disease by its French name until the sixteenth century, when all classes began to call it 'the clap'. John Aderne, physician to Richard II, recommended syringing a lead lotion into the urethra to relieve the burning sensation. Although actually a very different disease, syphilis when it first made its appearance was sometimes described in the same way as gonorrhoea as 'the burning'.[27]

Stricken with the seemingly novel illness of the pox, whatever its origins, Charles VIII of France and his army of mercenaries were forced to retreat from Naples and withdraw from Italy. In the wake of their passage across northern Italy, they left a terrible trail of victims afflicted by this frightening new epidemic. An outbreak was recorded in Cremona in 1495.[28] The notary Bernadino Zambotti reported its first appearance in Ferrara in December 1496 with the observation that it seemed to be incurable and for most of the sufferers proved fatal, following excruciating pains in the bones and nerves, accompanied by massive pustules all over the body.[29] These pains in the joints could be so intense, according to Sigismondo dei Conti da Foligno, secretary to Pope Julius II, that sufferers from them 'screamed day and night without respite, envying the very dead'.[30] The pustules and ulcers 'gnawed away as far as the marrow'.[31] In Perugia, a merchant was 'so consumed by the disease between the thigh and the torso that it was possible to see everything that he had inside his body'.[32] In Bologna, the pox 'ate away the nose and half the face' of another of its victims.[33]

Very soon this virulent disease had spread across the Alps with the disbandment of the French army and its bands of mercenaries. By 1496 its symptoms were being reported in France, Switzerland, Germany and Holland, a year later it had reached both England and Scotland, and by 1499 it was noted east of Prague in Hungary, Poland and Russia. It was taken to India in 1498 by the crews of sailors on Vasco da Gama's voyage that left Lisbon in July 1498. Early on an association was made between the spread of the pox and disbanded soldiers. The Swiss artist Niklaus Manuel in a painting of 1517 depicted Death in the tattered remnants of a soldier's uniform fingering the genitalia of a young woman.[34]

Yet there was also a measure of displacement of responsibility as nation after nation named the disease after enemy countries. The Italians called it the 'Spanish' or the 'French Disease'. The French, in turn, referred to it as the 'Pox of Naples'. In Japan, to which it had been brought in 1569, as indeed also to Africa and India, by

Portuguese explorers it was known as *manakabassam* or the 'Portuguese Sickness'. Later, the Tahitians in the eighteenth century called it *Apna no Britannia*, the British disease, to the chagrin of Captain James Cook, who thought that it was not his men who were to blame for spreading it to Tahiti but that it was the fault of the French.[35] To the Turks, it was simply the 'Christian Disease'.[36]

One of the early victims to have left a personal account of his sufferings was the Christian cleric Tommaso di Silvestro, a canon of Orvieto Cathedral. The symptoms first appeared at Christmas 1496, when he was afflicted with pains in his knees, followed in January by even greater pains at the top of his left shoulder and in his kidneys and buttocks. By May these symptoms had cleared up, only to return a year later.[37] In April 1498 he was suffering pains in his penis, and his head was covered with scabs, while his arms ached so much that 'I could never find rest'. The treatment at this stage of his affliction began with blood letting. He was confined to his bed for six days and then 'washed with a bath of wine and many herbs, such as bitter infusions, rue, mint, rosemary, mulberry, sage and other herbs'. Only then was he allowed to go outside his house, but he was left with an ulcerated mouth that proved so sore that he could hardly bear to eat bread. After a fortnight the pains in his arm and the pustules disappeared, but his mouth still remained painful and he was to suffer 'a great flux . . . from which I could have died'. A period of remission from his illness then occurred, only for a recurrence of the symptoms to begin in November 1498.[38] Tommaso di Silvestro continued to keep his diary for a further fifteen years without mentioning his symptoms again, so it is likely that he was one of those lucky enough to recover.

Most contemporary doctors, on the other hand, were sceptical of any effective treatment for this new disease. Luca Landucci, a Florentine apothecary, regretted that it was impossible to find any medicines that could treat it.[39] Fileno dale Tutte of Bologna and Sigismondo dei Conti da Foligno were equally pessimistic in the belief that the remedies, ointments and drugs of the physicians, doctors and apothecaries had no effect and that no one knew how to produce a cure.[40] This view of the incurability of the disease was shared by the majority of the physicians at the papal court faced with all too many clerical cases of it, although Gaspar Torella, physician to Pope Alexander VI, did not share the pessimism of most of his colleagues, an attitude that could only augment his prestige as someone confident of success in tending his patients.[41] Jacopo Cattaneo of Genoa was even more optimistic in claiming that, if treated early enough, the disease could be cured, although he admitted that relapses were common.[42]

It was the very strangeness of the disease and its sudden appearance that perplexed the doctors and made them despair of finding a cure. No one knew what had caused it or where it had come from. Seemingly the disease had appeared in Naples from nowhere, yet there must be an explanation for it. While there were also anti-Semitic suggestions that its progress had followed the diaspora of the Jews following their expulsion from Spain in 1492, Francis Bacon later reported rumours that it was the result of 'certain wicked merchants that barrelled up man's flesh of some that had been lately slain in Barbary and sold it for tunney', noting that cannibalism and the pox seemed to go alongside each other in the West Indies.[43] Most people, however, associated it with other sins of the flesh. Not surprisingly, the disease, which was soon linked with sexual contact and sin, was seized on by moralists as a divine punishment for the licentiousness of the age. In the apocalyptic preaching of the Florentine Dominican friar Girolamo Savonarola, the signs of God's displeasure and of the Last Days included the French invasion of Italy and the pox, twin calamities that reinforced his calls for radical moral and political reform in the name of God. The expulsion of the Medici from Florence in 1494 gave Savonarola predominance in the new Florentine Republic, which he saw as the 'New Jerusalem'; yet his 1497 'bonfire of the vanities', a collective act of expiation, merely foreshadowed his own burning at the stake in 1498.[44] Nevertheless, for many the pox remained a chastisement for sin. John Calvin in Geneva pronounced that 'God has raised up new diseases against debauchery'.[45] That sin was not merely sexual. At the Diet of Worms in 1521, the French pox became a symbol of the corruption of the Church of Rome and was denounced more as divine retribution for blasphemy than for licentiousness.[46]

Humanist scholars looked for an astrological cause of the scourge afflicting mankind, described by 23-year-old Joseph Grünpeck, later to be court historian to the Emperor Maximilian, as 'a disease so cruel, so distressing, so appalling that until now nothing so horrifying, nothing more terrible or disgusting has ever been known on this earth'. He had himself caught the pox at an entertainment organised by his fellow humanist Celtis and had no shame in publishing an account of his own symptoms in his attempt to understand the disease, even though his first attempts to conceal his illness from his friends had been unsuccessful and had resulted in them shunning him: he had an ulcerated penis and scrotum, pustule-covered body and putrid-smelling ulcers.[47] His metaphor for the disease was of a weapon hurled at mankind by the gods of the classical pantheon. This was reflected in Christian iconography in the frontispiece to his book, which showed the infant Jesus throwing thunderbolts at women, seen here as the main transmitters of the disease, while a prostrate male victim lay before them covered in deadly pustules. Meanwhile the Virgin Mary was shown rewarding a suppliant monarch.[48] Grünpeck was suspicious of doctors and their inability to cure or understand his illness. His own explanation of the origin of the French Disease was based on the belief from classical Arabic astrology that the 'Great Conjunction' of Saturn and Jupiter foreshadowed changes in kingdoms and brought on natural disasters by causing a corruption of the air, which could be prevented from affecting mankind only by the lighting of aromatic fires containing myrrh, white frankincense and juniper berries. This fateful conjunction of the stars had taken place at four minutes past six on the evening of 25 November 1484 at a time when Mars was at an unfavourable aspect in its own house. The combined evil forces of Mars, a hot and dry planet associated with war and sharp, acute disease, and Saturn, cold and dry and predisposed towards chronic diseases, were enough to overcome the benign influences of Jupiter. Although this happened ten years before the advent of the pox, the astrological event was followed by pestilences, wars,

12

famines and finally syphilis, which had the sharpness of an acute disease linked with Mars and the duration of a chronic disease influenced by Saturn. The first places and people to be affected by the new disease were those most susceptible to the influences of the planets that had caused the problem.[49] This explanation was accepted by Albrecht Dürer in a woodcut of 1496 depicting the syphilitic, a pox-stricken aristocrat covered with sinister pustules, standing below the zodiac, on which is inscribed the dreaded date 1484. Such an astrological explanation was popular in humanist circles when Grünpeck published his book in 1496, but in that very same year the leading humanist scholar of the age, Giovanni Pico della Mirandola, argued that the freedom of the human spirit was not restricted by the stars but rather owed its range to supreme providence.[50] As a result of Pico della Mirandola's ideas, many doctors downplayed the role of astrology in their conception of the pox, though not the role of religion.

If the disease was to be seen in moralistic terms, the practical response to it was equally moralistic, though clearly dictated by a rising sense of panic and fear. Some observers had from the start of the epidemic made the connection between it and sexual activity, such as Marin Sanudo of Venice and Giovanni Portoveneri of Pisa, who noticed that 'it is spread through having sex with women who have these sicknesses, especially prostitutes'.[51] Since the early commentators on the new illness were men, women were unjustly seen as the cause of the disease rather than as its victims, while men were most often assumed to be the victims rather than the contaminators. Others believed that it could be caught from sharing a bed, using the same bathwater or even from kissing.[52] Henry VIII was said to have caught it from a kiss from Cardinal Wolsey.[53] The canons of the Duomo in Florence feared that they might catch the pox from communicants and even demanded a separate cupboard for chasubles, chalices and liturgical vestments used in public.[54]

Panic evoked varied responses. In northern France, syphilitics were driven from the towns. When the pox first appeared in Paris in the autumn of 1496, the Hôtel-Dieu, the city's hospital, was besieged by pox-sufferers who were turned away for fear that they may have had a form of leprosy that might be caught by innocent people. The response of the Paris *parlement* was to issue a decree giving sufferers twenty-four hours in which either to confine themselves to their own homes or to accept expulsion from the city, the penalty for non-compliance with the edict being hanging. Such decrees were periodically renewed until the early years of the sixteenth century, when the illness had become so common that it was no longer viable even to consider such draconian measures.[55] In Scotland, the town council of Aberdeen issued an order on 21 April 1497 forbidding prostitution on pain of being branded on the cheek, and on 22 September 1497 the town council of Edinburgh passed a 'Grandgore Act' banishing all syphilitics and also anyone claiming to be able to cure the infection to the barren island of Inchkeith in the Firth of Forth.[56] Throughout Europe, anxiety about the spread of the pox led to a tightening of control over places in which sexual freedom could spread the disease. In some parts of Europe innkeepers were banned from accepting as guests travellers displaying any sign of the dreaded disease. Elsewhere there was a decline in the late medieval practice of communal bathing since bathhouses were seen as breeding grounds of syphilis; in France and Southern Germany bathhouses were compulsorily closed.[57] When Montaigne visited the spa at Plombières in eastern France in 1580, the regulations were strict in excluding anyone showing signs of plague or syphilis, and prostitutes, who were forbidden to come nearer the baths than one hundred paces.[58]

If bathhouses were dangerous places, even more so were the brothels with which many of them were associated, and these too were not exempt from suppression. In 1500 Gaspar Torella suggested that 'the Pope, the Emperor, kings and other lords should send matrons to investigate the disease, especially among prostitutes, who if they are found to be infected, should be confined to a place designated for the purpose . . . and treated by a physician or surgeon paid to do so'.[59] Martin Luther also called for the closure of licensed brothels in 1520.[60] Yet only slowly were initiatives taken to control or attempt to suppress prostitution. The bishops of Winchester had since the early Middle Ages derived a substantial income from the

Bankside brothels, known colloquially as 'Winchester stews', under their jurisdiction and close to the episcopal palace in Southwark. So notorious were the prostitutes of the stews that the term 'Winchester Goose' became a widely used euphemism for syphilis. In Shakespeare's *Troilus and Cressida*, Pandarus expresses his fear that 'Some galled goose of Winchester would hiss: | Till then I'll sweat and seek about for eases, | And at that time bequeathe you my diseases.'[61] Indeed, it has even been suggested that there are sexual overtones to the popular nursery rhyme 'Goosey, Goosey, Gander'.[62] Whatever the origins of the children's verse, the links between the licensed brothels of the Bishop of Winchester's stews and the spread of syphilis were so apparent that in 1506 Henry VII took action to close them, but only for a short time.[63] It was left to his son Henry VIII, fresh from the suppression of religious houses, finally to close them in 1546 in an attempt to extirpate 'their abominable and detestable sin . . . as not only provoke instantly the anger and wrath of Almighty God, but also engender such corruption among the people as tendeth to the intolerable annoyance of the Commonwealth'.[64] Paris followed, with the closure of its brothels in 1561, and the popes attempted to eradicate prostitution in Rome in 1555 and 1556.[65] Vice was not suppressed but merely driven away from any regulation.

Official attempts to control the epidemic were perhaps more prophylactic than therapeutic in aim, but there remained a need to do something to treat the poorer sufferers from the disease and thus prevent it from becoming a threat to the social order. Poor victims were an eyesore and a public nuisance, begging in the streets. Their smell was not only offensive but also might be considered a threat to their social betters at a time when some people thought that foul airs could spread disease. In Florence, Piero di Marco Parenti complained that 'this putrefaction stank and was a most awful filth'.[66] In papal Rome, syphilitics were rounded up and compulsorily hospitalised because they polluted the atmosphere.[67] Nevertheless, the impetus for the foundation of hospitals for sufferers from the pox, the *incurabili* hospitals in Italy, was often private charity rather than an official response to the problem.

In Italy the initiative came from religious fraternities such as the Oratories and Confraternities of the Divine Love operating in urban centres. This movement had begun in Genoa in 1497 with the foundation of the Company of Divine Love by a layman, Ettore Vernazza, who had been influenced by the noble-born mystic Caterina Adorna, dedicated to the twin principles of celebrating individual faith through the Eucharist and providing charitable aid for the sick. A refuge for the sick was established by Vernazza and his colleagues in 1497, and inevitably many of their patients were syphilis-sufferers. The movement spread throughout the towns of northern Italy, and alongside the religious impulse came the foundation of hospitals for the *incurabili*, the chronically sick among whom pox victims loomed large, culminating in the foundation of the Oratory of the Divine Love in Rome in 1517.[68] Two years earlier in 1515 the hospital of San Giacomo had been founded in Rome with a moralistic and reformatory atmosphere. Patients were forbidden from swearing, playing games, making a noise and, above all, displaying the 'dishonest parts of the body'. Even Camilo de Lellis, who, after being treated for the pox, contracted during military service, went on to found a nursing religious order, the Ministri degli Infirmi, dedicated solely to the service of the sick, was expelled for his addiction to card playing.[69] Other Counter-Reformation religious orders were active in treating the *incurabili*. The constitution of the Jesuits indeed laid down the requirement for a novice to spend a month of his training in a hospital, usually the Spedale di San Giacomo in Augusta in Rome. In 1537, the founder of the order, Ignatius Loyola himself, had nursed in the Spedale degli Incurabili in Venice, founded in 1522 and later famed both for its buildings designed by Sansovino and for the girls' choir of its attached orphanage. The Capuchin Order was founded in 1528 in a small house close to the Spedale di San Giacomo, and the monks cleaned the wards and nursed the sick in hospitals for incurables in Rome, Naples and Genoa.[70]

One group of victims of the new disease who could not be morally blamed for their affliction were children. Not only were babies being born who had been infected in the womb, but horror stories were also abroad of diseased wet-nurses infecting innocent children with the pox. The sixteenth-century London surgeon William Clowes warned of the dangers in the 'corrupt milk' of 'lewd and filthy nurses'. He cited the example of three children born in the same parish of the City of London who had been sent out to different wet-nurses at about the same time. After six months all three children had returned to their parents, 'miserably spoiled and consumed with extreme pains and great breaking out upon their bodies, and being so young, sick and weak, impossible to be weaned'. Their desperate parents did everything they could to care for them and 'ere those children could be cured, they had infected five sundry good and honest nurses'.[71] For the honest nurses, their health, reputations and livelihood were at stake. The dangers of passing on infection provoked criticism of the widespread employment of wet-nurses, although the practice continued despite the risks.

Sufferers from the pox also acquired their own patron saint to whom they could pray for relief. The Old Testament patriarch Job was seen as an innocent suffering from an undeserved grief, as many of the sufferers from syphilis also considered themselves to be afflicted through little fault of their own. Job had already been adopted as the patron saint of sufferers from worms, leprosy, skin diseases, melancholy and plague and, despite being born before Christianity, had been canonised.[72] Pox, which was identified with the mysterious disease inflicted upon him by God, was rapidly added to his expanding portfolio of ailments.[73] In Bologna, the religious confraternity of Santa Marina dei Guarini and its hospital were formally rededicated to St Giobbe in the early sixteenth century because the hospital now specialised in treating victims of the pox, who would otherwise have been reduced to wandering the streets as outcasts, forbidden even the relief of other hospitals.[74] If intercession to St Job failed to work, the syphilis-sufferer had three other patrons saints who might be better able to help: St George, the warrior patron saint of England, had already given his protection to lepers and sufferers from other skin diseases, so it made sense for him to be recruited to slay the new dragon of the pox; St Fiacre, a seventh-century hermit, had been noted in his lifetime for his gift of healing and was considered particularly effective against fevers; the martyred St Symphorian of Autun, a patron of students and children, was also considered effective against eye problems.

Protestant countries might be able to forgo the intercession of St Job and the other saints, but could not ignore the problem of the pox. As elsewhere, there was a prejudice against admitting such noticeable sinners to the wards of a general hospital, yet there was a need to accommodate them rather than leave them to pollute the streets. At St Bartholomew's Hospital in London, a quarter of the patients giving gratuities to the surgeons in 1547–8 had been diagnosed as suffering from syphilis. However, these patients were segregated in a separate ward with their own nurses, clothing and mattresses. At one time, the hospital needed twenty extra mattresses to cope with the demand from syphilitic patients and prevent contamination of others. A sweating ward, known as a 'stothouse', was set up where patients could be encouraged to sweat the infection from their bodies. Yet separate wards were not enough to accommodate this group of patients, and at St Bartholomew's it proved necessary to accommodate some syphilitics in houses leased to tenants of the hospital. There was also a solution to the accommodation problem to be found in the now empty lazar houses, originally established to house lepers but now eminently suitable for the segregation of their successors, the poxed. In London, former lazar houses attached to the medieval hospitals refounded after the Reformation, St Bartholomew's, St Thomas's and Christ's Hospitals, were turned into refuges for the new outcasts.[75] Such hospitals had originally been founded in the twelfth and thirteenth centuries for the segregation of lepers, but the decline of leprosy after 1350 had made them redundant. For the surviving lazar houses, syphilis gave them a new use. Many of these hospitals were known as lock hospitals, deriving their names from the enclosures in which the lepers had been confined, although it has also been suggested that 'lokes' may have been the rags in which these unfortunates were dressed.[76]

The pox not only posed an institutional problem, but also challenged the medical profession to find new responses and forge new ideas about the very nature of medicine. Renaissance medical theory and practice continued to be based on the ideas of the Greek Hippocrates, the Roman Galen and the Arab Avicenna, especially the idea that disease was the result of an imbalance of the four humours in the human body. It was believed that the world was made up of the four elements of earth, air, fire and water. In the human body these were paralleled by the four humours, each of which was characterised by paired qualities: the blood was hot and dry; red or yellow bile was hot and dry, black bile or melancholy was cold and dry; and phlegm was wet and cold. In the healthy body the humours were in proportion to each other, but, if this balance were to break down, disease would result. A poor health regime and bad diet or an innate weakness could make the individual susceptible to disease, which was seen as particular to the individual rather than something that could affect large groups of people simultaneously and in similar ways.[77] Physicians brought up on this Galenic model of medicine attempted to fit the new disease into the familiar pattern. Konrad Schellig, physician to Philip, Elector of the Palatinate, argued that the contagious pustules characteristic of the French Disease were the result of the excessive heating and putrefaction of the humours, especially black bile, which could be cured by a moderate diet of bland foods to reduce the excessive production of the humours and by abstention from sex to conserve the strength of the patient.[78]

Many traditionally trained doctors were unable to accept that the pox could be a new disease. For them, the medicine of the ancient world was the ultimate authority; if a disease had not been described by Hippocrates or Galen, it could not exist at all. Nicolo Leoniceno, a teacher of medicine at the universities of Ferrara and Bologna, influenced by the Greek scholars who had fled to Italy after the fall of Constantinople to the Turks in 1453, believed that it was only by applying the principles of classical medicine that disease could be fought. If a disease could not be named and a description of it not found in the classical texts, it would be wrongly treated and the patient might be harmed. He went so far as to aver that, 'When I see that men are endowed with the same nature, born under the same heavens and brought up under the same stars, I tend to think that they have always been subject to the same diseases, and my mind is unable to comprehend that this scourge, so suddenly appearing, has infected only our age and never earlier times.'[79] For him, the pox belonged within the group of diseases caused by a warm and humid intemperance of the air, very frequent in summer, as described by Hippocrates.[80] The genitals were more exposed to putrefaction because they were naturally hot and moist and thus more sensitive to changes in the air.[81] Other doctors believed that the pox was similar to the dermatological disease elephantiasis as described by Galen and Pliny the Elder, characterised by a swelling of the limbs and thickening of the skin.[82]

If the disease could be categorised according to traditional ideas, then it could be treated accordingly. However, the use of bleeding, the customary means of drawing out the corrupted humours, proved ineffective, and other means of expelling this morbid matter from the body had to be found. Ointments and baths of wine and herbs were employed to draw out the poisons. Sometimes olive oil was used as an alternative to bathing in wine and herbs. In 1498, the Health Board of Venice forbade the resale of 'wretched oils . . . of a very bad quality in which people who have or have had the *Mal Francese* have been immersed, for as a result of these bodies being in these oils there has been a great deal of filth, scabs and dirt'.[83]

Heat was seen as being particularly useful for driving the corruption from the body. Sores would be cauterised and attempts made to induce sweating through the use of dry stoves. A wine barrel big enough for a patient to sit in was heated up with hot stones placed in a bed of sand at the bottom of the tub. The patient was then seated on a large perforated seat placed in the barrel, which was further enclosed within a framework covered by a cloth to retain the heat, and left to sweat for as long as he could stand the high temperatures. This treatment continued twice a day for between three days and a week and throughout it the unfortunate patient was denied food in case it allowed noxious odours to build up.[84]

Diet was also considered important once the patient was ready to begin eating again. William Clowes, surgeon at St Bartholomew's

Hospital, forbade the eating of pork, salty meats, geese, ducks, fish, cheese, raw fruits and sweet wines by anyone wishing to be cured of syphilis. Instead he prescribed what he considered to be more easily digestible foods, such as mutton, veal, lamb, kid, hares, chicken, capons, hens, partridges and pheasants.[85]

So far the treatments for the disease were based on principles of medicine that had been developed in classical Greece, refined in ancient Rome and transmitted through the Middle Ages. However, the voyages of discovery to the Americas brought forth a new treatment that was felt to be appropriate to a disease that may have originated there, and was regarded as a sign that God provided remedies where He also inflicted suffering. Holy wood or guaiacum was the wonder cure of the early sixteenth century that rapidly became fashionable throughout Europe. This dark hard wood originally came from Isola Beata off the coast of Hispaniola and was later considered from its supposed healing qualities to have been the holy tree from which the Cross on which Jesus had been crucified was made. Portuguese sufferers, believing themselves to have been cured by the wood, called it *lignum sanctum* or holy wood and hung it in their churches in thanksgiving. Relics of the True Cross had traditionally been associated with miracles, so it was little surprise that the wood should also be looked on as miraculous, although its cures were crucially seen as also being dependent upon the person who had been cured leading a holier life of chastity and abstinence thereafter. The wood was prepared by being ground to very fine sawdust and then soaked in eight times its weight of water. This water was boiled and reduced to half its volume. The scum was removed and dried to provide a powder to be used on the sores. The remaining liquid was then boiled a second time and the patient, after having first been purged and starved to remove any morbid matter in the body, would drink the resultant decoction twice daily before being made to sweat, covered in blankets, in a heated room.[86]

One of the greatest proponents of guaiacum was the Protestant reformer Ulrich von Hutten, who with Luther was condemned in the first papal bull against those attempting to reform the Church. Von Hutten's reforming zeal was directed not only against the ecclesiastical authorities but also against the medical establishment. Guaiacum appealed to him precisely because it was new and untainted by associations with Galen and the hated university-trained physicians. He saw it as an empirical remedy from an unspoilt land that had no doctors, no medical aphorisms and no canons of medical theory and practice, one whose effectiveness indeed highlighted the inability of conventional medicine to deal with a new disease, although the sweating induced was actually in line with contemporary medical ideas about expelling the humours.[87] A zeal for reform may have inspired von Hutten, but he also had a personal motive for writing about the benefits of guaiacum, since the conventional approaches of the doctors had been useless in treating his own case of syphilis. Instead, he relied upon guaiacum as the most effective remedy for the pox and one that every patient could obtain for himself without the need for the ministrations of a physician. This refusal to accept the professional mystique of the doctor paralleled his rejection of the authority of the priest as an intercessor in matters of faith. Like the Saxon peasant who cured all his ills by drinking hot buttered beer, von Hutten thought the simplest remedies, and those provided by God, like guaiacum, to be the best. Yet, at the same time, he believed that there was a conspiracy to boost profits and reinforce professional authority between the merchants selling the wood and the physicians, whose status depended on the ignorant showing respect for anyone 'garnished with the name of master doctor',[88] who insisted that only they could safely and effectively administer it. Indeed, he accused the physicians of having attempted to prevent its use when it was first discovered and then of having tried to restrict its use to treatment under their direction once its benefits had become apparent.[89] The merchants specifically attacked for their restrictive practices by von Hutten were the Fuggers, who had a monopoly on the guaiacum trade. Ironically, in advertising the values of holy wood, he was acting to the benefit of the medical profession and the very merchants to whom he was so opposed. Other Protestant reformers were more suspicious of endorsing guaiacum because of its control by this dynasty of merchants, the

Fuggers, who had in 1517 underwritten the very indulgence of
Cardinal Albrecht of Brandenburg that had triggered the German
Reformation, and who had financed the bid of Charles V for the
Crown of the Holy Roman Empire. The Fuggers may have
established a pox house in their native Augsburg for the relief of
victims of the disease where guaiacum was used extensively, but
their financial support for Catholicism made them objects of
suspicion to the reformers.[90]

The sculptor Benvenuto Cellini was another great believer in the
efficacy of holy wood when he caught the pox in about 1532 while
working on a chalice commissioned by Pope Clement VII. He had
caught it from a servant girl. The infection began with a painful
inflammation of the eye, which he bathed in a distillation of the
roots, stalks and petals of irises, but this was followed by red blisters,
the size of farthings, all over his body. The doctors he consulted
refused to believe him when he told them that he had the pox.
Against their advice, he decided to treat himself with *lignum vitae*
and within fifty days of beginning the treatment was 'as sound as a
roach'. As soon as he felt well, he went out shooting, only to go
down with a fever. Once again he ignored the advice of the doctors,
who told him that, if he were to take guaiacum while he was feverish,
he would die within the week. Once more his self-treatment had
results; within four days the fever had left him and after fifty days he
considered his self-treatment to have left him 'completely cured'.[91]

A great critic of the use of guaiacum was the French surgeon
Jacques de Béthencourt, who, disdaining the implied slur to his
nation in the more common appellation *morbus Gallicus* or 'French
Disease', preferred to use the term *morbus venereus* to describe the
disease, in recognition of its origins in the pursuits of the goddess of
love. He admitted that guaiacum was a gentler treatment for the
patient than his own use of mercury to promote salivation. However,
he considered the health regimen associated with guaiacum was
'inhuman because of the extremely severe way of living which is
imposed on the patient', but his main criticism of it was that it could
be dangerous because it was not sanctioned by the authority of
Hippocrates and Galen, 'our venerable Popes of medicine'.[92]

Mercury was also the preferred treatment of the reformers of both religion and medicine. Paracelsus, dubbed 'the Martin Luther of medicine' for his radical medical views, shared with von Hutten the firm belief that every man should be his own physician, but was one of the strongest proponents of treating the pox with mercury and in rejecting guaiacum. In the view of Paracelsus, doctors were born with special gifts from God that enabled them to guide the sick towards the remedies provided naturally by God, including essences of plants extracted by distillation and chemicals, so that each individual could take on personal responsibility for his or her own health. Believing that local remedies were best suited to local expressions of disease, he advocated mercury as a cure because it was found all over the world rather than only in the Indies.[93]

Mercury, known as *unguentum Saracenicum*, had long been used in Arab medicine for the treatment of scabs, psoriasis, leprosy and other skin diseases. It was already used in West European medicine by alchemists as a common remedy for skin diseases and soon became the most popular treatment for syphilis, especially in Protestant countries, where its use chimed with traditions of alchemy and attacks on the hegemony of the pagan and Roman Catholic medical traditions, although Paracelsus himself never formally renounced the Catholicism he had been brought up with.[94] The use of mercury, however, was opposed by those who were profiting from the trade in guaiacum. Paracelsus's own writings on the French Disease were published in Nuremburg in 1529,[95] but suppressed on the recommendation of Heinrich Stromer, dean of the medical faculty of Leipzig, who had advised von Hutten in his promotion of guaiacum and was a friend of the Fuggers, with his own stake in the success of their trade in holy wood.[96]

Yet so effective was mercury in the treatment of syphilis that it remained in common use until the twentieth century; it became a commonplace that a night with Venus would be followed by a lifetime with Mercury. The drawbacks of this treatment were such unpleasant side effects as profuse sweating, corrosion of the membranes of the mouth causing gum ulcerations, the loosening of the teeth and the erosion of the bones, all problems of which

Paracelsus was fully aware.[97] The French physician Jean Fernel, who helped to popularise the name *lues venerea* for the disease, reinforcing the idea of it as a moral punishment for intemperate sexual appetite, investigated the effects of mercury poisoning on painters, goldsmiths and tanners. However, he found no means of minimising the damage it could do to patients to whom it was applied beaten up with oils and powders to make an ointment to be rubbed into the joints up to four times a day. Mercury, aided by the use of dry baths, induced sweating and excessive salivation by which the poison could be expelled.[98]

Paracelsus, as well as being the great promoter of mercury, reinforced through his writings the belief that the pox was a distinct disease, taking a similar course in all its sufferers. It affected multitudes simultaneously and could be seen as the result of people coming into contact with other sufferers from the affliction. This challenged the old ideas of illness as the result of a breakdown of the balance of the humours in the body of an individual. It also raised doubts about the role of malign conjunctions of the planets in causing sickness and laid the ground for the development of theories of contagion and infection. The Veronese physician and humanist Girolamo Fracastoro took this challenge further and built upon the ideas of the classical philosophers Epicurus and Lucretius to explain how contagious disease was spread by 'seeds' sown through human contact. This contact might be at a distance through the air, it might be from person to person, as with syphilis through sexual intercourse, or it might be through the means of textiles, which could harbour the seeds of contagion. Fracastoro did not think of these *seminaria* as microorganisms such as bacteria or viruses, which were unknown before the seventeenth-century revolution in microscopy, but rather imagined them to resemble spores. This theory offered an explanation for infectious diseases like syphilis, the Black Death and smallpox, and also raised the possibility of containing such diseases through the quarantining of the diseased to prevent further contagion.[99]

Not only was Fracastoro to offer a way of understanding how the pox might be spread; he was also to give it the name by which the disease has been commonly known since the eighteenth century, as the author of the poem 'Syphilis sive Morbus Gallicus', begun in about 1511 but not published until 1530, when it was dedicated to his friend and patron Cardinal Pietro Bembo, a humanist scholar and the one-time lover of Lucrezia Borgia.[100] In this poem, hailed in its day as the equal of Virgil's *Georgics*, the shepherd Syphilis blasphemes against the sun god Apollo and encourages his king Alcinthous to set himself up as a god. Enraged, Apollo retaliates with a pestilence characterised by all the symptoms of the pox. Syphilis, after whom the new disease was named, is the first to suffer from foul sores that could be washed away only with quicksilver and brought on 'sleepless nights and tortured limbs'.[101] The impious shepherd is offered as a scapegoat in expiation, but Juno and Apollo take pity on him and allow a bullock to be substituted for sacrifice. Showing compassion to mankind for what Apollo has unleashed, they also provide the sacred guaiacum tree, which will offer a cure. In naming the protagonists in his story, Fracastoro sought inspiration in classical mythology. Alcinthous probably derives his name from Alcithoe, who was changed into a bat for denying the divinity of Bacchus,[102] and Syphilis may be inspired by Sipylus, shot by Apollo because his mother Niobe had incurred the wrath of the sun god by trying to stop the worship of his mother Latona.[103]

The story of Syphilis and holy wood as a gift of the gods is not the only legend Fracastoro invented for his poem. He also wrote about the myth of mercury. In this section of the poem, the huntsman Ilceus, a figure probably inspired by Adonis, accidentally kills a stag sacred to the huntress goddess Diana. Whereas Venus in the Adonis story had sent a boar to wound the unfortunate hunter, Diana persuades her brother Apollo to inflict a dreadful pestilence on Ilceus. In the depth of his misery, the unfortunate youth prays for a cure to Callirhoe, named after the fountain in which the biblical King Herod had bathed when inflicted with gangrene and worms in his genitals as a punishment for his sins. She advises him to visit the Underworld, where he bathes three times in a sacred river flowing with the alchemical metals silver and quicksilver. After these ritual ablutions, he sheds his diseased skin like a serpent, summoning up images of the pox as the serpentine disease. He must then pray to the chaste virgin goddess Diana, an echo of the prayers of sufferers from the pox to the Virgin Mary.[104]

Sub-classical mythology and allegory may have been central to Fracastoro's attempts to make an imaginative poem out of a disgusting disease, but he also introduced reality and a modern romance into his tale with an account of Columbus's voyages that led to the discovery of the holy tree guaiacum. After voyaging like the Argonauts through uncharted oceans, Columbus and his men find an earthly paradise, peopled by noble herbalists and gardeners leading a simple, natural and sylvan lifestyle. Into this world of innocence the European travellers introduce a note of violence when one of the sailors uses that satanic weapon, the gun, to shoot parrots, birds sacred to the sun. As retribution for this sacrilege, they are predicted to endure many battles, monsters, arguments among themselves and a strange disease for which they will find a remedy in wood. This disease is endemic among the natives too, as a punishment from Apollo for the transgressions of their ancestors, depicted as the survivors of the catastrophe that struck the legendary city of Atlantis. Yet hope for them too lies in guaiacum.[105]

The poem is an amalgam of myth invented by the poet and a clear diagnostic portrait of the disease and its treatment described by an experienced physician. The infection is shown as beginning in the sexual organs, eating away the groin and spreading through the entire body, leaving severe pain in the bones and foul scabs and ulcers on the face and torso. Fracastoro gave a moving description of the ravages of the disease on 'a conspicuous youth, more brilliant and gifted than any in Italy', for whom 'gradually that glistening springtime, that flower of youth, perished utterly, that vigour of mind'. The body of the young man is disfigured with scabs, his bones are riddled with abscesses, and sores begin to 'devour his lovely eyes and his love of the holy light and to devour his nose, which was gnawed away leaving a piercing wound'.[106] At the time when Fracastoro was writing these lines, his acquaintance Giovanni Cotta, a writer of love poetry in the style of the Latin poet Catullus, died of an unnamed infectious disease or perhaps as a victim of love,

27

aged 29 or 30, the very age at which his Veronese poetic inspiration had also died.[107]

Fracastoro was not only a physician but was also deeply immersed in humanist circles, where it was considered only natural that he should express his views on medicine in stately Latin verse as well as in the prose more usual for scientific tracts. Ariosto had submitted *Orlando Furioso* to him for critical comment, and Matteo Bandello had sent him the text of his novella *Romeo e Giulietta*. As a student and teacher of medicine at Padua, he had been a contemporary of the astronomer Copernicus, and, through his close friend Cardinal Bembo, he had links with Erasmus, Raphael and Titian.[108] Poetry was for him the natural means of communication, though the subject may have been an unusual one. However, Fracastoro was not the first doctor to write a poem about the pox, an honour that must go to Francisco Lopez de Villalobos, a Spanish physician who served the Catholic King Ferdinand of Aragon and his grandson the Holy Roman Emperor Charles V. As a 24-year-old student at the University of Salamanca in 1498, he had published a medical treatise in verse 'on the pestilential *bubas*'.[109] Although Villalobos may have been the first to give the subject the poetic treatment, Fracastoro was the first to make a truly original, imaginative and in truth beautiful work of literature from the horrible malady.

The poem 'Syphilis' encapsulated the horror of a new disease that struck Renaissance Europe unaware and brought great suffering to those who caught it. It also invented the name by which the infection was to be known. Yet, even as it was being written, Fracastoro was becoming aware that, 'though the contagion is still flourishing today, it seems to have changed its character since those earliest periods of its appearance', and in 1546 in his work on contagion was to conclude that it was in decline.[110] It was far from that, though by the mid sixteenth century it had become weaker once the virulence and vigour of its youthful phase had subsided into maturity and familiarity.

TWO

'Gentleman's Sniffles'

The initial impact of the pox had been so draconian and frightening because the disease was so absolutely new in its manifestations, but with familiarity came the usual contempt. Moreover, doctors were in agreement that within a generation the disease had become less virulent and was displaying signs of being weaker as its vigorous youth subsided into maturity and then middle age. Indeed, it has been suspected by some historians that the almost hysterical response of horror and disgust to its onset was an overreaction, with mortality from it not rising until after 1500, and that early accounts of it suffer from the kind of literary hype not unknown among modern journalists.[1] Yet it is equally possible that the novelty of the disease meant that it may have been underreported, with many of its symptoms going unrecognised. It was so disgusting and had such a stigma attached to it that 'only hated persons, and such, whose very noses were eaten off, were reported . . . to have died of this too frequent malady', an attitude that later led to underreporting of its incidence in early seventeenth-century London.[2] Nevertheless, as the severity of the symptoms decreased after the 1520s, venereal infections became more commonplace and were looked upon with an almost cavalier disregard. In the romance *Gargantua and Pantagruel*, Rabelais commented in the words of his character Epistemon, describing his return from Hell where he had seen Pope Sixtus as an 'anointer of pox sores', that he had never seen so many people with pox, 'for believe me, everyone who hasn't had the pox in this world gets it in the next'.[3]

For Renaissance rulers in particular, the pox was almost an occupational hazard and the object of gossip. It was far too unpleasant for its association with the rich, talented and influential to make it a glamorous or fashionable disease, but it was equally inescapable for anyone leading the licentious lifestyle of court society of the time. Indeed, Erasmus commented in 1519 that any nobleman who had not suffered from the pox was considered to be an ignorant countryman.[4] Moreover, survival rates were better for those of higher social standing than for the poor, reduced to beggary or the receipt of charity. Francesco Gonzago, Marquis of Mantua, died of the pox in 1519, but not until twenty-three years after his first symptoms had manifested themselves. His court physician was the poet Battista Fiera, whose portrait was reputedly painted by the artist Lorenzo Costa in gratitude for the medical treatment he received when he contracted syphilis shortly after his arrival in Mantua in 1507.[5] Another 'survivor', Cardinal Francesco Soderini, was rumoured to have contracted the disease in 1510 but actually died of old age, not the pox, in 1524.[6]

Within families, the pox could spread rapidly. Francesco Gonzago had fought at Naples against the French army and had suffered from a fever during his stay at the court of his father-in-law Ercole d'Este in Ferrara on his way home to Mantua in 1496. The pox was subsequently to spread through the Este family. Duke Ercole's daughter Beatrice, wife of Ludovico Sforza, Duke of Milan, and his daughter-in-law Anna Sforza died of it in 1497. The heir to the dukedom, Alfonso, later to be notorious for his practice of walking around Ferrara stark naked on hot summer afternoons yet cultivated enough to commission Titian to paint a series of bacchanalian pictures for his private apartments, was so ill from the French Disease that he was unable to attend his young wife's funeral. The following year, Alfonso's younger brothers Ferrante and Sigismondo were also to suffer from it. Sigismondo had contracted it during a visit to the court of Francesco Gonzago at Mantua, which put an end to any hopes that he would lead the usual active life of a Renaissance prince. The Cardinal of Milan, Ippolito d'Este, another of the brothers of Alfonso, was probably another victim of the disease.[7] His sexual appetites were vicious enough for him to order a servant to stab his half-brother Giulio in the eye simply because he was a more successful rival for the favours of a woman the Cardinal lusted after.[8]

Alfonso's second wife was the scandalous Lucrezia Borgia. The papal court of her father Alexander VI was also riddled with the French pox, although the Pope himself seems not to have suffered from it despite his salacious reputation. However, his son Cesare, Cardinal of Valencia and reputed lover of Lucrezia, was one of the early sufferers from the disease, as were other members of the Borgia family. So too were other cardinals, including Giuliano della Rovere, who in 1503 succeeded Alexander VI as Pope Julius II, the patron of the artist Raphael whose productive amatory and artistic life was to be cut short by an unspecified violent fever following upon over-indulgence in the pleasures of love.[9] Gaspar Torella, physician to the Borgia court in Rome, in his writings on the pox, for which he had coined the neologism 'pudendagra' because it first manifested itself in the genitalia or pudenda, cited the case of 'Nicolo the Young', described as a servant of Cesare Borgia but possibly a pseudonym hiding the identity of Cesare himself, who caught the disease when 'corrupt vapours' from the uterus of the woman he was sleeping with entered his male member.[10] Torella, working in a male-centred world and dealing with male patients, believed that men were more susceptible to catching the disease because of their hotter complexions and should avoid infected women, but women need not avoid intercourse with afflicted men because the uterus was cold and dry and so not as easily damaged by the pox. Perhaps it would have been better advice to warn his patrons against promiscuity, but many of them anyway ignored their doctors when it suited them. Cardinal Bertomeu Marti of Segorbe, a close friend from childhood of Rodrigo Borgia, later Alexander VI, fell ill with the pox in March 1499 and died a year later. Racked by so terrible a pain that he could not sleep at night, he was grateful when a Portuguese visitor offered him the promise of a cure with an ointment made of litharge, ceruse, incense, mastic, pine resin, pork fat, roseate oils and quicksilver. The court doctors all believed that this ointment, for which extravagant claims had been made, contained too much quicksilver, but the Cardinal was so desperate

31

for relief that he continually rubbed it in himself, briefly deadening the pain but at the expense of increased anxiety and sleeplessness. However, what eventually killed the Cardinal was another ointment, containing pork fat, the ashes of the white grape vine, juice of lemon balm and even greater quantities of mercury, which he rubbed into his armpits and groin.[11]

Undoubtedly, syphilis was endemic in the courts of early modern Europe, but it is dangerous to assume that everyone of importance had it, especially if sexually active. Henry VIII of England is assumed to have been a syphilitic, partly on the basis of his colourful marital and extramarital career, and partly because some aspects of his recorded medical history suggest that he suffered from syphilis, though they could equally be symptomatic of other ailments. Henry's decline in middle age from the handsome, charming, physically active prince to the bloated, suspicious tyrant has been ascribed to syphilis. In about 1528, he first began to suffer with an ulcer on his leg that was to afflict him until his death. This was most probably either a varicose ulcer or an ulcer caused by osteomyelitis resulting from a jousting injury, but it has been interpreted as being syphilitic. Further clues suggesting that the King may have had the pox come from his failure to achieve his dynastic ambitions. It has been suggested that the failure of Catherine of Aragon to produce a healthy male heir could be because she was infected with syphilis by her lusty husband. The ill-health of Henry's surviving children has also been adduced to support the notion that they may have inherited congenital syphilis through him. Edward VI, the longed-for male heir, died at 15 of tuberculosis, a year after he suffered from a skin rash probably caused by measles. Mary and Elizabeth were both short-sighted. Mary's nose had a flattened bridge and discharged such foul-smelling pus that her husband Philip of Spain found it, and her, repellent. These factors in the medical history of the King's children have all been seen as possible indications of congenital syphilis – or not. It is all circumstantial evidence, none of which proves that Henry VIII had the pox. What is perhaps most telling is the negative evidence. There is no record of the King's physicians having ever administered mercury or guaiacum in their treatment of his ailments, and they would have used the conventional and accepted treatments available to them had they themselves diagnosed the pox. One of the most famous syphilitics in English history probably did not actually suffer from it.[12]

Syphilis provides a surer explanation for the savagery of another ruthless and capricious sixteenth-century ruler, Tsar Ivan the Terrible of Russia, whose bones were exhumed in the twentieth century and found to have lesions typical of the disease. A reformer and despot, Ivan had already showed a streak of sadism from childhood, when he would climb to the top of the towers of the Kremlin and throw small animals out of the window, but it was after the death of his first wife, Anastasia, in 1560 that he really began to act in a paranoid fashion, striking out against imagined conspirators. However, it was in 1564, when he was 34, that he began to display what has been interpreted as signs of cerebral syphilis, the result of infection caused by incessant whoring in his youth. Suddenly, without any warning, Ivan loaded up his treasures and decamped from Moscow to establish himself in a weird parody of a monastery at Aleksandrov, outside Moscow, which he ruled as abbot, with his personal bodyguards and supporters, the *oprichniks*, acting as monks when they were not oppressing and terrorising Ivan's subjects. At Aleksandrov, he would prostrate himself before the altar with such vehemence that his forehead would be bloodied and covered with bruises before he rose to read homilies on the Christian virtues to his drunken retainers, themselves fresh from torturing and raping their victims in the cellars of the monastery. Often Ivan presided over the ritual tearing-out of the ribs from men's chests with sharp and hissing hot pliers. His reign of terror lasted for nineteen years, culminating in the murder, using a steel-tipped staff, of his son in 1581. By the time of his own death in 1584, Ivan would wander through his palace howling, surrounded by soothsayers and fondling his jewels, fancying that they changed colour as a sign that he was poisoned by disease. As his heir he left a congenital idiot.[13]

The dynastic effects of syphilis were of utmost concern to rulers. Mary Queen of Scots was said by her son to have refused to allow

Archbishop Hamilton to use his spittle, as was then customary, at the baptism of James VI of Scotland and the future James I of England, for fear of infection, stating she would not have 'a poxy priest to spit in her child's mouth'. Her worries might more correctly have been concentrated on her husband, the alcohol- and sex-addicted Lord Darnley, described by contemporaries as 'poisoned' and as a 'pockish man' by his own wife. At the age of 21 he was said to have had smallpox, but it is more likely that this was syphilis. When Mary visited him she thought 'I should have been killed by his breath', and noted that his rash was fading but that he had alopecia. Later he sent Mary a letter that made her immediately consult her physician and then declare that she wished she were dead. Although the actual contents of the letter are not known, it is thought that he was informing her that he had the pox. Certainly at the time of his murder in 1567, he had moved to Kirk O'Fields in order to convalesce and was receiving special baths, which may have been linked with the treatment of syphilis by mercury salivation. If Darnley did indeed have the disease, Mary's next husband, Lord Bothwell, may also have suffered from the same and possibly died of general paralysis of the insane.[14]

The rich, famous and powerful were not the only ones to suffer from the scourge. By the 1590s it was so commonplace that William Shakespeare, whose plays and verse contain clusters of pox imagery representing corruption, decay and disgust,[15] could write: 'A man can no more separate age and covetousness than he can part young limbs and lechery. But the gout galls the one and the pox pinches the other.'[16] Treatment by salivation with mercury or guaiacum to produce more phlegm to expel the poison remained standard. Rabelais waxed lyrical in his description of victims of the pox after their treatment with mercury, with their faces glistening 'like a larder lock-plate and their teeth rattling like the keys on the manual of an organ or spinet when it is being played' and their mouths foaming 'like a wild boar which the hounds have driven into the toils'.[17]

By the early seventeenth century tobacco, newly brought to Europe from the Americas, from which the pox had perhaps been an earlier import, was being lauded as a cure for venereal disease.

It was claimed that indigenous Amerindians had been the first to observe that tobacco was 'a preservative or antidote' against the loathsome disease. James I of England thundered against both the infection and its alleged cure, preferring to put his faith in nature's own healing powers rather than in a cure that could cause men to smoke themselves to death. He deplored the import into Christendom of 'a stinking and unsavoury antidote for so corrupted and execrable a malady, the stinking suffumigation whereof they yet use against that disease, making so one canker or vermin to eat out another'.[18]

Tobacco was yet another New World remedy from nature that could be self-administered without the intermediary role of a doctor, and in time other weeds, woods and roots were brought into use, most of them sharing with guaiacum the property of promoting sweating and salivation. Root of China, also known as China smilax, was introduced from the Portuguese colony of Goa in the 1530s, to be followed by sarsaparilla from North America and sassafras wood from Florida. The physician and anatomist Andreas Vesalius recommended cinchona bark, which had traditionally been used by South American natives to treat fever, skin diseases and the symptoms of the menopause. Some doctors were so anxious not to neglect any avenue of treatment that they would prescribe an infusion of the four sudorific woods, root of China, sarsaparilla, sassafras and guaiacum, preferring to use all available means at their disposal indiscriminately rather than lose out by being too selective.[19] Water-germander, which did not need to be imported into Western Europe, formed the main ingredient of the *electuarum diascordium*, a herbal preparation with a honey base.[20]

These newer cures, like guaiacum, may not have been very effective, but at least they were mild and did no real harm, unlike the widespread popular belief that the pox and *chaud pisse*, as gonorrhoea was then generally known, could be cured by deflowering a virgin. The principle behind this unsavoury piece of folk lore was that, if the disease could be passed on to another person, it would leave the original sufferer. Effectively, the virgin was being made into a scapegoat. This belief put young women and children at risk of rape and infection. It was to persist well into the nineteenth century in many parts of Europe.[21]

For many men, though, there was to be no cure, and perhaps the most visible stigma resulting from their infection was the collapsed or missing nose, only too clearly identifiable with uncleanness and immorality. Face visors could be used to cover the mutilation, which might be disguised and passed off as a battlefield or duelling injury, but many people would have preferred to have a nose like everyone else. The Bolognese doctor Gaspare Tagliacozzi set out to find an answer to the problem of restoring what nature had given and misfortune had stolen away. He developed a technique of replacing the nose with a flap skin graft, which he described in 1597. A flap of skin was partially detached from the flesh of the upper arm and left so that it could establish itself as a viable tissue. Then, still attached loosely to the arm, it was roughly shaped and sewn to what was left of the nose. For the next 14 days the unfortunate patient would have his nose attached to his arm until the surgeon considered it time to cut the flap of skin from its original site. After a suitable interval, the flap would be reshaped to form a new nose. In using this procedure, Tagliacozzi laid the foundations of the western tradition of plastic surgery, although rhinoplasty, or nose reconstruction, had first been developed in ancient India and, more recently had been practised in Southern Italy. Aesthetically his grafts left scars on the very roughly formed new nose and on the part of the body from which the graft had been taken. Compared with modern plastic surgery or even classical Indian plastic surgery, the results were primitive, and other surgeons and physicians found it difficult to imitate his art. The French surgeon Ambroise Paré recommended as a better alternative the use of an artificial nose that could be held in place by a clasp or a pair of spectacles.[22]

The anatomist Gabriele Falloppio also advised on means of avoiding infection in the first place and in doing so has been credited with the invention of the contraceptive sheath or condom. Ever since the realisation that the great pox was sexually transmitted, it was understood that abstention from casual sex was the best way of avoiding the disease. However, human nature and the lure of forbidden fruits being what they are, it was unrealistic to expect that fear of infection would prevent men and women from having intercourse, so prophylactic measures were devised to minimise the risks. Niccolo Massa in 1532, following advice first given as early as 1502 by another doctor, Juan Almenar, advised any man having sex with a woman he suspected of being infected first to wash out her vulva with hot white wine or vinegar and then penetrate and withdraw as quickly as possible. Immediately after intercourse, both the man and woman should wash their genitals with the same concoction.[23] Falloppio refined such prophylactic measures out of a desire to protect young men unable to resist the lure of beautiful but syphilitic sirens. He recommended that the man should wash himself after sex and then cover his penis with a piece of cloth soaked in a concoction of wine, guaiacum shavings, copper flakes, precipitated mercury, gentian root, red coral, burnt ivory and burnt deer-horn ashes. This sheath was then left on for some four or five hours. Falloppio claimed success in 1563 in 1,100 cases with this method and advised men to be prepared by carrying a supply of such cloths around with them cut to the precise size of the penis.[24] Falloppio's sheaths may often have been seen as the forerunner of modern condoms, but they were no such thing; they were intended to prevent infection rather than conception and, significantly, were used after copulation rather than before.

Falloppio's advocacy of prophylactic measures reflected the increasingly common view that the disease was an everyday hazard that should be avoided if possible but not at the expense of sexual appetite. For the Puritans of the first half of the seventeenth century, however, the pox was to be regarded with contempt as the wages of sin. It was 'a very fit punishment for whores, for their exorbitant and untameable lust; and it is perhaps the harder to be removed, that the repentance for it may be the more severe'.[25] Thomas Sydenham, the most influential of the seventeenth-century English physicians and known to his contemporaries as 'the English Hippocrates' on account of the breadth of his medical teachings and his emphasis on practical observation, remarked: 'I have met with several, that have affirmed (either upon a good design, that they might affright incontinent persons from sin by the fear of the following punishment, or because they would be thought very chaste) that the cure of the French Pox ought not to be taught.' Sydenham disagreed with this extreme view, since in upholding it 'there would be scarce any room left for charity or for doing good turns . . . it belongs to God Almighty to punish the guilt, but it is our duty to help the miserable as much as we can . . . and not to search too nicely into the cause or vex them with our censures'.[26]

Sydenham had been educated in a hotbed of Puritanism at Magdalen Hall in an otherwise predominantly Royalist Oxford, and had fought for Parliament during the Civil War, but had come to professional renown in the more licentious days of the Restoration, when sexual restraint was as rare as venereal disease was common at the court of the Merry Monarch. During the godly years of the Commonwealth, an underground sexually liberated culture had survived among the clerks of Whitehall, the taverns of London and the shopkeepers of Westminster to vie with the official ideals of continence and wrestling with temptation. With the return of the monarchy, the high life of the court soon outdid the low-life culture of the inn in bawdiness and disease. Charles II, with his posse of mistresses, presided over a court in which aristocrats dallied with actresses and great ladies were said to be infected with the pox and to think nothing of aborting their unwanted bastards. A doctor who could help great ladies 'to slip their calves' and 'great men in curing of their claps' could expect to 'do what he please with the King'.[27] It was a matter of common chatter that the Duke of York, later James II, had caught the clap soon after arriving in London at the Restoration.[28] Gossip 'made nothing' of the illness of Prince Rupert of the Rhine, once the dashing cavalier hero of the Civil War, when it was feared that he was dying from the pox. Indeed the Prince overcame his apprehensions of dying and when 'we told him that we believe he would overcome his disease, he is as merry, and swears and laughs and curses and doth all the things of a man in health, as ever he did in his life'.[29] Similarly, even when he was dying of syphilis, the actor and dramatist John Lacy did not repent of the lifestyle that had led to his deathbed, despite the exhortations of a

bishop, and insisted on his mistress lying alongside him 'to look on
. . . though he can do no more'.[30]

Such apparent indifference to the risk of catching the disease was
common in high society, but no one wanted actively to court it.
There was a rumour that James II had caught the pox as a result of
an act of revenge by a cuckolded husband, who had discovered his
wife and the Duke of York 'too kind'. On the bullying insistence of
the husband, the wife had continued to allow the Duke to
'dishonour' her. Meanwhile, he had sought out 'the foulest whore he
could find' in the hope of catching syphilis so he could infect his
wife and, through her, her lover. Having thus accomplished his aim
of 'the most pernicious and foul piece of revenge' imaginable, the
man had then been able to congratulate himself on his triumph,
although it may have been a pyrrhic victory at the cost of a chronic
disease that could lead to his own death as much as it contributed to
the ill-health and eventual death of his ultimate victim James II,
who, like his brother Charles II, did actually suffer from the disease,
from whomsoever he may have contracted it.[31]

For the libertines of the Restoration, the pox was considered the
norm, especially among the group of wits in the circle of the
notorious John Wilmot, Earl of Rochester, whose short but
debauched life probably ended with tertiary syphilis at the age of 33.
In that time, he could claim to have been continually drunk for five
years, to have had countless lovers of both sexes, kidnapping an
heiress and buggering his page, and to have written both tender love
lyrics and explicitly pornographic verse. One of his associates, the
poet Charles Sedley, shocked a crowd of worthy London citizens by
dipping his 'private member' in a glass of wine from which he drank
the king's health before urinating on his audience. With such a
lifestyle it is little wonder that Rochester should have caught the pox
in 1669 and sought mercury treatment at Madam Fourcard's
bathhouse in Leather Lane, London. Thereafter his health rapidly
declined and the dashing rake became a crippled, almost blind
misanthrope.[32] On the fringes of Rochester's circle was the dramatist
William Wycherley, who was to use syphilis to good effect as a
trigger for the plot of *The Country Wife*. In this play, first performed

at the Theatre Royal, Drury Lane, in 1675, the rakish man-about-town Harry Horner pretends to be impotent as a result of treatment for the pox. This ruse allows him to pose as a suitably neutered escort for the bored and neglected wives of London businessmen, acceptable to the husbands because safely neutered, and, at the same time, free to seduce the wives. In Lady Fidget he meets his match as she enthusiastically moves in on Horner actively to help cuckold her husband, an aggressive entrepreneur more interested in money than sex. However, things become more complicated when one of Horner's victims, Margery Pinchwife, falls in love with him and threatens to expose his deception right to the end of the play, when she returns from her dynamic young lover to her unsuspecting older husband. In terms of morality the ending is ambivalent, with breaches of the old moral code left unpunished.[33]

The licence of the court was copied at lower levels of society, where it was observed with varying mixtures of disapproval and fascination. The diarist Samuel Pepys could never shake off the Puritan ethos of his upbringing despite the alternative attractions of 'clubbing' with his fellow clerks in the alehouses of the Commonwealth, the sophistication and easy-going morals of the Restoration court he visited as a rising young official in the Navy Office, and the pleasures of theatre and tavern in a London recently released from the straitjacket of moral rectitude. An insatiable voyeur of beautiful women, Pepys, married to a woman whose suspicions of his philandering were as well founded as his jealousy of her admirers was groundless, was lacking in the sexual confidence he so much admired in others. His philandering often failed to progress beyond ogling and daydreaming or fondling and masturbation; once he even ejaculated in church while fantasising about a pretty young married woman. With this object of his obsession, Betty Mitchell, as with so many of his other pursuits, the height of his success was to grope her under her petticoats since knickers were not yet common, and thus there was no protection for a woman against roving hands, and to get her to rub his penis; of the twenty women he had designs on in the course of the nine years that he kept his diary, he succeeded in seducing no more than three or four.[34] A cautious man with an eye to promotion and advancement, Pepys never allowed his desires to interfere with his career nor ever seriously contemplated sex with an unmarried woman for fear of the consequences of an unexplainable pregnancy; but there was also another dread that constrained his sexual impulses, that of contracting a venereal disease. This ensured that he avoided contact with prostitutes, although they were hardly necessary, considering both his personal charms and his willingness to use his official position for the benefit of the husbands of the women for whom he developed an obsession. He was shocked when he heard that his brother Tom was dying of the pox and that the maid had tales to tell of Tom's disquieting sexual practices of staying up at night 'doing something to himself'. Tom assured his brother that he did not have the pox, which prompted Samuel to celebrate by sending for oysters for a celebratory dinner. However, having enjoyed his meal and just to make sure that Tom was indeed clean, Samuel called in another doctor for a second opinion, with whom he 'searched my brother again at his privities; where he was as clear as ever he was born'. The unfortunate Tom was actually suffering from tuberculosis, which was often inaccurately thought to be associated with venereal disease, and was already unconscious and close to death during the examination that exonerated him of having the shameful disease so distressing to middle-class respectability but treated with contempt in high society.[35]

The prevalence of the disease had its influence on fashion in an age when conspicuous show was of prime importance. One of the features of the milder form of syphilis that became common after about 1520 was alopecia. Such hair loss had helped to create a new fashion for beards which could demonstrate wholeness and purity in men.[36] Fashion could also be used to cover up the ravages of the disease. Powder covered up pockmarks, whether they originated from venereal disease or smallpox. The signs of hair loss could also be concealed by periwigs, introduced to Britain from France in the 1660s, which were worn by all men of status during the seventeenth and eighteenth centuries until a tax on wig powder during the Revolutionary and Napoleonic wars encouraged men and women to reveal their own hair once more, where they had it. The fashion for wigs also meant that no one need go grey or lose their hair in public, and noblemen could assume an air of authority from under a uniform mass of curls that stifled expressions of individuality in portraits of the period. With the external signs of syphilis hidden under wigs, gloves and face powder, high society could easily downplay it as no more than the 'gentleman's sniffles'.[37]

There was little advance in the treatment of the disease as the seventeenth century gave way to the eighteenth. The 'English Hippocrates' Thomas Sydenham continued to rely on the by-now long-established salivation method of expelling the disease from the body with mercury or guaiacum, although he linked it to mid-seventeenth-century ideas of medical knowledge. He was a strong believer in the primacy of accurate and skilled clinical observation over more academic and speculative medical theories, and emphasised that treatment should be appropriate to any one particular case rather than conforming to more generalised and abstract theories about the causes of disease. Although, like many of his contemporaries, he incorrectly believed that the pox and gonorrhoea, actually two separate venereal diseases, were different stages of the same infection, with gonorrhoea as the first stage of infection leading on to the true pox if the humours putrefied, he did notice that 'though the salivation is much better for the curing of the confirmed pox than any other medicine whatever, yet it can not cure a gonorrhoea when it accompanies the pox'.[38] His recommended treatment remained conventional, with the use of purging medicines to evacuate the 'peccant matter', the use of an ointment made of 2 oz of lard and 1 oz of quicksilver, and bleeding after a month of purgation; yet he also believed that excessive sweating out of diseased matter might be harmful, and advocated as an alternative a 'cool therapy' of a cooling diet, copious fluids and moderate bloodletting to assist nature against the fever.[39] He also sanctioned the custom of many wealthier syphilitics in going to France to recover their strength because the climate was healthier and clearer there, compared with 'our thick and moist air'. What he did deny was that French physicians could be any better in treating the disease than their English colleagues.[40]

French physicians, while they may not have had anything original to contribute to the understanding and treatment of the disease in the late seventeenth century, were to take a prominent role in studying the disease in the early eighteenth century, led by the physician to Louis XV, Jean Astruc, who, in contrast to Sydenham's practical approach based on experience, was more famous for his theoretical writings than for his practice. Astruc did not aim at originality in his writings and teachings on what he called *lues venerea* or venereal diseases, but rather sought to record and systematise what his predecessors had written. This approach was historical rather than aimed at better therapeutic practice, although he realised that the changes that he recorded in the disease since its first appearance could well have included a reversion to its original virulence. Knowledge of earlier treatments might be useful should that happen, although his own feeling was that it seemed to be declining in severity so rapidly that it might well become extinct before too long. That initial savagery had paradoxically stimulated medical developments in the same way that warfare was a stimulus to the improved art of fortification. Astruc believed that all venereal infections, including gonorrhoea, buboes, genital sores and warts in the early stages, and venereal pain, tumours and bone lesions later on, were caused by a *virus venereum*, by which he meant a slime or poison that entered the body through direct sexual contact and spread through the blood and disturbed the balance of the humours.[41] This so-called chemical theory of venereal infections as the result of poisonous acids spreading through the body was challenged by Nicolas Andry and Antoine Deidier, Professor of Chemistry at the University of Montpellier, who proposed that the infection was spread by worms entering the genitalia, copulating and laying eggs that enabled them to multiply through the body. These worms were then supposed to sting, pierce and bite the body, causing ulceration and inflammation.[42]

A more influential theory about the transmission of venereal infection was advanced later in the eighteenth century by Paul-Joseph Barthez and popularised by the London surgeon John Hunter – the doctrine of sympathy. Barthez denied the possibility that the infection could be carried within the body and suggested instead that it first of all produced symptoms in that part of the body that it entered. It then had an effect on the other body organs by sympathy with the first parts affected.[43] Hunter went further in believing that the inflammation in the body produced by the presence of the venereal poison could act simultaneously on all parts of the body susceptible to such irritation. He was also a strong supporter of the unicist theory that gonorrhoea and syphilis were different stages of the same infection, which he carefully identified and then differentiated between the external signs of the first phase and the lasting internal damage done by the disease.[44] These observations on the internal ravages of syphilis were confirmed by the surgeon Giambattista Morgagni, whose autopsies confirmed the existence of lesions of the heart, brain and nervous system, and aneurisms in the aorta of the corpses of the victims of venereal disease.[45]

Teaching about the disease now became more popular and fashionable in the late eighteenth century. Under the influence of Astruc, the term 'venereal diseases' became more widespread and cemented the moral link between sexual transmission, moral sin and the infections. At the same time, the name 'syphilis', derived from Fracastoro's poem, now became the more usual title of the disease, displacing 'the pox' and 'Morbus Gallicus' in the medical literature.[46] Medical atlases graphically showing the symptoms of the disease were published, and the medical publications on the subject multiplied.[47] Dermatological manifestations of syphilis appeared prominently in the great anatomical collections of the age, including those of the surgeon and anatomist John Hunter, which form the basis of the Hunterian Museum of the Royal College of Surgeons, despite losses of specimens during the London Blitz. As an alternative to teaching using human specimens, wax models illustrating anatomy and disease were sometimes used, especially in Italy and the Habsburg dominions. Particularly important was the work of a group of wax modellers active in Florence in the late eighteenth and early nineteenth centuries who, with anatomists at the hospital of Santa Maria Novella, dissected corpses, exposed the organs to be modelled and then produced a plaster cast into which a mixture of waxes, resins and dyes was poured.[48]

Among the waxes now displayed at La Specola in Florence is an interesting and unusual wax tableau depicting the *Morbus Gallicus* by the late seventeenth-century Sicilian wax modeller Gaetano Giulio Zumbo, who specialised in models of decomposing bodies in macabre scenes. The *Morbus Gallicus*, long hidden away in a cupboard in Palazzo Corsini in Prato until it was badly damaged in the 1966 floods that devastated the art treasures of Florence, suggests the misery inflicted by the pox, with suppurating wounds and decaying bodies. A contorted and emaciated male torso, his genitalia covered, shows the typical sores and damaged nose of the sufferer, while dead female corpses lie on a rocky base among the skulls and bones of earlier victims. A baby suffering from hereditary syphilis looks down upon them.[49]

Zumbo's wax tableau was didactic in a different way from the Florentine anatomical waxes in that its purpose was moralistic rather than dispassionate. It was not intended for the teaching of medical students. In it and his other works he pointed to the contrast between the glory of the human body and the crude reality of nature and the cruelty of disease, and showed the results of sin. Equally moralistic was the allegorical depiction of syphilis by the Neapolitan painter Luca Giordano in his *Allegory of Youth Tempted by the Vices* of 1664. In this large and impressive painting, an attractive young man is assailed by temptation. Bacchus and satyrs offer him wine, Venus and Cupid tempt him with the charms of love, and Saturn looks on with the weight of the world on his back. Meanwhile the virgin Minerva tries to defend his virtue. Venus spurts milk at him from her breast, which a winged Minerva catches in a bowl, a possible reference to the fears that milk from syphilitic wet-nurses could contaminate infants. Meanwhile, the sinister loathsome figure of the shepherd Syphilis, marked by the characteristic flattened nose with a dip in it, scabs, bumps on his head and alopecia, reaches out to the unfortunate youth. In his mouth is a gnawed-away bone, symbolic of the disease eating away the bones. He is a warning of the results of giving in to the allurements of vice, whereby the beautiful youth could be reduced to such a hateful condition.[50]

An earlier artistic representation of syphilis had been made by the Florentine artist Angelo Bronzino in 1545 in his *Allegory of Venus, Cupid, Folly and Time*, now in the National Gallery, London, in which the agonised background figure traditionally identified as Jealousy bears all the signs that he suffers from syphilis, including patchy hair loss, reddened eyes, missing teeth and bumps. He is an admonition against lust and the crime of incest implicit in the adolescent Cupid's kissing and fondling of his mother Venus. The painting was a gift from Bronzino's patron Cosimo di Medici to François I of France, noted for his profligacy for which he paid with the suffering of syphilis.[51]

Such moral exhortations to avoid the temptations of the flesh that led to disease were generally ignored. In Georgian London, sexually transmitted diseases were rife at all levels of society and often not even considered worthy of concern.[52] One student, on being asked about his health by his tutor, fearing the young man might be 'clapt', replied, 'No, Sir, but I am pox'd.'[53] Sowing one's wild oats, like heavy drinking, was seen as part of the rite of passage by which a well-connected young man came of age. Frequent sex was even seen as a salubrious way of expelling excess humours from the body in sperm, and thus maintaining a healthy balance of body fluids. Catching the clap or the pox was an unavoidable risk, yet one that might not be altogether shameful. For those unfortunates who 'sacrific'd their noses to the god of Priapus, and had unluckily fallen into the Aethiopian fashion of flat faces', whose noses had been eaten away by syphilis, there existed an exclusive London club known as the 'No-Nose'd Club'.[54]

As always, travel increased exposure to sexually transmitted infections, and the fashion for undertaking the Grand Tour as a means of finishing off the education of an accomplished gentleman was to be the ruin of many a noble family. Not only did innocent, impressionable young men find themselves seduced by the ostentatious and expensive fashionable dress and affected manners they observed among the dandies of Italy and France, and the expensive aesthetic tastes of the connoisseur of art, but they also found themselves the prey of the famed Italian courtesans.

Lord Chesterfield warned his illegitimate son Philip Stanhope not only against the common prostitute but also about the more insidious dangers posed by the more refined sort of courtesan: 'I will by no means pay for whores and their never failing consequences, surgeons . . . a young fellow must have as little sense as address to venture or more properly to sacrifice his health with such sort of creatures in such a place as Paris especially where gallantry is both the profession and practice of every woman of fashion.'[55] The famed courtesans of Venice were a particular draw for young men who 'by aiming at breeding abroad . . . return with those diseases which hinder them from breeding at home'.[56] Twenty-one-year-old William Beckford, for whom women had fewer charms than the young son of the aristocratic Cornaro family, found Venice full of dissipated men and women lulled into a post-coital stupor as a result of 'their nerves, unstrung by disease and the consequence of early debaucheries'.[57]

Fears that sexual adventures abroad might be the undoing of the health and careers of promising young men and harm the chances of securing heirs were by no means unfounded. The death from syphilis caught in Italy of the 22-year-old Charles Howard, Viscount Morpeth and heir to the Earl of Carlisle, precipitated an inconvenient by-election in 1741. Henry Pelham Clinton, heir to the Earl of Lincoln, succumbed to the disease at the age of 28 in 1778, seven years after being infected by a Venetian dancer and prostitute at Florence. Even if they did not die of the disease, many distinguished visitors to Italy, including the future prime minister, the Marquess of Rockingham, were left with permanent reminders of their travels that were not so welcome as their almost obligatory swagger portraits by the artist Pompeo Batoni or their fashionable collections of Italian art.[58]

Prostitutes, whether home grown or of the more exotic continental variety, were still seen as the main source of contagion, but there was now perhaps a greater acknowledgement that the philandering husband might have some part to play not only in his own plight but also in infecting his innocent wife. One prominent courtesan, Fanny Murray, was in no doubt that the initial blame lay with her own profession: 'Many an antique gonorrhoea and even confirmed pox have they transplanted, by a drunken libidinous husband, to an innocent wife, and to the blood of their posterity; glorying at their chicanery, and wishing everyone as infected as themselves.'[59] What is perhaps surprising is that neither the clap nor the pox is a problem for two of the most famous women of pleasure in the literature of the age, Daniel Defoe's Moll Flanders or John Cleland's Fanny Hill, although Amy, the trusty servant of Defoe's harlot heroine Roxana, is punished with an unpleasant death from the French Disease and its treatment by salivation in the sequel to *Roxana: The Fortunate Mistress*.[60]

For the innocent woman infected by her husband, infection often came as a shock, especially when he tried to treat her without her knowledge. The quack doctor Robert James recommended his own remedy for the pox, which could be slipped into the spouse's hot chocolate drink without her suspecting anything, so as not to upset the harmony of the household.[61] That did not stop the actress Sarah Siddons from being a 'ball of resentment' after catching the pox from her husband in 1792. If she found out this subterfuge, the wronged wife had no legal recourse. When Martha Robinson filed for a divorce in 1775, after her husband had beaten her and almost killed her by slipping a powder to treat gonorrhoea into her wine, her suit was refused.[62]

Not all men admitted that they had contracted the disease from sexual intercourse with a woman. John Marten cited one case of a man with a dose of gonorrhoea who emphatically denied that he had had sex, admitting at most that he had picked up a woman at the playhouse and had been 'accomodat'd by her hand'. Marten conceded that such mutual masturbation might be enough to transmit the infection and that 'by friction or rubbing the yard with a warm hand, just wet with a virulent venereal matter, the pocky contagious miasms may enter into the pores of the erected heated yard and prove infectious'. Marten also stated that 'one man's conversing with, or having the carnal use of another man's body' and oral sex could also transmit venereal infections, a rare acknowledgement of the medical problems of gay men.[63]

For homosexual men, there was resort to the criminalised underworld of the molly-house or male brothel, such as that kept in Holborn in 1726 by the notorious and appropriately named Mother Clap, as potent a source of contagion as the more regular brothels or the women and boys touting their rather cheaper charms on the streets of London.[64]

James Boswell was not averse to seeking his gratification with women wherever he could find it, and looked upon venereal disease as 'that troublesome companion and bar to my innocent pleasures'.[65] Boswell caught nineteen doses of the clap spread over thirty years of promiscuity and was lucky not to acquire the full-blown pox as well, although like his contemporaries he believed them to be different stages of the same illness. Each time he went through a cycle of infection, treatment, remorse and determination to reform, only to return to his accustomed wenching as soon as he felt better. His first bout of the disease in the spring of 1760 lasted for ten weeks, and the pain of the urethral discharges and a recurrence of the illness after a visit to an Edinburgh brothel at first discouraged him from seeking further sexual adventures, since he had suffered 'severely from this loathsome distemper', and he was conscious once he had moved to London that the 'surgeon's fees . . . come very high'.[66] Resolved to avoid the company of whores, he attached himself to the actress Anna Lewis, also known as Louisa, only to find himself infected by her with 'Signor Gonorrhoea' once more.[67] At first he tried to convince himself that it was impossible that Louisa could have infected him and half-heartedly he tried to pretend that he had merely 'got a gleet by irritating the parts too much with excessive venery'.[68] In the end he was forced to admit that he had caught gonorrhoea, but 'it is merely the chance of war'.[69] Louisa admitted that she had had a dose of the clap three years previously but had been clear for fifteen months and had slept with no one but Boswell in the past six. It was the end of the affair, despite Louisa's protestations of innocence, which were probably true, as the infection could have lain latent in her without any further symptoms that she still had it.[70] Boswell, feeling sorry for himself, thought that he suffered more than most people, since 'I am of a warm constitution: a complexion . . . exceedingly amorous, and therefore suck in the poison more deeply'.[71]

Despite being forced to take to his room for five weeks, living on bread, broth and water taken with his medicine, within a month of being cured, Boswell picked up a prostitute in St James's Park. This time, though, he was careful for the first time to 'engage in armour, which I found but a dull satisfaction'.[72] His dislike of using a condom was soon overcome and six days later he had sex with the first prostitute that he met, 'free from danger, being safely sheathed'.[73] Despite his revulsion at the brutishness of his behaviour and a loathing for the sickness he brought upon himself, Boswell remained addicted to casual sex, however much he tried to stiffen his resolve to overcome his lust or avoid the clap. By 1767, a recurrence of what seems by now to have been a chronic gonorrhoeal infection of the prostate would invariably be reactivated by any venereal or alcoholic excess.[74] Even marriage could not curb his need for prostitutes, although the fear of passing on any infection to his wife racked him with guilt.[75]

Unlike Boswell, his contemporary Giacomo Casanova rarely felt any self-loathing about his sexual adventures and their consequences, preferring to portray himself in his memoirs as a dashing Enlightenment intellectual endowed with looks, charm and charisma. Syphilis was a disease that he knew from experience how to overcome, and he was to comment in old age that 'the French disease does not shorten life when we know how to cure it' but merely leaves its marks on the body, which have the consolation of having been 'acquired during pleasure, just as soldiers enjoy looking at the scars from their wounds as evidence of their courage and the source of their glory'.[76] His first sexually transmitted infection had been contracted when he was a youth in Venice and too inexperienced to resist an 'ugly, destitute whore' throwing herself at him, only to leave him with the marks of a shameful disease.[77] At the age of 20, a one-night stand with a courtesan was a turning point in his life. Before being stricken with the pox, he was 'rich, lucky at cards, wise, liked by everyone and adored by the prettiest women'. Afterwards he 'lost my health, money, credit, good humour, consideration, wit and the ability to express myself for I was no longer persuasive'.[78] Nevertheless, the experience did not change his cavalier attitude towards sex and disease, nor alter his behaviour. He contracted venereal diseases in Mantua, Parma, Paris, Munich, Dresden, London and wherever his restless wanderings took him. Invariably he recovered after following a strict diet of nitrate water for six weeks, during which he gallantly refrained from sex so as not to pass his 'incense' or 'Celtic humours' on to any woman. These bouts of illness usually punctuated the various phases of his life and prompted him to turn over a new leaf, albeit briefly. When he fled from London in 1764 after being accused of having delivered a false bill of exchange, another bout of illness left him feeling at the age of 38 that he had entered the twilight of his life. This time his physician treated him with mercury pills, sweat-inducing herbal infusions and a rigorous diet. He was permitted the company of young girls doing their needlework, but otherwise inaccessible to this thin, sallow creature with swollen glands confined to his bed. It was apparent to him that there was a difference between the healthy and free man and the man in prison or suffering from severe illness.[79] Yet the life of the ageing libertine continued down its self-destructive path.

There was now some protection against catching the dreaded pox available in the use of the condom, which was worn during intercourse rather than after, as had been recommended by Falloppio. First appearing in the late seventeenth century, condoms did not become common until the eighteenth century, and even then they remained difficult to obtain outside London and Paris. As with the disease itself, names for the sheath reflected national antagonisms, Casanova calling them his 'overcoats from England', the French referring to the 'capote Anglais' and the English to 'French letters'. One supplier in 1776 advertised his shop as premises where 'all gentlemen of intrigue may be supplied with those bladder policies or implements of safety, which infallibly secure the health of our customers'. For Lord Hervey, the confidant of George II and Queen Caroline, they were 'preservatives from the clap and impediments to procreation', although for most users their

51

value was as a prophylactic against disease rather than their utility as a form of birth control. The sheaths in use were made of sheep gut and were tied around the scrotum by a red ribbon. Clumsy to use as they may have been, it was better to be cautious when having casual sex rather than have to undergo painful treatment for any infections caught later.[80]

Even abstention from sex with a partner was not considered to be free from risk, since it was even believed that masturbation could cause venereal infections through the irritation caused to the sexual organs. The eighteenth-century Enlightenment was marked by a rising phobia about the dangers of self-abuse, culminating in Jean-Jacques Rousseau's exhortation of 1762 in his influential *Émile* to guard against 'the most fatal habit which a young man can acquire'.[81] Fears were also stoked by the Swiss physician S.A.A.D. Tissot's 1756 treatise *Onanism* attacking masturbation, named after the Old Testament figure of Onan who had scattered his seed, a book destined to remain the basis of attacks on the practice for the next two centuries.[82] Tissot ignored the moral implications of self-abuse and concentrated on the physical consequences, including stunted growth, weak eyesight, general debilitation, fainting fits, epilepsy, impotence and even gonorrhoea.[83] For Tissot and his followers, masturbation was more pernicious for a young man than casual sexual gratification with a woman. By implication it was better to resort to a prostitute and the risks of sexually transmitted infection than to indulge in self-pollution. Some doctors even advised this as a way of avoiding self-abuse, although they then had to treat the consequences.[84]

It was not only the qualified physician or experienced surgeon that men sought out for the treatment of their disease, much to the disapproval of established medical men such as Daniel Turner, who in 1727 devoted many pages in his writing on venereal disease to attacking the claims of quacks.[85] An array of mountebanks and charlatans sprang up to offer the promise of speedy recovery without pain, preying on the fears and hopes of those 'children of Venus' who had 'anchored in a strange harbour'. Many advertisements for patent cures traded on fears by running through the symptoms in such detail that it was possible to make any reader of them fear that he or she might have the disease.[86] One advertisement listed these as 'the gonorrhoea or running of the reins, shankers, buboes or swellings in the groin, pain in the head, arms, shoulders and legs, or ulcers in the mouth, throat, scabs, itch, and breaking out over the whole body'.[87] What the quack doctor offered to the sufferers from these symptoms was a painless alternative to mercury, as used by more conventional medical practitioners. In doing so they returned to the old staples of guaiacum, sassafras and sarsaparilla, although generally the exact ingredients were kept secret, as in the case of 'an Herculanean antidote against the pox', ostensibly 'so as not to give encouragement to vice'.[88] One advantage of not using mercury was that there was no need for the patient to be confined to bed, and the side effects of the cure which made its use so conspicuous, such as excessive salivation, swollen gums, loose teeth and a foetid smell, were not present to advertise the malady to the world. Speedy cures with money-back guarantees were promised, with the 'chymical physician' G. Dean even undertaking that 'all injuries sustained by mercury where the parts or faculties are not perished' are 'faithfully repaired with the blessing of God'.[89] The quack doctor Anthony Bellan claimed to cure the French pox 'without obliging his patients to keep their chambers, nor leaving their daily occupations',[90] and James à Tilbourg claimed that his cures were 'so private that the wife shall not know whether her husband be cured of that distemper, nor the man of his own wife, nor none of their relations shall take any notice of their cure'.[91] Secrecy and utter confidentiality were further promised by the furtive manner in which many of these self-styled physicians conducted their consultations. In one case a lamp was left lighted at the door in the evening so patients could seek out treatment without having to enquire of anyone as to the location of the pox doctor,[92] and Gilbert Anderson offered two entrances to his patients, one of them in a private court, so that they could sneak in by whichever way they pleased.[93] Such patent cures as Isaac Swainson's Velno's vegetable syrup, Keyser's pills and Kennedy's Lisbon diet drink were readily available over shop counters in such diverse settings as bakers and booksellers, and thus readily recognisable. In his satirical cartoons of the Prince Regent such as the 1792 *Voluptuary under the Horrors of Indigestion*, James Gillray included Velno's vegetable syrup and Leake's pills alongside empty port bottles and dice.[94]

William Hogarth also included popular anti-venereal remedies in his satirical engravings, confident that the references would be fully understood by his audience. In *Marriage à la Mode*, Viscount Squanderfield visits the quack Monsieur de la Pillule, in a consulting room festooned with such trappings of the medical profession as apothecaries' jars, anatomical specimens, an Egyptian mummy and a crocodile, and holds out a pill box containing an anti-venereal remedy to a distressed young lady.[95] The same physician appears again in the *Harlot's Progress*, this time under his true identity of Jean Misaubin, arguing with Dr Richard Rock, whose anti-venereal pills litter the floor, while the prostitute Moll Hackabout dies of syphilis, her teeth loosened by the disease lying on a piece of paper marked with Dr Rock's name.[96] Rock was a high-profile quack, depicted by Hogarth in other works, including the *March to Finchley*, and noted for his 'anti-venereal, grand, specific pill'. Misaubin, however, was a regular physician, a French university graduate and a licentiate of the Royal College of Physicians, not the quack that Hogarth's deflating of his pretensions might suggest.[97] As Hogarth subtly suggested, in their approach to venereal disease, there was perhaps less difference between the reputable physician and the quack than might have been expected. Neither of them could deliver the safe, effective and painless remedy their patients sought.

In a society where there was an openness about sexuality and where the effects of promiscuity were also recognised as commonplace, there was an acceptance of the pox as a hazard that might have been far from welcome but that could not always be avoided. In the higher levels of society, where fashionable sexual licence and gratification made it commonplace, it was accepted as something unpleasant but that could be covered up in a fashionable style. Yet even for the highest in rank, syphilis might deprive a man of both looks and dignity. George II died while sitting on his privy stool in his closet from an aneurysm resulting from syphilitic infection.[98] His great-grandsons, George IV and William IV, were both pilloried for their chronic infections by the satirists of the day. William IV as a bluff young man had indeed sighed in vain for the type of girl who 'would not clap or pox me every time I fucked'.[99]

For those lower in social rank, there was the degradation suffered by Voltaire's Pangloss, whose optimistic philosophy that everything was for the best in the best of all possible worlds might be expected to be sorely tested by the repellent beggary syphilis had reduced him to: 'covered in pustules, his eyes dead, the end of his nose eaten away, his mouth twisted, his black teeth, speaking from his throat, tormented by a violent cough and spitting out a tooth with every exertion.'[100] It was not an attractive picture, even if he did claim to have caught it from a maid, who had it in a direct line of aristocrats, monks and soldiers from a companion of Christopher Columbus.[101] The glamour of syphilis was never more than superficial, with shame ever lurking below the skin. In the more puritanical climate of the nineteenth century, the disguises used by the wealthy to cover their shame at their loss of attractiveness were to be replaced by the hypocrisy-trimmed mask of respectability whereby venereal disease became more of a mark of ignominy rather than the wounds of Venus.

THREE

Containing the Contagion

What in many ways epitomised the change from the open libertinism of the eighteenth century to the moral repression of the nineteenth and twentieth centuries was the buttoned-up dark suit, which has held sway since the French Revolution swept away the gaudy extravagance of the rakish fop. It really came into its own in the nineteenth century as the epitome of discretion, modesty, professionalism and respectability among all social classes. It has given way to more relaxed casual dress when old moral rigidities have loosened, but in times of economic depression and neo-puritanical ethics it has invariably defied predictions of its demise and become once again the uniform of conformity. As such, the dominance of the dark suit coincided with the age of sexual inhibition. Yet below the appearance of respectability lay other realities under which darker fantasies and hypocrisies could hide, symbolised by the demand for fancy male lingerie noted by the French Syndicate of Men's Underwear Manufacturers in 1908.[1] Sexual fantasies and marital infidelities were hidden beneath a sartorial display of modesty. However, the sharper and flashier the seemingly austere suit, the more representative it was of business machismo and authority, and of a masculine dominance that sought to hide away sexual licence and moral contagion.[2]

In public places, likewise, there was a veneer of respectability beneath which lurked vice. Andrew Mearns, a Congregationalist social investigator, was aware when writing his 1883 pamphlet *The Bitter Cry of Outcast London* that in the seediest of areas all might not be what it seemed: 'Here you pass a coffee house, there a wardrobe shop, there a tobacconist, and there a grocer's carrying on a legitimate trade no doubt, but a far different and more remunerative one as well, especially after evening sets in.'[3] In one street in the East End of London in 1883, 32 of the 35 houses were known to be brothels, while another district could boast of 43 brothels and 428 'fallen women', some of them girls as young as 12.[4] The coexistence of criminals, heavy drinkers and prostitutes with the respectable poor seemed a rich source for corruption of the innocent, especially when the attractions of alcohol and the lure of prostitution as the means of escape were only too obvious to even the most virtuous of social reformers. William Booth, founder of the Salvation Army, admitted that 'the profession of the prostitute is the only career in which the maximum income is paid to the newest apprentice',[5] but also warned that 'this life induces insanity, consumption and all forms of syphilis'.[6] General Booth was also conscious that a prostitute was more likely to be condemned for having sinned than the man with whom she had slept: 'while the man who causes their ruin passes as a respectable member of society, to whom virtuous matrons gladly marry – if he is rich – their maiden daughters, they are crushed beneath the millstone of social excommunication.'[7]

Women, especially prostitutes, had been blamed from the very first appearance of the pox for spreading syphilis and gonorrhoea, not the men who had slept with them and then spread the disease to their innocent wives, and often to their as yet unborn children. Even that model of Victorian domesticity Isabella Beeton was to suffer numerous miscarriages as a result of her unwitting infection by her dashing, upwardly mobile but sexually reckless husband Sam, who patronised the prostitutes plying their trade near his publishing firm in the Strand.[8] Prostitution was seen as a conduit through which venereal disease could contaminate society and as such was something to be channelled and hidden away. It was a source of contagion that must be contained. In the Middle Ages, lepers had been segregated in lazar houses, many of which had been subsequently adopted for the use of syphilitics in the sixteenth century when leprosy had become rarer and the pox had become a serious social and medical problem. The sufferer from syphilis not only shared the unsightly skin disease of the leper, but also the stigma that went with it. Many general hospitals refused to admit such patients, whose smell was often 'so offensive that . . . where even one ward was appropriated . . . it pervaded the whole house',[9] not only for fear of the disease spreading to other patients, but also for fear that undeserving patients who had brought on their own plight might corrupt the morals of their innocent fellow patients. Sufferers from venereal disease, seen as the result of their own transgressions, were deemed unworthy of medical treatment. As a result, many voluntary hospitals, dependent upon the charitable support of their patrons and subscribers, excluded the admission of 'venereals'. At the Middlesex Hospital, one patient who had been admitted with a fever in 1753 was discharged as soon as he had been treated because his venereal disease made him 'unfit for this house'.[10] Some hospitals, such as St Bartholomew's, St Thomas's, Guy's and the Westminster, would admit 'foul patients' only if they paid special fees and thus did not benefit from the subscriptions and donations made to the charity for the free treatment of the deserving poor in the general wards of the hospital. One patient was even told by his doctor: 'you have had the disease one year and I hope that it may plague many more so to punish you for your sins and I would not think of treating you.'[11] At the London Hospital, founded in 1740, it was decided that syphilitics were the 'proper objects of the charity', but patients were required to leave a deposit of 10*s* 6*d* as security for their good behaviour and were kept apart from the main hospital in a special house reserved at first for them and sufferers from smallpox and other fevers, but which later for a time also provided lodging for nurses, in an age when the commoner type of nurse was often popularly regarded no more highly than a prostitute.[12]

The scantiness of provision for venereal diseases in the general hospitals meant that an institution dedicated solely to the treatment of such infections was desirable, especially as it would have the additional advantage of isolating the morally weak from society. The London Lock Hospital, which opened in January 1747 in a converted house amid open fields near Hyde Park Corner, was the first modern hospital in Britain to offer treatment for venereal disease and provided a model for similar institutions set up in large towns in the nineteenth century.[13] Its foundation was the initiative of William Bromfeild, a surgeon at nearby St George's Hospital who also numbered Frederick, Prince of Wales, among his practice. Bromfeild, although never pretending to be a specialist in venereology, had seen for himself the plight of many syphilitics denied access to the general hospitals either on moral grounds or because they could not afford the deposits demanded as surety for their good behaviour. He had even bought the leasehold of the site for the hospital for £350 with his own money and had the right contacts to recruit support from the aristocracy and the world of entertainment. After he had performed a cataract operation on Frederick Handel, the composer promised to write an oratorio in aid of the hospital, just as he had previously written music for the benefit of the Foundling Hospital. Meanwhile, Bromfeild himself had staged a play, *The City Match*, at the Theatre Royal, Drury Lane, for the benefit of his charity, and had recruited the support of the actor–manager David Garrick.[14]

The London Lock Hospital offered a place of refuge as much as the promise of a cure, although in its first two years it claimed that, out of 695 patients received, it had discharged 646 cured.[15] The hospital, though enjoying patronage from the nobility, did not receive the same widespread support as other charities, including the Magdalen Hospital, which had been founded to save 'fallen women', since its aims were to offer succour to those who had sinned and might not be repentant. In such circumstances the governors of the hospital were quick to counter any accusations that they might be encouraging vice by making it a rule that patients could not be readmitted for a second time after they had once been either cured or simply discharged for whatever reason without a cure.[16] All applicants for admission with a letter of recommendation from a governor were interviewed once a week by a small committee formed from the hospital governors, who had the power to veto anyone considered likely to cause trouble or who was not suffering from a venereal infection. Once admitted to the hospital, the patients were expected to help in the kitchen and laundry, and were forbidden to bring in alcohol, use bad language, be unruly or visit the wards occupied by the opposite sex. Such regulations were very little different from those in force in all the voluntary hospitals of the time, but reinforced the punitive and penal atmosphere of the institution. After 1762, compulsory attendance at a newly constructed and for a time fashionable chapel, with a strongly evangelical character, assumed an important role in the moral rehabilitation of the patients. Then in 1792 an asylum for fallen women was established nearby for 'those desirous of giving up their evil life'.[17] Whereas the men discharged from the hospital had homes and jobs to which they could return, for many of the women there was no option but to return to prostitution and disease unless they entered the Lock Asylum for the Reception of Penitent Female Patients, where they were subjected to a strict regime of studying the Bible, sewing, cooking and laundry duties as preparation for being sent out into domestic service once their moral rehabilitation was complete.

As the nineteenth century progressed, lock hospitals routinely began to treat men as outpatients and concentrate their inpatient work on women. It would have been impossible to offer inpatient beds to all men seeking a cure if only on account of the overwhelming numbers of them, whereas there were fewer women in need of treatment. However, the emphasis on the admission of women perhaps had most to do with the role of the lock hospitals as places in which the perils of prostitution could be controlled. One official in the Colonial Office, when writing of hospitals in the British colonies, even stated that the main purpose of lock hospitals was 'to put diseased prostitutes during the most venomous period of their career out of position in which they can spread disease'.[18] The segregation of the unrespectable from the deserving patients was based on moral considerations rather than medical ones, since the former's infections were sexually transmitted rather than airborne or transmitted by touch, which would have been the other justification for the isolation of the sick. There was a fear that not only would women patients be offended by the loose morals and bad language of the prostitutes, but that in some way they would also be corrupted by them. Underlying such attitudes was the assumption that prostitutes came from an underclass and that there would have been no need for segregation if they had been 'mostly immoral in the sense in which certain great empresses, actresses, lady noodists [*sic*] and soprani [*sic*] are known to be immoral'.[19]

Yet respectable women did contract venereal disease through no fault of their own and had to be treated for it alongside common prostitutes. At the London Lock Hospital in the early 1850s, out of 217 women admitted, the assistant chaplain noted that 129 were prostitutes, 18 were living 'in concubinage', 50 had 'yielded privately' and 19 were 'unblemished', infected unwittingly by their straying husbands.[20] Elsewhere there was concern about the transmission of syphilis to the unborn child. In France, the foundation of the Vaugirard Hospital in 1780 had been an Enlightenment response to the problem and recognition of the importance of healthy children to a strong state. Pregnant syphilitic women were brought from other public institutions, treated with a small amount of mercury and then they breast-fed their own babies or other newly born babies with congenital syphilis in the hospital. The small amount of mercury in the mother's or wet-nurse's milk was believed to act as an antidote for the babies, who received no direct doses of mercury themselves. Vaugirard was considered a model establishment, with each woman and child having her own bed or cot. Within 15 months, it was claimed that the Vaugirard had saved the lives of more than a third of the babies born there with syphilis. Vaugirard Hospital was one of the first attempts by a government to deal with venereal disease as a medical problem rather than as a social one; in the France of the Revolution and Napoleonic Empire generally there was a conscious attempt to run hospitals for sufferers from venereal diseases as therapeutic institutions rather than simply as punitive institutions or refuges for paupers. Nevertheless, the reform of fallen women was still seen as an important way of stamping out the disease.[21] If prostitution could be eradicated or controlled, then so could syphilis.

It was also, however, a service that many men sought out, and, if the dangers of contracting an infection could not be eliminated, then they must be minimised; and prostitution must be regulated so as to contain the contagion within supposedly safe bounds. In 1769 Restif de la Bretonne had argued that prostitution should be made a public institution, with regulated public brothels where 'the utmost care will be taken to protect the prostitutes from the horrible disease which makes an establishment of this sort so desirable'.[22] It was not until 1800 that the revolutionary government in France did introduce state regulation of prostitution, with the police given the duty of inspecting brothels and the power to insist on compulsory treatment of any diseased girls to prevent the spread of contagious disease. In 1802 all prostitutes, whether or not they worked in a brothel or whether they were working independently, had to register with the police if they wished to continue to be allowed to work, and in 1804 new regulations gave the police even tighter control over the monitoring of brothels.

The keystone of the system was the obligatory medical examination at regular intervals, which would be held at the brothel, a dispensary or a police station, including the special infirmary created for such purposes in Paris in 1843 at the Préfecture de Police. No more than a minute was set aside for examining each woman, which hardly gave time for the doctor to display much sensitivity towards his client.[23] Toulouse-Lautrec depicted one such medical inspection at an up-market brothel in the Rue des Moulins in his series of paintings of Parisian brothels, one canvas of which sympathetically shows two prostitutes with their chemises hitched up over their hips queuing for their examinations while the fully clothed madam goes about her business in the background.[24] Awaiting them was the degradation of the speculum, nicknamed 'the government's penis' by many of the girls. This was used to search out signs of disease in the course of very personal examinations, once a week for women living in official brothels, known as *maisons de tolérance*, and anyone found with symptoms of a venereal disease was detained and sent for compulsory treatment, often in prison hospitals such as the notorious Saint-Lazare in Paris, which had changed little in its wretched squalor from the dark days when such victims of the Guillotine as the poet

André Chénier had awaited their fate there at the hands of the Revolutionary Terror.[25] Here the unfortunate inmates wore a distinctive uniform, were badly fed and were not allowed to speak during their working hours. Attendance at Mass was compulsory, and the nuns responsible for supervising the women were unforgiving in their attitudes to their charges. Yet even this was not punitive enough for some physicians, such as the physician Alexandre Parent-Duchâtelet, a respected expert on the connections between prostitution and syphilis for whom the trade of the whore was 'as inevitable as the sewers, rubbish dumps and dust heaps'.[26] He urged that the prostitutes should be subjected to a military regime and even suggested that their punishment might include the use of treadmills, which would make the women fitter just as they could help to fatten oxen.[27] France led the way in recognising that, if vice could not be suppressed, it might as well be controlled though never condoned. Other countries followed suit and enacted their own legislation.[28] Britain, proud of its tradition of civil liberties and suspicious of any state interference that smacked of continental authoritarianism, remained aloof, though as riddled with venereal disease as any other country.

Not surprisingly, the British armed forces had long been a focus of concern about the spread of venereal disease. In 1846 the surgeon William Acton claimed that an average of 181 out of every 1,000 soldiers admitted to hospital each year had primary venereal sores, of which a quarter went on to develop constitutional syphilis. Meanwhile in the navy, every seventeenth sailor had gonorrhoea and every fifteenth suffered from syphilis.[29] Acton believed that this high rate of infection was down to the ready availability of prostitutes, who also endangered more respectable young men of the middle classes, but accepted that prostitution was ineradicable given the powerful sexual urges of young men and what he believed to be the lack of similar urges in well-brought-up young women. Convinced that the greatest hope of successful treatment lay in early diagnosis, he recommended the regular inspection of prostitutes working in brothels as a means of control.[30] What already existed was provision for the inspection of serving soldiers for signs of infection.

Nevertheless, in 1857, acting upon the recommendations of the Royal Commission on the Health of the Army, set up as a result of the scandalous conditions during the recently ended Crimean War, these regular inspections had been discontinued because they were considered to undermine the self-respect of the men.[31] However, the recommendation was not always acted upon, and the Duke of Cambridge, Commander-in-Chief of the British army, continued to insist that inspection be continued in the elite Guards regiments.[32] Yet the emphasis continued to be upon regulation of women as the source of infection. In 1862 a committee set up to investigate the prevalence of venereal diseases in the army and navy recommended the establishment of more voluntary lock hospitals in garrison towns but shied away from the continental system of regulated brothels and compulsory treatment, although it admitted that 'a coercive system of registration and surveillance, when properly enforced, may under certain conditions diminish the frequency of venereal disease'.[33] Yet something needed to be done when it was realised that a third of soldiers were being treated for venereal infections annually and that, with treatment usually lasting twenty-three days, this was equivalent to the loss of 8.69 days of service for every soldier each year, with the equivalent strength of two battalions being constantly disabled.[34] Dr W.C. Maclean, Professor of Military Medicine at the Army Medical School, thundered that 'prostitutes should be regarded as the enemies of the common weal, and not allowed to do the mischief they now do without let and hindrance'.[35]

A Contagious Diseases Act to deal with this threat to national efficiency was introduced without any fuss in the House of Commons on 20 June 1864 and passed almost surreptitiously at a late-night sitting on 21 July. It took only six days for the bill to pass through the House of Lords, and it received the royal assent on 29 July 1864. During the five weeks of its progress, there was very little debate about the Act, which introduced state regulation of prostitution and through its element of compulsion posed a threat to the liberty of the individual, albeit for the common good. The measure had been prepared in secrecy and circulated only to a small number of interested parties. Florence Nightingale, the redoubtable heroine of the Crimea, was of the opinion that such an Act would never be passed by a British parliament and warned of the danger that 'any honest girls might be locked up all night by mistake by it'. The writer Harriet Martineau protested against a bill that 'promises to secure soldiers and sailors from the consequences of illicit pleasures' and, as well as condoning immorality, was the first step towards a curtailment of civil liberties 'which can never be retracted as to leave us undamaged'.[36] Yet it was not only in the armed services that the new legislation had its supporters. Within the medical profession there was some support for compulsory inspection of prostitutes for disease in the same way that other public health measures, such as compulsory vaccination, sanitary inspections and the imposition of fines on butchers caught by inspectors selling bad meat, were accepted as necessary for the public welfare: 'if the butcher's shop may be occasionally visited and inspected for diseased meat, why should the brothel be exempted?' The doctors were urged 'to call upon the Government to arm science with the social powers necessary to destroy this spreading cancer of civilisation'.[37]

The lack of debate around the passage of the Act was largely due to a lack of popular understanding about what it involved. Many people, including, it was alleged, Queen Victoria, believed that it dealt with veterinary disease rather than infection in humans. Had they read the Act they could have been in no doubt about what it actually meant. The Act applied only to eleven port and garrison towns and was never in force outside those designated districts.[38] Any woman suspected of prostitution by a plain-clothes member of a special metropolitan police squad stationed within those towns could be arrested, examined by a doctor for disease without giving her consent and, if infected, forcibly admitted to a lock hospital for up to three months or until she was considered 'cured'. If any woman refused to be examined or refused treatment, she could be imprisoned for a month if it was her first offence and for up to two months if she reoffended against the Act.[39] The Act applied for only three years, but in 1866 a second Act made the system permanent and extended the maximum period for which women could be detained to six months; then in 1869 a third Act extended it to cover eighteen military areas in all.[40]

Effectively, the legislation ensured the provision of a healthy and disease-free supply of women available to service the lusts of the other ranks, enshrining in law the sexual double standards of Victorian England, which condemned the erring woman and made it easy for the straying man to satisfy his illicit desires hidden under the outward cloak of respectability. The Acts enjoyed some influential support in the Church of England and from the medical establishment, including the Regius Professors of Medicine at both Oxford and Cambridge. The *Lancet* considered that 'it cannot be wrong to prevent disease any more than to cure it . . . to compel women when diseased to cease from infecting the soldiers whose destruction by venereal poison costs the nation so dear'.[41] However, Henry Markham, editor of the *British Medical Journal*, denounced the Act as the work of legislators 'totally ignorant of the nature of the disease' and considered that 'a more iniquitous interference with the liberty of the subject has never been sanctioned by British Houses of Parliament', though no mention was made of the sexual hypocrisy also implicit in the law.[42]

For the War Office and Admiralty all that really mattered was whether or not the Contagious Diseases Act was effective in its operation. A committee set up in October 1864 under the chairmanship of F.C. Skey, a surgeon at St Bartholomew's Hospital, reported that the regulations needed amending and extending if they were to prevent a daily loss of men hospitalised by venereal disease 'equal to the loss of . . . such a vessel as the Royal Oak'.[43] One of the major difficulties in applying the Act was that it was nigh impossible to 'seize upon and eradicate disease at its source' because of the difficulties of diagnosing the infection early enough. Many of the men were drunk when they contracted the disease and then failed to show any symptoms for between twelve and fifteen days after intercourse, making it difficult to trace the girl they had slept with and allowing time for other men to be infected in the meantime. Moreover, brothel-keepers were admitting that they employed diseased girls only when they were totally unfit to work. At the same time, some girls were actually being reported to the authorities for 'being poxed' by their fellow prostitutes, who were 'frequently actuated by spite'. What was necessary was the regular examination of all known prostitutes in all garrison towns and sea ports, as well as a ban on prostitutes living in beer shops and public houses, where they might prove too great a temptation to inebriated customers.[44] However, just as essential was the provision of more beds for the treatment of any infected women in lock hospitals, since, without them, women having 'no alternative but starvation or prostitution . . . must return to the streets and engender more disease'.[45]

The Skey Committee was equally realistic in stressing that regulation of prostitution was severely limited without similar measures aimed at 'preventing the men from carrying infection to the women'. There was, however, great opposition from many military medical officers to periodic inspections of men for venereal disease, which had indeed been customary until as recently as 1857; in their routine medical examinations of the other ranks 'the genital organs, so prone to disease, whether contagious or not, are not examined'.[46] In the absence of medical inspections, it remained the responsibility of the individual soldier and sailor to check for signs of disease and he could be punished under military regulations for concealing it. In general, men were urged to wash themselves immediately after intercourse and to check more often for signs of disease when washing themselves. It was a recognition that the servicemen had some personal responsibility for catching and spreading infection, but there remained a strong feeling that it was prostitutes who were the major problem, and the best means of prevention was to avoid them altogether. If the armed forces could improve the comfort of barrack blocks and ships and provide opportunities for healthy and manly exercise and other recreations for off-duty hours, then there was some hope of 'reducing indirectly the amount of venereal disease in both services, by lessening the temptation of the men to resort to beer shops and brothels'.[47]

While, as ever, avoidance was better than treatment, there was little that could be done to prevent bored and drunken soldiers and sailors from seeking diversion in sex. The Contagious Diseases Acts offered some hope of containing the contagion in garrison towns and ports, but did nothing to deal with the dangers besetting respectable young middle-class men who were considered especially vulnerable to the seductions of ladies of the night. In France, visits to prostitutes began for these young men in their schooldays, and on holidays and half-days the brothels swarmed with schoolboys.[48] In London, 'it is amongst the middle classes . . . that the chief mischief is done by the evil they are the most persistent in ignoring', according to the medical reformer Thomas Wakely, who painted a lurid picture of such parents seeing their 'sons lured into debauchery'.[49] In the face of such fears for vulnerable young manhood, there were calls for the extension of the legislation to cover civilians too.

A glowing picture was painted to the Epidemiological Society of the success of the systematic regulation of brothels by naval and military medical officers in India and China, with one doctor idealistically dreaming of the days when there would be a state system of district medical officers policing the system, houses of recovery for afflicted prostitutes and a Health Union dispensing philanthropic aid.[50] The continental system of regulation was eulogised at the 1867 International Medical Congress,[51] and the Harveian Society of London began to address the question of instituting a similar regulation of brothels in Britain.[52] In response to such recommendations for wider regulation, the Society for the Extension of the Contagious Diseases Act to the Civil Population was set up. Among the leaders of the movement were Ernest Hart, editor of the *British Medical Journal*, the fashionable psychiatrist Henry Maudsley and the young surgeon Berkeley Hill. Hill had impeccable reforming credentials as the son of the criminal law reformer Matthew Davenport Hill and as the nephew of Rowland Hill, who had introduced the penny post. Berkeley Hill had studied with the French doyen of venereology Philippe Ricord in Paris and with the influential pathologist Rudolph Virchow in Berlin, giving him the scientific base that not only underlay his later success as Professor of Surgery at University College, London, but also gave him professional authority as the leading advocate of extension.[53]

Hill, surgeon to the Lock Hospital, was an especially effective exponent of regulation: his mastery of an array of statistics and his scientific objectivity underpinned the eloquence of his arguments. Moreover, he could draw upon personal experience of treating prostitutes and cite examples of women who were themselves in favour of any system which could alleviate the misery of their situations. One girl aged 20, who expressed a willingness to be examined by a doctor 'as often as was necessary', had eked out her work in the mantle trade by part-time prostitution until she had caught 'the disease'. She was admitted to the Royal Free Hospital and was a patient for three months, during which time 'she had a sore throat, spots on her skin and scabs in her hair'. On her discharge from hospital, she had returned to prostitution but had started to attend the Lock Hospital as an outpatient, ignoring the dangers of spreading the disease further. She and other prostitutes living in the squalid courts and alleys between Drury Lane and Gray's Inn Road all declared themselves willing to submit to compulsory medical examination and detention if it preserved their health. They freely admitted that, if they were diseased and could not gain admission for treatment in a hospital, they would attend for outpatient treatment but continue to ply their trade. When asked if they ever gave up walking the streets while they were diseased, one woman said, "Taint likely; if they did they must starve'.[54] Hill had not investigated higher-class prostitutes in the better districts of the West End but believed that they would also see the advantages of regular examination, since their prosperity depended upon them being free of disease, attractive and able to dress well. His findings among the prostitutes of London were similar to those of medical men in the towns already covered by the Acts, where, when they were first introduced, there had been very little opposition from the women themselves, who appreciated their value to them and 'would be tolerant of even further interference, having their health for its object'.[55] Some prostitutes, calling themselves 'Queen's Women', considered themselves 'a privileged class' and were able to charge higher prices as state regulation was a guarantee to their clients that they were free of disease.[56]

Not all doctors were as pragmatic and non-judgemental in their approach to the Acts as Hill and the medical men of the garrison towns. Samuel Solly, a surgeon at St Thomas's Hospital, was opposed to any measures to protect either women or men from the consequences of their addiction to vice, for syphilis was 'intended as a punishment for our sins and we should not interfere in the matter'.[57] By contrast, John Simon, medical officer to the Medical Board of the Privy Council, was dubious about the value of the Acts and resisted their extension to civilian areas for the very reason that he thought they did little good and were far too expensive.[58] Opposition to the Contagious Diseases Acts gathered momentum only gradually but when it did rally, in response to their extension in 1869 to cover large areas of Kent, Surrey and Hampshire, it brought together a wide spectrum of society, from religious groups concerned about the encouragement of sin to sanitary reformers who doubted that the Acts did much good, from early feminists concerned about their inherent discrimination in applying compulsory treatment only to women to supporters of civil liberties worried about the threat to individual rights. Men and women of all classes joined in the protests throughout the country.[59]

The first major popular expression of protest came from the Ladies National Association for the Suppression of the State Regulation of Vice in their Women's Manifesto published on New Year's Eve 1869, with the signatures of 130 women linked to Unitarian, Quaker, radical and independent free-thinking circles. Foremost among them was Josephine Butler, the wife of the principal of Liverpool College and herself a social reformer interested in the education of women and the reform of fallen women. Their protest centred on the threat to civil liberties of legislation passed without full public debate and on the degradation of the women caught up in the legislation. The Acts 'remove every guarantee of personal security, which the law has established and held sacred, and put their reputation, their freedom and their persons absolutely in the power of the police'. Not only did they remove the rights of British subjects to civil liberty, but they were unjust in punishing 'the sex who are the victims of vice, and leav[ing] unpunished the sex who are the main cause, both of the vice and its dreaded consequence' while violating the feelings of the women compelled to undergo inspection and treatment and 'further brutalising even the most abandoned'. Above all, the Contagious Diseases Acts were deplored as officially encouraging immorality so that 'the path of immorality is made more easy to our sons and to the whole youth of England'.[60] Support for the opinions expressed came from all quarters, and the Ladies National Association garnered support through public meetings and the publication of a newspaper *The Shield*, which chronicled abuses of the Act.

A by-election at Colchester, one of the garrison towns affected by the legislation, in November 1870 offered the chance to campaign against the Acts, since the government candidate Sir Henry Storks, former governor of Malta, was a strong supporter of them. Although many of the supporters of the Ladies National Association were themselves Liberals like Storks, and the Conservative candidate was also in favour of regulation of prostitution, they put up Dr Baxter Langley as a candidate to split the Liberal vote. The by-electioneering became increasingly rowdy, and when Langley attempted to hold a public meeting he was driven from the platform covered in flour, with his face bleeding and his clothing torn. Josephine Butler, who took a prominent part in the campaign, almost provoked riots in the streets by her very presence. The result was that the Liberal majority was overturned and the Conservative candidate returned. Josephine Butler and her allies saw it as a victory, but Gladstone and his government viewed it as of little significance.[61]

Nevertheless, the campaign for the repeal of the Acts had already been taken into the House of Commons. The leader of the parliamentary group against the Acts was Henry Fowler, a Liberal and a Quaker. His bill for the repeal of the Contagious Diseases Acts, introduced to the House of Commons in May 1870, met with the immediate announcement by H.A. Bruce, the Home Secretary, that a Royal Commission would be set up to investigate the matter.

Josephine Butler gave evidence and called for nothing less than total repeal of the Acts although she had few specific proposals for measures in their place. For her the focus of attack should be on the evil of prostitution rather than any attempts to deal with the consequences. Her suggestions were that 'the State may check profligacy, not with the object of curing disease only, but to check the vice which was the cause of the disease'. She called for severe punishment for the seduction of women, especially by 'the rich profligate', and demanded that men should be made more responsible for the care of their illegitimate offspring, rather than the burden lying with the mother. In suggesting this alteration to the laws of bastardy, she underlined her fervent belief that men and women should be treated equally in any attempts to stamp out vice, since 'legislation, however pure its aim, which is directed against the weaker sex only, will fail to accomplish any reduction in the amount of misery and sin there is amongst us'. She was, however, in favour of voluntary lock hospitals and believed that women who sought admission to them of their own free will would agree to remain in them until they were cured.[62] Yet the usually charismatic and inspirational Mrs Butler gave a somewhat disappointing performance before the Royal Commission with her unspecific proposals and her admission that her experience of the areas affected by the Acts was limited and that she knew nothing at all of Portsmouth and Devonport.[63]

The final report of the Royal Commission was issued in July 1871, and little action was taken. It recommended that the Contagious Diseases Acts should continue to be enforced, but made the concession of curtailing the periodical compulsory examination of prostitutes, which had been the most controversial aspect of the Acts. It also recommended against extending the legislation to the north of England or London, and ruled out covering the civilian population.[64] The 23 members of the Commission were themselves divided over the issue, with 7 of them being convinced supporters of extending the Acts and 6 of them equally committed to their repeal from the start. In such circumstances, a clear consensus for extension or repeal was unlikely and allowed the government to take as little action as possible. A bill was introduced by the Home Secretary to modify the law so as to end compulsory examination, but this was withdrawn in the face of cross-party support for maintaining the Acts as they were.

The campaign for repeal continued over the next decade with little result. The campaigners attempted to repeat their tactics from the Colchester by-election in another by-election at Pontefract in August 1872. Once again there were scenes of violence, and Josephine Butler found herself trapped with Mrs Wilson, the wife of the Sheffield manufacturer who was funding the challenge to the Liberal candidate, in a hayloft by ruffians trying to smoke her out. They failed, and so did the repeal movement, since the Liberal candidate H.C.E. Childers downplayed his support for the Contagious Diseases Acts and won the seat. The repealers rejoiced at the fall of Gladstone's ministry in 1874, not realising that the incoming Conservatives were even less likely to listen to their arguments and that they themselves had lost many of their supporters in the Commons in that general election, including Henry Fowler.

The leadership of the parliamentary wing of the repeal movement was now taken up by James Stansfeld, former Liberal President of the Poor Law Board and a vice-chairman of the Ladies National Association. Stansfeld insisted that all future agitation should be confined to the floor of the Commons. Within the House, he concentrated on putting pressure on Disraeli's Conservative administration by challenging the annual army estimates. In 1879 the government set up a select committee into the workings of the Acts, which reported in 1882 with no consensus as to what action should be taken. By this time, Stansfeld had built up greater support within the Liberal Party, now once more in office, and had mustered medical support for repeal. He also decided to concentrate his efforts on the area of the Acts that aroused most controversy and that had least support – the compulsory vaginal examination of suspected prostitutes. When, in April 1883, he called for the suspension of the compulsory examination clauses, his motion was carried by 182 votes to 110.[65] This wrecked the system of regulation, and, despite the predictable objections of the armed

73

services, the Contagious Diseases Acts were finally repealed in March 1886 as a result of political manœuvring. Gladstone's third ministry had been torn apart over the question of Irish Home Rule, and the President of the Local Government Board Joseph Chamberlain was expected to resign over the issue. James Stansfeld was the obvious replacement, and the final repeal of the Contagious Diseases Acts was the price of his joining the Cabinet, as well as a shrewd move to placate northern Liberals, Radicals and Nonconformists whose support was wavering in the face of divisions over Home Rule.[66]

It was a triumph for the Ladies National Association and for Josephine Butler as much as it was a vindication of Stansfeld's tactics. It was also an indication that the Contagious Diseases Acts had not been so efficient in eliminating disease as their supporters had initially hoped. In the absence of any effective form of treatment for venereal diseases, compulsory examination and hospital treatment could not perform this role. However, prostitutes hospitalised under the system were believed to leave with a greater concern for cleanliness, personal hygiene and their health, just as the supply of ablution blocks and personal towels by the War Office and Admiralty after 1867 was seen as encouraging servicemen to look after themselves by using soap and water on their genitalia as soon as possible after intercourse. Nevertheless, there was not the anticipated dramatic fall in the incidence of syphilis and gonorrhoea that might have justified any curtailment of individual liberty.[67] Moreover, it was reported that there had been reductions in the incidence of venereal disease in Glasgow, Edinburgh, Manchester and Leeds, which had not been covered by the Contagious Diseases Acts but where active, somewhat heavy-handed, policing had chased prostitution from the streets.[68] Meanwhile, justices of the peace in the southern garrison towns and ports were lamenting the 'disastrous effects' of the withdrawal of the Metropolitan Police, who had enforced the Contagious Diseases Acts, notably 'the increase in prostitution, and especially of youthful prostitution, in the more reckless conduct of prostitutes in the streets, in the increase of disease and in its more virulent character'.[69]

The triumphant reformers now turned their attention to demands for 'social purity', with campaigns for censorship and crusades against 'white slavery',[70] masturbation and homosexuality, thus driving vice further into hiding below the tight waistcoat of respectability. Meanwhile, successive governments shied away from attempting to deal with the problem of venereal disease after the failure of the Contagious Diseases Acts. In 1897 there was an outcry from the moral purity lobby at calls for the reintroduction of regulation of brothels and control of prostitutes in India as a result of concern over the prevalence of syphilis and gonorrhoea among troops stationed there. Legislation along the lines of the British Contagious Diseases Acts had been enforced from 1866 until 1888 despite the opposition of the Indian civil administrators and prominent Indians, and had continued on a semi-official basis using cantonment legislation, which allowed the compulsory hospitilisation of anyone suspected of having an infectious disease. Despite such measures, familiar in many British colonies and naval stations, admissions to hospitals in India of troops suffering from venereal diseases had actually risen and had reached a peak in 1895.[71] Now Florence Nightingale and the novelist Mrs Humphrey Ward both signed a petition to the government from a group of socially prominent women calling for better protection for British soldiers in the Empire, although they added the proviso that they favoured an independent inquiry. Nightingale had previously been a staunch opponent of such regulation at home, but now saw the need for legislation to preserve the efficiency of the army overseas and protect 'the innocent from contagion'. Josephine Butler had no such second thoughts and signed a counter-petition from the Ladies National Association. The prime minister Lord Salisbury, believing that 'public opinion was not sufficiently informed and enlightened' on the issue, took no action and similarly ignored a call in 1899 from members of the medical profession and women involved in philanthropic work for an inquiry into the prevalence of venereal diseases and the efficacy of existing arrangements for their treatment.[72]

Many venereal cases went untreated in the absence of adequate medical facilities. Voluntary hospitals remained unsympathetic to such patients, and treatment in the poor law infirmaries carried legal disabilities and a stigma additional to the one attached to the disease itself. Most friendly societies refused sick benefit to sufferers from sinful diseases. Fear of social disgrace drove many people into the hands of chemists and herbalists.[73] There was a debate over whether circumcision might act as a protection against syphilis, although the concern was perhaps more linked to discouraging masturbation than anything else.[74] Ignorance meant the continuance of the old superstition that a man could be cured of the infection if he slept with a virgin and transmitted the disease to her. In Liverpool in 1884 a man with syphilitic ulcers defended himself against charges of having raped a 14-year-old girl with the excuse that he had not set out to harm her but merely wished to cure himself. Another man had similar motives for raping a 9-year-old girl, and her parents, who at first believed that the ulcers on her genitals were the result of the child having swallowed a 6*d* piece, were reluctant to give evidence against him. 'Quack doctoresses' in Liverpool were said to have kept special brothels in Liverpool to provide such cures, often using mentally handicapped children.[75]

Allied to ignorance and fears of venereal disease was a sense of alarm about threats of contagion from abroad. Venereal disease could weaken the race, morally as well as physically. Since the time of the Grand Tour of the eighteenth century, travel abroad had been associated with sexual licence and its downside, venereal disease. The British Empire in the late nineteenth century was a source of pride, but was also a source of infection. Concern about the coupling of white British colonial administrators and soldiers with native women throughout the Empire, especially prostitutes, who shouldered the burden of blame for infecting these innocent men, meant that contagious diseases ordinances had been introduced in the colonies earlier than in Britain and implemented in a much more draconian way.[76] The relationship between colonialism and prostitution, though, could be viewed in another way. For the Irish nationalist, British civilisation was actually 'their syphilisation', a pun coined by James Joyce in *Ulysses*, and given to a character encountered by Leopold Blum in a pub in the course of his meanderings around Dublin on 16 June 1904, an Irish citizen who then goes on to curse the 'bloody thicklugged sons of whores' gets' whose language is fit only for the toilets of Europe.[77] More usual was the belief that any corruption or degeneration of the British race would lead to a decline in British influence in the world.

It was a threat dramatised by the theatrical manager Bram Stoker in his 1897 novel *Dracula*. A sufferer from syphilis himself, Stoker told the story of the attempt by the vampire Count Dracula, who had sucked dry the sources of blood of his native Transylvania and now sought to reinvigorate himself with the fresher blood of England, to infiltrate Britain and corrupt its bloodlines with his poison. Stoker's portrayal of vampirism had many similarities with the symptoms and social implications of syphilis. The vampire's kiss, the penetration of the body with its sharp teeth, which take on a phallic symbolism, and the exchange of body fluids all resembled the sexual transmission of syphilis. In attacking the young and rather staid solicitor Jonathan Harker during his visit to Dracula's castle, the vampire's wives, like prostitutes preying on the naive Englishman abroad, seduce him into a helpless state of 'languorous ecstasy' with 'the soft shivering touch of the lips' on the 'supersensitive skin' of his throat.[78] Dracula's own attacks on young women in England are penetrative in nature, and, just as sores first appeared on the body where syphilis had entered it, the teeth of the vampire left their mark where vampirism had corrupted the blood. Both Lucy and Mina, the young women infected by Dracula, suffer from such symptoms of secondary syphilis as tiredness, weight loss and fever. Lucy, thoroughly infected with the contagion, joins the living dead and starts to prey on others, including helpless children.[79] As with syphilis, women are seen as dangerous carriers of the infection, even if the original contagion came from a man, albeit a foreigner. In the novel, modern science is used effectively against the vampire, but as yet there was little that it could do to combat the very real problem of venereal infection.

Syphilis as a metaphor for foreign contamination was not confined to the sensationalist prose of Bram Stoker, but was also alluded to by Richard Wagner in his opera *Parsifal* as the result of a fall from virtue in the face of temptation. Amfortas had set out on a mission against the corrupt Klingsor, who was tempting the Knights of the Grail away from the path of virtue with his magical garden of delights full of diabolical flower maidens, a reference to the longstanding association of syphilis with contacts between soldiers and prostitutes. On his way to give battle, he had been seduced by the witch Kundry, losing as he did so the lance that had pierced Christ's side on the Cross. In the course of losing both his chastity and the lance, Amfortas had been wounded by the lance. This wound, a syphilitic result of his encounter with Kundry and a visible mark of his shame and sexual weakness, would not heal. Only the pure and compassionate knight Parsifal, personifying the redemptive power of Christianity, is capable of recovering the lance and curing the sinning king, though only once he has himself resisted the temptations of Kundry.[80] Wagner's musical motif for the suffering of Amfortas, with its heavy, dragging rhythm, is expressive of the physical and mental agony he has brought upon himself by not resisting the temptation of the forbidden.

Yet the forbidden had its allure enhanced by its very dangers, both to health and of the risk of being discovered. For the avant-garde, syphilis acquired a certain glamour from the myth that it contributed to genius by providing creative drive and restless energy. Leon Daudet wrote that the syphilis microbe was 'as much the power behind genius and talent, heroism and wit as that behind general paralysis, tabes and almost all forms of degeneration'. It 'makes a great poet of a maid's son, a satyr of a peaceful bourgeois, an astronomer or conqueror of a sailor' and 'fosters at once the dramatic intensity of life, the sterility of which is its opposite and the hardest of scourges'.[81] The syphilis of the philosopher Friedrich Wilhelm Nietzsche and of writer Guy de Maupassant has been cited in support of the thesis that tertiary syphilis in its general manifestation as paralysis of the insane corresponded to the peak of their creativity. Madness and genius may have been seen as allied, but the price exacted was high.

Nietzsche is usually claimed as the prime example of a man whose masterpieces were written as he declined into the dementia of tertiary syphilis. In 1888, aged 44, he completed his autobiographical *Ecce Homo* in Turin before lapsing into acute mania that was diagnosed as 'progressive paralysis' by the physician at the Jena asylum to which he was admitted.[82] Lucid at times and able to talk intelligibly to his mother, he would on other occasions urinate in his drinking glass and break windows. Two years later, after suffering two strokes, he died of pneumonia, having been confined to a wheelchair for much of that time. His manic behaviour, flights of fantasy and delusions of grandeur did not affect his memory or his ability to deal with abstract ideas. He had played a piano in a brothel as a young man and it was believed that the primary syphilis he had contracted in his youth had developed to the tertiary stage. However, his symptoms would also be consistent with schizophrenia.[83] There were no diagnostic tests for syphilis at the time of his death, and in the absence of such proof it is impossible to say definitely whether or not he was a sufferer from the pox. Attempts by much later doctors to diagnose the ailments of the famous from contemporary reports of their symptoms can be as misleading and wrong as the diagnostic attempts of their original doctors working without the advantages of subsequent advances in knowledge and technology.

Guy de Maupassant had no doubts about what he suffered from and, for one, gloried in his disease:

> My hair is beginning to grow again and the hair on my arse is sprouting. I've got the pox! At last! Not the contemptible clap . . . The majestic pox . . . and I'm proud of it . . . I don't have to worry about catching it any more, and I screw the street whores and trollops, and afterwards I say to them, 'I've got the pox'.[84]

Indeed Maupassant was probably prouder of his sexual prowess and the syphilis it brought him than he was of his writings. He boasted that he had once had intercourse with six prostitutes in the course of an hour in front of witnesses and that he could have an erection at will anytime that he wanted. He had also painted a chancre on to his penis to convince his mistress that he was infected, before proceeding to rape her so that she would believe that she too was in danger of being diseased.[85] His short story 'Le Lit 29' had told the story of a handsome soldier who had returned to Rouen from the Franco-Prussian War of 1870 to find his once-beautiful mistress Irma, now almost unrecognisable, dying of syphilis in a hospital ward. She had been raped by Prussian soldiers but, rather than seek treatment, had had her personal and patriotic revenge on the invaders by sleeping with as many of the Prussian soldiers as possible.[86] Maupassant himself succumbed to general paralysis of the insane and died in 1894, eighteen months after a suicide attempt and his admission to a fashionable sanatorium, where Vincent Van Gogh's brother Theo had previously received treatment for the same syphilis-induced dementia.[87]

Although Maupassant had no qualms about writing of venereal disease in his fiction, it is surprisingly absent from many nineteenth-century novels. Writing for family audiences, Charles Dickens and William Makepeace Thackeray had avoided mention of the disease and were perhaps more decorous than many of their predecessors in their depictions of low life. Even a more explicit and brutally realistic writer such as Émile Zola did not dwell on the scourge of syphilis. His prostitute heroine Nana dies of smallpox rather than of the syphilis her lifestyle might have suggested as a suitable end for her, perhaps because her death could be swift rather than long drawn out as with the great pox. Honoré de Balzac never specifically mentioned the pox, but in *La Cousine Bette* of 1846 described something very similar to it. In this novel Valérie catches a disease from her Brazilian lover and fatally passes it on to her husband. Valérie is punished for her sin by losing her looks as her hair and teeth fall out and her swollen hands are covered with 'green pustules', her nails falling off and remaining embedded in her flesh when she scratches the sores, and her extremities are eaten away.[88] The disease is never specified, but the symptoms suggest mercury poisoning as a result of treatment for syphilis, an unappealing picture of the effects of the disease.

Earlier, venereal disease had enjoyed glamour through its association with Romanticism in literature, music and art. The mad, bad and dangerous Lord Byron, despite his reckless sexual escapades, had managed to avoid syphilis, but was a martyr to gonorrhoea, prompting his desire to die 'standing' if he had to die young.[89] Even the supposedly chaste and consumptive John Keats seems to have contracted the clap, but, having trained as a doctor, he knew how to treat himself with 'a little mercury' which 'corrected the poison'.[90] Later in the century, syphilis became associated with genius and creativity, although often ending in the general paralysis of the insane. The composer Gaetano Donizetti managed a prodigious operatic output until syphilis reduced him to a virtually vegetative state at the age of 47 in 1844. Gustave Flaubert bragged, after a sybaritic round of sexual activity in 1850, of having 'collected 7 chancres' in Beirut 'which have ended by "joining up" into a single chancre on his penis', which he dressed daily with a mercury ointment. Despite losing his teeth and hair, giving him 'the bald head of a clerk or a worn-out notary', he felt that his scars merely added to his sexual allure and his creativity.[91]

The poet Charles Baudelaire also considered that syphilis represented a coming of age, commenting that 'the day a young writer corrects his first proofs, he's as proud as a school boy who has just caught the pox'.[92] Rite of passage though it may have been, syphilis terrified Baudelaire once it got a grip on him, and his mental faculties began to decline from 1862 onwards, gradually burning out the very creativity with which the disease was associated. By 1866 he was 'rolling about and falling over like a drunkard' without any apparent reason, despite obeying his doctors' advice to abstain from coffee, beer, wine and brandy and to drink only Vichy water. The doctors, ignorant of his earlier infection with syphilis, put his symptoms down to hysteria. During a sightseeing visit to a church in Namur, he collapsed and suffered a mild stroke. Paralysis and mental confusion soon followed. Once noted for his lyrical flow of words, Baudelaire was soon incapable of expressing any coherent ideas and indeed of finding the words to express even the most simple of requests. He lingered on in this deplorable state, sometimes recovering his mental faculties and then relapsing, for another seventeen months until his death at the age of 46 in August 1867, never again able to wield his once-mighty pen.[93]

For the Impressionist artist Paul Gauguin, syphilis was the curse he introduced to the island paradise of sunshine and solitude he had sought out for himself in Tahiti. Shortly before leaving Paris in 1895 for his second sojourn on Tahiti, he had contracted syphilis, and this he passed on to his Polynesian lovers, who 'come to my bed every night as if possessed'. Some of the beautiful female nudes in his paintings of the primitive and innocent state of nature he believed that he had found there were to become the victims of his diseased condition. He developed a running sore that failed to respond to the medical treatment he could barely afford. From 1897 onwards his work took on a gloomier tone, and the following year he attempted suicide. By now wracked with syphilis and no longer so attractive to the local women, he moved to Dominique, where he built his 'House of Pleasure' and found a new lover. Increasingly he longed to return to his native France but that would have destroyed the myth of the South Seas painter who had returned to the state of nature, and in 1903 he died in his lost paradise.[94]

Gauguin may have flaunted his sexuality, but others preferred to cover up the results of their sexual licence. Oscar Wilde dramatised this in *The Picture of Dorian Gray*, where the corruption that disfigures the portrait of the debauched hero while he retains his unchanging, youthful beauty mirrors the effects of syphilis on the body. Only on his death does Dorian Gray's corpse take on the 'withered, wrinkled and loathsome decay' his lifestyle might have been expected to bring on.[95] For Erik, the 'Phantom of the Opera' of Gaston Leroux's 1911 novel, a real mask actually hides his disfigurement, in which his eyes are like 'two big black holes, as in a dead man's skull', his skin is 'a nasty yellow' and 'his nose is so little worth talking about that you can't see it side-face'.[96] Erik's missing nose, sunken eyes and stench of rotting flesh were the stigmata of hereditary syphilis to contemporary readers of the novel, with the absence of the nose being perhaps the most horrific feature.[97] It is this that dooms his love for the soprano Christine and that he must cover with a mask or a false nose.

For real, rather than fictional, sufferers from syphilis, it was not so easy to hide the shame that went with the symptoms of syphilis, although their decline and deaths might be far from the public gaze. Even the innocent were not exempt. The angst-ridden Swedish dramatist Auguste Strindberg suffered from eczema, but to his shame was admitted to a VD ward in the early 1890s because of the continuing perception that the nastiest of skin diseases were manifestations of sexually transmitted infections and remained the particular province of dermatologists.[98] Sometimes prominent victims received their treatment more confidentially. In 1894 Lord Randolph Churchill made his last public speech at a City Livery Company appeal dinner in aid of the London Lock Hospital in which he passionately declared that the Lock was perhaps the greatest public charity in London and deserved full charitable support. The dinner raised £2,767 for the charity thanks to Churchill's eloquence.[99] What his audience did not know was that he had just been diagnosed by his doctors as suffering from general paralysis of the insane and given only a year to live. He had probably contracted syphilis in 1883, and from 1893 his speeches in the House of Commons had become increasingly incoherent, cutting short a brilliant career that had taken him to the post of Chancellor of the Exchequer.[100] Syphilis was merciless when it struck.

The blighting effects of syphilis on hopes and ambitions evoked fear in the last quarter of the nineteenth century, especially when, as with hereditary syphilis, the sins of the fathers might be visited on the next generation. It was not normally a subject for open discussion. When Henrik Ibsen actually raised the subject of hereditary syphilis on stage in 1881 in his play *Ghosts*, he scandalised audiences, for whom it was not considered a suitable subject for entertainment. Osvald Alving's promise in life is doomed as the result of his dead father's debauched and dissolute lifestyle. His mother Mrs Alving recognises that there is no moral difference between fallen women and debauched men and rues the way in which it was male sexual immorality that has damned her child.[101] She had sent Osvald away to shield him from exposure to paternal vices and, not wanting 'my son to inherit anything whatsoever from his father', also metaphorically denied him his financial inheritance. Yet she could not prevent him from being 'more or less riddled from birth' and at the end of the play is faced with the dilemma of whether or not to hasten the end of the life of her cursed son as he sinks into mental decline, asking for the sun.[102]

The silence of despair at the end of *Ghosts* echoes the contemporary inability to treat syphilis. Seemingly there was nothing that could be done except to contemplate death as a release, especially once the disease had reached its secondary and tertiary stages. This reflected a profound ignorance about the cause of the disease and its nature. Only when its cause was discovered could an effective treatment be found, but this was not yet even a distant hope for Osvald Alving and his real-life counterparts, their all-too-genuine suffering hidden under their outward garb of respectability.

FOUR

The 'Magic Bullet'

It is hard for a doctor to treat a disease effectively if he does not know precisely what causes it or how it differs from other illnesses. Yet that was what many medical men were expected to do before the nineteenth century, when advances in the new science of microbiology finally made it possible to identify the specific causes of bacterial diseases. Until then many questions remained unanswered for specialists in venereal diseases. What caused syphilis and gonorrhoea? Were they separate diseases or different stages of the same one? Until these questions could be answered and the exact nature of syphilis established, there could be no great advance either in understanding its character or in developing more effective treatment. Indeed, it was not until the nineteenth century that the difference between syphilis and gonorrhoea was fully recognised and the two infections were no longer seen as different manifestations of the same infection. Only once the two infections had been differentiated and their causes identified could the search for a more effective treatment begin as the twentieth century dawned. Even then the search was not to be simple, but, as medicine began to become more scientific, the quest for the causes of and cure for syphilis took on a central role in the development of medical science.

Since the sixteenth century, it had been difficult to distinguish between gonorrhoea and syphilis. Many of the most distinguished doctors involved with treating sexually transmitted infections believed in the unitary nature of the two diseases, including Paracelsus, Ambroise Paré, Thomas Sydenham and Jean Astruc. Alexander Pope reflected the popular view when he referred to 'Time that at last matures a clap to a pox'.[1] The clap was seen as a local manifestation of the pox affecting only the genitalia and was

85

believed often to disappear of its own accord. When the more serious symptoms of syphilis appeared, they were commonly attributed to the venereal poison having spread itself around the body, starting from the hard chancre on the genitals, and become 'constitutional'. The concept that there was only one venereal disease did not go unchallenged by doctors, who noticed that syphilis might be found even where there had been no earlier case of gonorrhoea, which itself was not invariably followed by the development of full-blown syphilis.

John Hunter, who had established for himself a primacy of reputation among London surgeons in the second half of the eighteenth century, set out to settle once and for all the question as to whether the pox and clap were different stages of the one disease or two very specific diseases. The tenth child of a Lanarkshire farmer, he had sought fame and fortune in Georgian London, where his elder brother William had established himself as a surgeon and teacher of anatomy. Starting off as an assistant in his brother's dissecting room, John Hunter had trained as a surgeon at Chelsea Hospital under William Cheselden, who had developed an operating technique for the removal of the stone, and at St Bartholomew's Hospital under Percivall Pott, after whom the compound Pott's fracture of the ankle and spinal tubercular Pott's disease are named. Having completed his surgical training with these eminent medical men, he had returned briefly to working with his elder brother before building up his own successful practice as a surgeon. Above all, though, he remained a prolific and indefatigable experimentalist, and through his studies of inflammation, shock and disorders of the vascular system, teeth, gunshot wounds and blood circulation, he played a major part in the transformation of surgery from a manual craft inferior to the work of the physician into a serious scientific discipline based on physiological investigation. Yet his search for knowledge of the human body and his appetite for dissection drew him into the murkier world of the body-snatching resurrection men, whose activities were paralleled by his building-up of a huge collection of anatomical and biological specimens that after his death became the nucleus of the Hunterian Museum of the Royal

College of Surgeons.[2] It also drew him into an energetic study of venereal disease, which affected many of his patients and gave him the opportunity to test his theory of the unity of syphilis and gonorrhoea.

By 1767 Hunter could bask in his professional and personal success. At the age of 39, he had a thriving practice, had recently been elected to membership of the Royal Society and was newly engaged to marry Anne Home, daughter of an army officer. His coarse language, disregard of etiquette and unkempt, casual appearance were not barriers to either professional or social advancement. Then in May 1767 he decided to undertake what would now be regarded as a risky and perhaps not entirely ethical experiment by inoculating gonorrhoea into a man not suffering from the disease. He could then monitor the progress of the disease for signs that syphilis might be developing. If, as he indeed anticipated, the symptoms of gonorrhoea were followed by those of syphilis, then he would have undeniable proof of the unity of the diseases. If, however, there were no signs of syphilis, then the two infections must be distinct from each other.

Taking up his lancet, he made two punctures into a human penis, one in the foreskin and the other in the *glans penis*. Into these punctures he rubbed a 'lancet dipped in the venereal matter from a gonorrhoea'. This he did on a Friday. By the Sunday, he recorded a 'teasing itching in those parts which lasted till the Tuesday following'. On the Tuesday morning he recorded that 'the parts of the prepuce where the puncture had been made were redder, thickened and had formed a speck', which within a week had 'increased and discharged some matter', and 'there seemed to be a little pouting of the lips of the urethra'. So far the symptoms were those of gonorrhoea. Now reassured that he had successfully inoculated the clap, he began to watch for signs that the pox might be developing. Within ten days, an ulcer had formed on the foreskin and a gland in the right groin began to swell to form a bubo. Two months later 'a little sharp pricking pain was felt in the tonsils', indicating an ulcer. Seven months after beginning the experiment, 'copper coloured blotches' broke out on the skin and there was no doubt that the infection had developed into syphilis. Hunter now began to treat the festering sores on the genitals and tonsils with a mercury ointment to control the disease, and continued to monitor the symptoms for three years. By the time the last symptoms of the disease had disappeared, either as a result of the use of mercury or because it had entered the latent stage, Hunter was satisfied that he had proved the unity of venereal diseases.[3]

The identity of his victim Hunter would never reveal. He could have been a paid volunteer or perhaps one of Hunter's unwitting patients, experimented on in good faith but without having given anything approaching informed consent. It is more likely, though, that he was rashly experimenting on himself. It had not been difficult for him to find a patient infected with gonorrhoea from whom he could obtain the requisite suppurating matter. However, finding the right subject for the experiment was not so easy. He needed to be absolutely certain that he would be infecting someone clean of any previous infection and who could be observed on a daily basis over a long period for signs of disease. Hunter himself was the obvious subject, perhaps the one person he could be sure of being free from infection, courageous and knowledgeable enough of the consequences to take the decision to risk his health, and available for regular examination. Yet, in writing up his experiments in his *Treatise on Venereal Disease*, not published until 1786, he gave no clues as to the identity of his subject, provoking much debate ever since as to whether it was indeed self-inoculation or not. Some of his pupils later claimed that he had revealed his own identity as the experimental subject in lectures with the statement 'I have produced in myself a chancre from the matter of a gonorrhoea' and also in an article in the *European Magazine* in 1782 where he endorsed self-experimentation.[4]

Sadly, Hunter's courage in inoculating himself, far from definitively settling the question, was merely to confuse the issue as to whether or not he was dealing with one disease or two. He had taken the pus from a man who was most likely suffering from both gonorrhoea and syphilis, and had unwittingly infected himself with both diseases. Yet on the basis of only one experiment he felt confident enough to assert that a 'gonorrhoea will produce chancres'. His authority was deemed enough to put an end to the debate over the unity or duality of venereal diseases and was to delay considerably progress in the proper understanding of the disease. Since further experiments in inoculating patients with matter from their own secondary ulcerations failed to produce a chancre, he wrongly concluded that the rashes and mouth ulcerations could not pass on the disease. He also denied that syphilis could affect the brain, another aspect of the disease about which he was to be seriously mistaken.

Despite his dominance in the medical firmament, Hunter's views did not go unchallenged by his contemporaries. His main opponent was a younger surgeon with pretensions to an expertise in venereal disease and a personal animus against him, Jesse Foot, who ridiculed Hunter's *Treatise* within months of its publication. Foot attacked it for generalising from only one case, failing to refer to other authorities on the subject and using obscure language to do so.[5] Yet Foot accepted that syphilis and gonorrhoea were actually one disease. It was just that he disliked Hunter and distrusted his methods. Meanwhile Hunter's supporters rallied in defence of the validity of his findings against this and other attacks.[6] Following his experiment, Hunter went on to greater success, being appointed surgeon to St George's Hospital in 1768 and surgeon-extraordinary to George III in 1776. Yet within a few years his health had begun to deteriorate with angina, which may have been the result of his syphilitic infection.

Only in Edinburgh did the question as to whether the two diseases were separate entities remain an important issue. In 1797 Benjamin Bell, building on work started by Andrew Duncan in 1778, carried out a series of similar experiments to the one undertaken on himself by Hunter, but with very different results. A number of intrepid medical students self-inoculated in order to demonstrate that gonorrhoea produced only gonorrhoea and that syphilitic chancres could be produced only by infection with syphilitic pus. The first of these young men used a lancet to inoculate matter from a syphilitic chancre into his urethra. None of the signs of gonorrhoea were noticed, but after five or six days he developed a painful and inflamed chancre before further developing a suppurating bubo on his groin and then an ulcerated throat. He was confined to his room for thirteen weeks for treatment with mercury. This and similar cases involving foolhardy but committed young men established the duality of the diseases but were ignored for many years.[7] Supporters of Hunter's views cited him in support of the existence of only one disease, while some of the more eclectic critics of Hunter, such as F.X. Swediaur, even claimed that one prostitute might infect one man with the clap, another with the pox and a third with both diseases.[8]

It was not until 1837 that there was any further advance in establishing that syphilis and gonorrhoea were two very different infections, once again through a series of experimental inoculations from syphilitic chancres, this time by the fashionable French physician Philippe Ricord. Born in Baltimore in 1800, the son of a bankrupt ship-owner, Ricord had left the United States in 1818 to study medicine in his parents' native France. His interest in venereal disease had been aroused by his appointment in 1831 to the staff of the Hôpital des Vénériens, later renamed the Hôpital du Midi, which specialised in treating sufferers from venereal diseases. There he quickly built up a reputation as the national expert on syphilis, and with it a prosperous medical practice. His Paris house, befitting the reputedly richest doctor in France, contained five separate magnificently decorated waiting rooms for his patients. One of them, for ordinary men, was always so crammed that the queues were controlled by giving each patient a number on his arrival that would be called out when it was his turn. Women had their own waiting room reached by a separate staircase. Patients with letters of recommendation had their own reception room, and yet another salon was set aside for Ricord's friends and fellow doctors. A fifth, much more grandiose, salon, decorated with paintings by Rubens, Van Dyck and Géricault, was reserved for the elite of society. Ricord's own library and consulting room were no less magnificent, with a gallery of busts of the great physicians of the past, a collection of medical instruments and a portrait of Ricord by the then fashionable painter Couture.[9] However, it was at the hospital that he developed his theory that gonorrhoea was a localised disease caused by inflammation of mucous tissues and that syphilis was very different in its nature and could not be the result of a gonorrhoeal infection.

Ricord believed that clinical observation of the symptoms of gonorrhoea and syphilis was not enough to establish proof of his theory. Instead he turned to the technique of 'experimental inoculation', which he considered to be more 'in line with the needs of modern science'.[10] At first he tried to experiment using animals, but failed to make much headway because 'the inoculable principle of syphilis is specific to man'.[11] Yet, unlike both Hunter and Bell in the previous century, he had ethical scruples about experimenting on healthy human subjects and infecting them with the dreaded disease.[12] He decided instead to experiment with patients already infected with syphilis and gonorrhoea, drawing pus from an existing sore and reinoculating it elsewhere in the same individual from whom it had been taken. What he found was that the pus from gonorrhoeal infections failed to inoculate, as did the pus from the secondary symptoms of syphilis such as buboes, ulcers and pustules, but that pus from a primary chancre invariably produced another chancre when inoculated.[13] These findings provided evidence that syphilis was a specific disease caused by a particular agent, the *virus syphilitique*, and that gonorrhoea was 'incapable of communicating syphilis either in its primitive form to another subject, or in its constitutional form to a person already infected' by gonorrhoea, which accordingly was not the initial stage of the disease but a completely different infection.[14] Ricord also categorised the different stages of syphilis starting with the primary ulcer on the genitals before progressing to the rashes, pustules and swollen glands of the secondary stage. After a latent or transitional phase, tertiary syphilis could develop, with its gumma, rubbery tumours affecting any part of the body. However, he wrongly concluded that syphilis was contagious only from its primary chancres and could not be passed on in its later stages.

Most controversy revolved around the very question as to whether or not secondary syphilis was contagious, although not all doctors at first accepted that syphilis and gonorrhoea were distinct diseases. By the 1850s many younger doctors who accepted the distinction between the two diseases were less willing to agree with Ricord that syphilis was infectious only in its primary stage, since their own clinical observations had led them to believe otherwise. For Ricord, the science involved in his experimental inoculation work could not be misleading, and he refused to listen to the arguments of his critics or accept the evidence of their eyes. In 1859 the Lyons physician Joseph Rollet demonstrated by clinical observation that secondary syphilis was indeed contagious,[15] but it was felt that the only way to refute Ricord's ideas would be deliberately to infect healthy subjects with pus taken from the symptoms of secondary syphilis.

The cudgels were taken up by two of Ricord's bitter rivals, Camille Gibert and Joseph Alexandre Auzias-Turenne, both of them resentful of his success and wealth, and smarting from his curt dismissal of their views on syphilis. Auzias-Turenne, moreover, was ambitious to develop a form of vaccination against syphilis similar to the smallpox vaccination developed by Edward Jenner, who had been a pupil of John Hunter. He believed that repeated inoculations of successively weaker forms of the syphilitic poison or 'virus' would eventually make the individual resistant to further infection. Although he used his vaccines, derived from human beings with the infection, only on people already suffering from the disease, his ultimate aim was to develop it as a preventative measure that could eventually eradicate syphilis completely.[16] It was Auzias-Turenne's belief that syphilis gradually lost its virulence as it progressed through its various stages, but remained infectious. Ricord's failure to produce an infection from secondary syphilis reinoculated into someone already thus infected was due to the acquisition of immunity from the infection and to the weakening of the infection.[17] Auzias-Turenne blamed Ricord for obstructing acceptance of his theory of syphilisation and for having used his influence to withhold permission for him to test out his theories and vaccines on the prostitutes detained at Saint-Lazare. The National Academy of Medicine had condemned Auzias-Turenne's ideas and methods as dangerous to the patient in 1852 at Ricord's instigation, and six years later he sought his revenge by reopening the debate about secondary contagion. In January 1859, with Camille Gibert, he began a series of experiments on seriously ill men in their early twenties at the Hôpital Saint-Louis, who were inoculated with pus taken from a patient suffering from the secondary stage of syphilis. Each of the men involved duly contracted syphilis.[18] Even Ricord was forced to admit that he was wrong. The contagiousness of secondary syphilis had now been proved beyond doubt, yet the way that it had been done raised important ethical issues. Non-syphilitic patients in a public hospital had been infected deliberately with the disease without their consent. For the doctors concerned, what mattered was the advance in knowledge obtained. The individual patients were sacrificed to a greater good, and there were few controls to restrain the doctors, although some did speak out against these experiments. Generally the rights of the patients to be told about what was being done to them and to be asked to give their permission were given very little consideration. It was an attitude that was to prevail well into the twentieth century, particularly with regard to syphilis.[19] The doctors and their Olympian judgement reigned supreme.[20]

It was a pupil of Ricord's, Alfred Fournier, who was to make the next major advances in the study of syphilis. Fournier, arguably the greatest syphilographer of the late nineteenth century, dedicated his professional life to the study of syphilis and was appointed to the first chair of cutaneous and syphilitic diseases established especially for him by the University of Paris Faculty of Medicine in 1880. After qualifying as a doctor he had been Ricord's houseman at the Hôpital du Midi before taking up appointments at the Hôpital de Lourcine, then the main Parisian hospital for the treatment of venereal disease, and at the Hôpital Saint-Louis. In addition to being active in the practical clinical treatment of syphilis, he also made major contributions to the theoretical understanding of the disease on such topics as the incubation period of syphilis, the classification of the various stages of the disease, the symptoms of the infection in women, syphilitic abortion and the contagiousness of the secondary stage of the disease.[21] He also demonstrated that there was a latent phase in both acquired and congenital syphilis.[22]

However, his major contribution was in establishing the relationship between the tertiary stage of syphilis and diseases of the nervous system, thus ensuring that the importance of neurosyphilis was recognised. In 1875 he asserted that *tabes dorsalis*, a disease of the spinal cord and sensory nerve roots in which positional sense and sensation are lost, was caused by syphilis.[23] Then from 1879 onwards he made the even more revolutionary claim that syphilis was also the cause of general paralysis of the insane. This condition, characterised by impaired speech, loss of memory, loss of voluntary movement in the arms and legs, disintegration of the personality, delusions of grandeur and dementia, had been observed as a distinct condition since the eighteenth century but had not been connected with syphilitic infection until the 1850s.[24] Fournier's beliefs were opposed by the psychiatrists, who laid more emphasis on the role of alcoholism, overwork and overwrought passions in bringing on the onset of general paralysis of the insane. Fournier countered with an impressive array of statistics demonstrating that the cerebro-spinal system had been affected in 2,009 cases out of 4,700 cases of tertiary syphilis, using examples of general paralysis of the insane among syphilitic juveniles who were not old enough to have developed general paralysis from long-term alcoholism or overwork. His critics acknowledged the existence of general paralysis in syphilitics, but not the condition of syphilitic general paralysis of the insane. It was not until 1913 that Fournier's views were definitively proved correct when Hideyo Noguchi discovered the bacterium that causes syphilis in the cerebral cortex of people who had died from general paralysis.[25]

Fournier was also concerned about hereditary syphilis and undertook a systematic study of the subject, noting that the most frequent signs of this were nerve deafness, a saddle-nose, inflammation of the cornea of the eyes and the dental deformation known as Hutchinson's teeth, where the teeth are peg-shaped, broader at the gum than at the cutting edge.[26] These diagnostic features of congenital syphilis, known as Hutchinson's Triad, had first been identified by the nineteenth-century English clinician Jonathan Hutchinson in his work at the London Hospital, the Blackfriars Skin Hospital and Moorfields Eye Hospital.[27] Fournier's interest in hereditary syphilis was especially strong because the whole question of the transmission of the infection to future generations posed a major and seemingly insoluble social problem. Undaunted in his approach to understanding the disease and seeking to get his ideas accepted by sceptical fellow professionals, he was equally energetic in launching a social campaign against the disease whose study and treatment had been his life's work; he founded the Société Française de Prophylaxie Sanitaire et Moral to fight against the scourge. He argued for prostitution to be monitored, for soldiers and sailors to receive regular medical inspections, for better provision for the treatment of the disease in hospitals and for syphilis to be a routine subject taught in all medical schools. He warned of the repercussions of syphilis in marriage, having treated women patients who had been unknowingly infected by philandering husbands,[28] and recommended the setting-up of free outpatient clinics where treatment would be confidential.[29]

The psychological effects of syphilis and the fear it engendered in the offspring of syphilitic patients was also of particular concern to the Viennese psychiatrist Sigmund Freud. He had observed that in many of the most severe cases of hysteria and obsessional neurosis that he saw on his consulting couch, the fathers of his patients had been treated for syphilis in their youth. Freud's patients themselves showed no physical symptoms of congenital syphilis, but he concluded that there was a link in that their sexual problems were the 'last echo of their syphilitic heritage'.[30] His patient 'Dora' believed that she had inherited syphilis from her father, whom Freud had treated for gonorrhoea many years previously, and that this was the original cause of her hysteria. In coming to such a conclusion, she confused the two diseases and made no distinction between a hereditary disease and a congenital condition, a very common error. Freud refrained from divulging his own belief that 'the offspring of luetics were very specially predisposed to severe neuropsychoses'.[31] Another of his patients, the young lawyer dubbed the 'Rat Man', linked syphilis with the gnawing of rats and again ascribed his own obsessional behaviour to his father possibly having had syphilis.[32] Fear of syphilis recurred among many of the occupants of Freud's couch, since in the opinion of the famed psychiatrist it represented a modern form of castration as a 'punishment for the indulgence of sexual desires'.[33]

Although there was a greater understanding of the natural history of syphilis and its psychiatric impact as a result of clinical observation, it was only with the growth of the new science of bacteriology that the cause of the disease could be discovered. The basis of bacteriology was the idea that some diseases could be caused by microscopic organisms, a notion that was nothing new in the case of theories of the transmission of syphilis, where contagion through sexual intercourse had long been accepted. Fracastoro had built on hints in Galen to write of disease seeds being carried by the wind or transmitted by contact with infected objects, but it was only with the development of the microscope in the seventeenth century that the presence of bacteria was confirmed. Yet the connection between bacteria and infection was not fully established until the nineteenth century. Louis Pasteur had championed the germ theory of disease and, a skilled microscopist, he had identified the existence of disease-causing bacteria, but it was left to his younger German contemporary Robert Koch to demonstrate that a specific disease could be caused by a specific microorganism. Koch, Professor of Public Health in Berlin, set out a series of principles, later known as Koch's Postulates, for establishing whether a particular bacterium produced a particular infection. The microorganism must be present in every instance of the disease. It must be capable of being cultivated in a culture medium such as agar jelly. If an experimental animal was then inoculated with the culture, it must reproduce the disease. Finally, the organisms must be capable of being recovered from the inoculated animal and grown again in a pure culture in the laboratory. If, and only if, all four of these conditions were met could a scientist prove that a particular disease was caused by a particular bacterium.[34]

Venereal disease was an obvious field for bacteriological investigation and where Koch's Postulates could form the basis of the scientific approach to finding the cause of infections. In 1879 Albert Neisser, a Breslau dermatologist, identified the gonococcus bacterium as the cause of gonorrhoea.[35] These small bead-like microbes were among the first to be identified as the cause of a specific disease, only three years after Koch's seminal work on the anthrax bacillus. His work was carried on by Ernst von Bumm, who cultured the organism in the laboratory in 1882 and developed methods of staining so that the gonococcus could clearly be differentiated from other bacteria under the microscope.[36] Meanwhile, in 1883, Karl Sigmund Credé of Leipzig developed a new treatment for gonococcal ophthalmia in newborn babies, infected in the womb by their mothers, by using silver nitrate eye drops to cure the infection, having first observed the action of such solutions on bacteria in test tubes.[37] However, it was not until 3 March 1905 that *Treponema pallidum*, which causes syphilis, was isolated from a secondary syphilitic lesion by the zoologist Fritz Schaudinn and his colleague the venereologist Erich Hoffmann at the Imperial Health Institute in Berlin. The first samples of this elusive pale-coloured, spiral-shaped microbe, known as a spirochaete, were small, very mobile and difficult to study, but, when Schaudinn and Hoffmann also discovered the same bacterium in syphilitic ganglions, chancres and in the spleen, there was little doubt that they had discovered the bacterium they were seeking.[38]

Now that the cause of syphilis has been identified, the first diagnostic test for it was developed the following year. August von Wassermann, the 40-year-old fastidiously dressed Professor of Medicine at the Friedrich Wilhelm University in Berlin, had originally tried to develop a similar test for the diagnosis of tuberculosis based on the complement fixation test devised by Jules Bordet and Octave Gengou to detect antibodies in the blood and further developed by Fernand Widal to detect typhoid antibodies in his patients. Having failed to establish such a test for tuberculosis, Wassermann had turned his attention to the development of a test for the antibody produced by syphilitics in collaboration with Albert Neisser and Karl Bruck at the Robert Koch Institute for Infectious Diseases in Berlin. The son of a Bavarian court banker, Wassermann had studied with Robert Koch and had worked with the chemist Paul Ehrlich on antitoxins. His colleague Neisser was ten years his senior and had considerable experience with sexually transmitted diseases, having previously discovered the bacterium that causes gonorrhoea when only 24 and having studied the contagion of syphilis in man and beast. Inspired by the infection of a monkey with human syphilis by Elie Metchnikoff, one of the founding fathers of modern microbiology, and the physician Emile Roux in 1903,[39] he had set off on an expedition to Java to study the transmission of the disease among apes and also human beings, finding plenty of material among the Dutch soldiers stationed on the island. Karl Bruck at 27 was the youngster of the group and was to make his name with this new project.

The three researchers began by using a watery extract from the liver of a syphilitic foetus as an antigen to stimulate an immune response through the production of antibodies, since they believed that it would contain large numbers of spirochaetes. They found that, when this was used in tests on the blood serum of syphilitic patients, a relatively large amount of complement within the blood was fixed as it combined with the antibodies. However, when the serum from people who did not have syphilis was used, little or no complement fixation took place.[40] Here, it seemed, was a reliable diagnostic test for syphilis. However, the Wassermann reaction was difficult to perform, needed more blood for testing than could easily be taken from a skin prick and was often unreliable unless undertaken in large batches in a laboratory dedicated to carrying out the test.[41] Neisser and Bruck attempted to refine the detection of syphilitic antigens in the blood, but within a few years it had been standardised and a better appreciation of the possible sources of error in the test made it an invaluable diagnostic tool that reinforced the importance of the bacteriology laboratory.[42] Yet it remained 'more of a fine art than a scientific procedure' for many years, to such an extent that the Swedish bacteriologist Hans Ericsson was to stress that it was as important not to make 'one false positive diagnosis of syphilis as it is not to make one false negative' since 'the social and medical consequences of the disease are still so serious that no mistakes are acceptable'.[43]

Despite all these advances in the understanding and diagnosis of the disease, its treatment had remained substantially unchanged for centuries, with mercury retaining its primacy in therapeutics. Fumigation with mercury was rarer than it had been, but in the nineteenth century could now be administered easily at home. The patient was advised to expose his naked backside on a cane-bottomed chair, under which a metal plate containing 5 grams of calomel was suspended over a bowl of hot water, heated by two spirit lamps. The fumes of the calomel would waft round the patient and the mercury would be absorbed through the skin.[44] Mercury could also be administered externally as ointments applied to the ulcers, one variation of which was a short-lived fashion in seventeenth-century Italy for anti-venereal underpants coated with mercury, or internally through enemas or oral preparations. Mercurous chloride in the form of calomel could be taken by mouth, as could Van Swieten's liquor, devised by Gerard van Swieten, the physician to Maria Theresa of Austria, which comprised mercuric chloride dissolved in water and brandy.

The effects of mercury nevertheless remained so destructive that for a time some physicians preferred to use hot baths, enemas and laxatives to counteract the irritation to the tissues caused by the infection. However, the development of new mercurial compounds, such as acetate, nitrate, phosphate and sulphide of mercury, in the 1860s encouraged a revival in the popularity of mercury at a time when injections were added to the old repertoire of ointments, pills and liquors. Potassium iodide, copper iodide salts and chalk were also introduced as alternatives to mercury, and cauterisation or excision of chancres was also sometimes employed in treatment. Newer arsenical compounds, such as atoxyl, were also developed and were mildly effective but just as injurious as the older options.[45] These alternatives for the patient were not pleasant, and more damage might be done by the treatment than by the disease. However, within a few years of the discovery of the spirochaetes, a modern treatment had been developed for syphilis based on scientific methods.

Salvarsan, developed in 1909, was the first modern use of chemotherapy to treat disease and was a great advance in the treatment of sexually transmitted infections. It was the achievement, after a long search, of Paul Ehrlich, the 55-year-old director of the Royal Prussian Institute of Experimental Therapy in Frankfurt and joint winner with Elie Metchnikoff of the 1908 Nobel Prize for Medicine for his contribution to medical and biological research in the field of immunology. Yet, despite his academic brilliance, he had been an indifferent student whose hatred of examinations and reluctance to study any subject he did not find challenging were redeemed only by the passion with which he immersed himself in chemistry, which did interest him. In his doctoral thesis at Leipzig University, he had studied histological staining and its relationship to the dyeing of textiles, a subject that fascinated him to such an extent that the dyes he used for staining left their mark over his hands, clothing and all over his laboratory and lodgings. In this work he was influenced by his cousin, the bacteriologist Karl Weigert, who had developed his own methods for staining bacteria and tissue sections for study under the microscope and had contacts with the German chemical industry, which was producing a large number of commercial aniline dyes. Ehrlich observed that specific chemicals interacted with particular tissues, cells or microbial agents in both stains and dyes, with the result that not all dyes stained everything. This suggested to him that chemical structures could not affect a cell without becoming attached to it in some way and that there could be no reaction unless the dye attached itself to a receptor on the chemical structure. Starting from this idea of receptors, he raised the possibility that, if there were dye receptors, there might also be similar chemical structures that might act as drug receptors. This led him to the search for chemical substances that would act on microbes but not on the human body tissues.

Continuing with his work on dyes, Ehrlich turned his attention to the development of a fast method of staining the newly discovered tubercle bacillus only six months after it had been revealed by Robert Koch to be the cause of tuberculosis. Ironically, as a result of this work, Ehrlich discovered that he was himself suffering from TB and was forced to leave his work for two years and seek a cure in the drier climate of Egypt. On his return to Berlin, he took up an unpaid position in Koch's new Institute for Infectious Diseases and in 1892 began an unhappy collaboration with Emil von Behring and Shibasaburo Kitasato on the development of vaccines against diphtheria, a major cause of death among children at the time, and tetanus. Ehrlich's precise and painstaking methods of quantifying and standardising the antiserum were crucial to the success of the project. However, after Behring reneged on a promise to include Ehrlich in a commercial contract for producing the resultant diphtheria antiserum, which brought a fortune to Behring, there was an acrimonious split between the two men, who had been born a day apart and who never saw each other again after this quarrel. However, Ehrlich's success with antitoxins brought him appointment in 1896 to the prestigious post of Director of the newly established Institute for Sera Research and Sera Therapy, originally located at Steglitz outside Berlin before moving to Frankfurt. For the first time he had a real salary and, more importantly, adequate research funding.[46]

The main purpose of the Institute was the state control of therapeutic sera and Ehrlich was able to use his work with von Behring's anti-diptheritic serum to standardise sera in units related to a fixed and invariable standard, which formed the basis of all future standardisations of vaccines. However, there was also the opportunity for him to carry out further original work in immunology. He was determined to understand how the tetanus antitoxin worked and to do so he advanced a series of hypotheses that formed the basis of his revolutionary side-chain, or chemical affinity, theory. In this he proposed that cells have specific receptors for antigens and that they shed these receptors in the blood when they come into contact with the antigen. He compared the process to a key fitting a lock, with each molecule of a toxin combining with a particular amount of antitoxin. Thus the tetanus toxin would become bound to the cells of the central nervous system by attaching itself to the chemical side-chain of the cell nucleus, thereby blocking their functions. The cell would then produce new side-chains to replace those that had been blocked, these being the antibodies produced by the action of the toxin.[47]

The theory was based on the idea that these reactions were chemical in nature and involved agents that were toxic to specific bacteria and would have no effect on the host. These antibodies could thus act as 'magic bullets which find their target by themselves' and would be capable of killing only the specific organism that had invaded the body. Just as the antibodies in blood serum engulfed the bacteria that could cause disease, so must there be chemical compounds that could target a particular infection without harming anything else in the human body. He enthusiastically and loudly expounded this theory to his friends, the British pathologists William Bulloch and Almroth Wright, on the night train from Berlin to Frankfurt after he had presented his findings on side-chains to a scientific conference, with so much passion and making so much noise that the conductor thought that the three friends were arguing and threatened to put them off the train if they did not quieten down.[48] The real challenge was to find tailor-made chemicals capable of acting against particular infective bacteria. His first experiments using methylene blue, one of the aniline dyes originally discovered by W.H. Perkin, for the treatment of malaria were promising. He then turned his attention to finding a form of chemotherapy that would target the trypanosomes that caused sleeping sickness. Atoxyl and other arsenical compounds proved fairly effective here but caused neurological damage and blindness. Syphilis, though, offered a more fruitful field of research using arsenical compounds, since one of them, atoxyl, had already been used with some success in its treatment. If Ehrlich could find a compound safer and with fewer side effects than atoxyl, then there was a chance that he might have found what he was seeking.

By now, Ehrlich's research empire had expanded since the move to Frankfurt of his Institute in 1899, which had been renamed the Royal Prussian Institute of Experimental Therapy at the time of its relocation. In 1902 he had established at his own expense a department devoted to cancer research, a subject that was to continue to interest him for the rest of his life. Then in 1906 he had been appointed Head of the Georg-Speyer Haus for Chemotherapy, a research institute founded by Franziska Speyer in memory of her husband, a Frankfurt businessman, and built next door to the Royal Institute that Ehrlich continued to head. In this dual role, he controlled every aspect of the activities of both institutes from his cluttered office, piled high with books, journals, magazines and papers that covered every space and left nowhere to sit. Each day he wrote out detailed instructions for his staff on what he wanted them to do, with different-coloured pencils on colour-coded note cards or 'blocks' delivered by his devoted porter Kadereit. Only he knew the key to the colour codes. An excitable and hard-working man, he was, according to his secretary Martha Marquardt, 'driven by an inward urge, not from egoistic motives, but from a burning desire to help humanity. His life and work were like a candle burning at both ends.'[49] To sustain all this energy, he smoked twenty-five cigars or more a day. His stamina and persistence were to stand him in good stead in his search for the magic bullet for syphilis. He was also to need what he called the four 'G's, essential for all scientific progress: 'Geduld, Geschick, Geld und Glück', patience, ability, money and good luck.[50]

Patience and ability were certainly much needed when Ehrlich began his investigation into the action of arsenical compounds on first the trypanosomes and then the spirochaetes, his new interest spurred on by the identification of the cause of syphilis, which meant that he knew what the enemy actually was. By 1907 he had synthesised and tested more than 600 different preparations,[51] ably assisted by the chemist Alfred Bertheim, the only member of the Chemical Department of the Georg-Speyer Haus not to have walked out of the Institute in protest at Ehrlich's insistence that he knew more about the chemistry of arsenical compounds than the qualified chemists did.[52] Throughout all these experiments, Ehrlich worked in his private laboratory at the Institute, with its dominating central laboratory bench and single Bunsen burner amid a clutter of bottles containing chemicals and test tubes. Such clutter and seeming chaos were not unique to Ehrlich's laboratory, but what was unusual was the absence of cylinders, retorts, funnels, beakers, bowls or thermometers, which were by then standard equipment in most chemical laboratories. Ehrlich preferred to use only the test tube when conducting his experiments and making his observations, prompting Ludwig Benda of the Cassella Chemical Works to style him 'a virtuoso in the art of test tube experiments'.[53] Among the arsenical drugs tested was compound 606,[54] which he set aside when his then research assistant reported that it had no effect whatsoever on infected animals, although he was cautious enough to have taken out a patent on it in 1907. Then in 1909 he set a new research assistant to work on retesting the entire series of synthetic compounds for their action on the spirochaetes, only to discover that 606 was actually very active against syphilis.

Ehrlich was lucky in his collaborator in his investigation of the action of arsenical compounds for the treatment of syphilis. Despite the acrimony with which his collaboration with von Behring had ended, Erhlich had enjoyed better relations with their Japanese co-worker Kitasato, who after his return to Tokyo had begun to send some of his best students to work at the most important European research institutes. The first of these students to be sent to Ehrlich, Kiyoshi Shiga, had proved a good researcher in the work on sleeping sickness. Now, in 1909, Kitasato had sent a new bacteriologist to work with him. Sahachiro Hata, then aged 36, had already undertaken work on inoculating rabbits with syphilis at the Kitasato Institute for Infectious Diseases in Tokyo when he arrived in Frankfurt and seemed the ideal collaborator for the new project. He was immediately set to work on infecting rabbits with syphilis and then injecting each arsenical compound into them. It was a slow and meticulous process, but, after a laborious series of tests on 605 compounds, he was able to report successful results with the 606th[55] to Ehrlich, who then insisted that the tests be repeated[56] so that they could be sure that they had at last found their magic bullet.[57]

However, innumerable experiments on animals were not enough to prove that compound 606, arsphenamine, which Ehrlich named salvarsan, was effective and safe in a human being. For this, it needed to be tested on human patients. Two physicians volunteered to act as human guinea pigs to test its safety, and then a series of clinical tests was begun with a group of doctors administering intramuscular injections of salvarsan into their most hopeless patients. This group was spread across the world, testing the effects of the compound in Bremen, Breslau, Magdeburg, Bonn, Sarajevo, St Petersburg, Pavia, Catania, Zurich, London and New York.[58] Despite their wide geographical distribution, Ehrlich expected each doctor to follow his instructions exactly. For their benefit, he gave precise instructions as to how salvarsan was to be injected and warned of the risk that the injection might induce fever if the needle was not absolutely sterile; he recommended painting the patient's skin with iodine before injecting salvarsan.[59]

Everywhere, Ehrlich's collaborators noticed that the improvement produced by a single injection was staggering. Reports on the results of treatment were sent to Ehrlich so he could follow for himself the action of his discovery.[60] One patient, a 28-year-old married man was described with evident disapproval by his doctor as 'dissipated' and a heavy drinker. He had been infected on 12 July 1910 and his physical condition in November 1910 was very poor, no doubt exacerbated by rubbings with mercury and potassium iodide. After his first injection with salvarsan on 14 November 1910, his next Wassermann reaction had been only slightly positive and a second injection on 11 December cleared the infection completely.[61] Another 33-year-old patient in New York, identified only by his initials as 'LB', had been infected for eight months and had developed crust-covered ulcers on his cheek and lower lip, which had not responded to treatment with mercury or iodides. He had even been fumigated with mercury with no result. Meanwhile he had also lost considerable weight before being injected with 0.5 grams of salvarsan on 23 November 1910. Within ten days of the injection, the disfiguring ulcer had disappeared completely. Five and a half months later, he had gained 16 pounds in weight and his Wassermann reaction was negative. 'LJ', aged 28, had suffered from secondary syphilis for two years and his throat had become so ulcerated that he found it 'practically impossible' to speak or even swallow. Mercury and iodides had again proved useless, but, within ten days of the administration of the new drug, his throat had become normal and he could leave hospital. Six months later he had gained over 30 pounds in weight.[63] The results in these cases were repeated around the world. By the end of 1910, over 10,000 sufferers had been successfully treated with salvarsan and there was great demand for this treatment with such spectacular cures as its results were publicised.[64]

In getting salvarsan into mass production, Ehrlich was fortunate in having already built strong links with two local chemical companies, Cassella, and Meister, Lucius and Brüning at nearby Hoechst.[65] Now agreements were made between the Georg-Speyer Haus and the two firms for the manufacture of the drug.[66] Ehrlich retained control over its quality control,[67] and one of the chemists at the Georg-Speyer Haus, Alfred Bertheim, undertook much of the chemical work in connection with the agreement.[68] Such was the demand for the new drug that, in launching it on the market in December 1910, the firm of Meister, Lucius and Brüning reminded pharmacists that they must apply to the authorised agents of the pharmaceutical wholesalers and not directly to the manufacturers or to Ehrlich himself.[69]

The main disadvantage of salvarsan was that it was still toxic, as might be expected from any treatment derived from arsenic. It could cause abdominal pains, vomiting, convulsions, jaundice and skin complaints as its side effects. In 1914 a modified form of salvarsan was developed from Ehrlich's compound 914, although the great man was less enthusiastic about it and believed that the original compound 606 was superior. The newer preparation, neoarsphenamine or neosalvarsan, was less toxic in its effects and more soluble, but because it was milder required many more painful injections into the bloodstream before a cure was complete. It was far from being the single shot of a magic bullet that Ehrlich had dreamt of. His worries over the progress of his drug were compounded when the First World War broke out that August. Although a fervent German patriot, he felt that no good could come from the war. Serum testing for the imperial army took priority over all other work at both the Royal Prussian Institute of Experimental Therapy and the Georg-Speyer Haus. The invaluable chemist Alfred Bertheim was called up by the cavalry but, catching his spurs on the stair carpet of the house in Berlin in which he was billeted, fell down the stairs and fatally fractured his skull before ever seeing active service. Contact with Ehrlich's scientific colleagues and friends in France and Britain was cut off. However, he was able to continue with some of his work on silver salvarsan with the help of a new chemical assistant, Paul Karrer from Zurich, who was to go on to win the 1938 Nobel Prize for Chemistry. Already sensitive to criticisms of salvarsan, he was more than ever concerned that under war conditions his instructions on the administration of salvarsan might be ignored and that there would be far more adverse reactions to the drug than there already were. Overworked and depressed, he suffered a slight stroke in December 1914, only to die from a massive attack in August 1915.[70]

Ehrlich's death came at a time when he was concerned that he no longer had control over the quality of production of salvarsan outside Germany. The outbreak of the First World War cut off access to salvarsan for nations that were now fighting against the German Empire. Allied belligerent nations were compelled to develop their own local generic alternatives if they wanted to prevent syphilis from incapacitating their troops as much as they wanted to battle against the enemy. Modern warfare is no respecter of patents. For Ehrlich, it was not so much the loss of patent income that worried him as the fear that, if other nations were producing the drug under less stringent conditions than he had laid down for its German manufacture, any substandard batches being distributed might discredit salvarsan in general. He need not have worried about Britain, where the Ministry of Health took care to ensure that production of a generic alternative to salvarsan was tightly controlled from the moment that the war had cut off supplies from Germany. Meister, Lucius and Brüning had a British subsidiary company at Ellesmere Port, Cheshire, but had never manufactured the drug there. Burroughs Wellcome, however, had done some developmental work on organic arsenical drugs and was given the go-ahead to produce its form of the drug, which was licensed under the brand name of Kharsivan.[71] In wartime an effective and relatively safe treatment for syphilis was more necessary than ever.

Arsenic was not only the basis of modern chemotherapy for syphilis, but was also the poison of choice in many a murder case. Since arsenic was widely available in forms that were easier to administer to an unsuspecting victim than salvarsan, it is not surprising that the treatment for syphilis was never used as an agent for poisoning, but the fact that it contained arsenic and was poisonous could suggest to a murderer that arsenic might be usefully employed. In 1922 Major Herbert Armstrong, a Herefordshire solicitor, was brought to trial for poisoning his wife with arsenic and for the attempted murder of a rival solicitor, Oswald Martin. In the course of the evidence it emerged that Armstrong had been treated by his doctor for syphilis and had seemingly idly enquired about how large a dosage of arsenic would be needed if it were to be fatal, while he was given his shots of salvarsan.[72] A short time afterwards, he had bought large quantities of weedkiller, containing arsenic, from a local chemist. Mrs Armstrong was taken ill within days of her husband's purchase. As she started to show signs of a mental disturbance, she was admitted to an asylum, but was discharged on her husband's insistence, only to die a month later, after Major Armstrong had bought more weedkiller. Although Mrs Armstrong had displayed clear symptoms of arsenical poisoning, her death was not regarded as suspicious. However, the case was to be re-examined after an attempt on the life of another victim. Oswald Martin was a younger and more successful solicitor, who aroused Armstrong's envy. After a professional disagreement between the two men, Armstrong had invited Martin to tea and handed him a buttered scone with his fingers, a breach of etiquette that seemed surprising at the time. Martin felt unwell. Tests on him revealed traces of arsenic poisoning. A box of chocolates laced with arsenic was also sent to him anonymously. Once suspicions of Armstrong were aroused, Mrs Armstrong's body was exhumed and it was found that she too had been poisoned. Armstrong's interest in arsenic, prompted by his treatment with salvarsan, was cited by the prosecution as part of the case against him. Any implied possibility that the traces of arsenic found in Martin's body may have originated from a similar origin rather than from an attempt to murder him was dismissed by the medico-legal expert witness William Willcox, nicknamed the 'King's Poisoner' by the press on account of his knowledge of poisons.[73] The jury found Armstrong guilty. Salvarsan, while not itself a murder weapon, had suggested the possibilities of a means of murder to at least one person treated with it, although it was already a commonplace means of murder.[74] Ironically, Willcox considered that Armstrong would have had a strong case for a defence of insanity on the grounds that his actions might have been the result of him suffering from general paralysis of the insane, the result of his infection with syphilis. Instead of being committed to Broadmoor, he was condemned to an appointment with the hangman at Gloucester gaol.[75]

The nauseous side effects of salvarsan and neosalvarsan nevertheless remained a problem, and attempts were made to find ways of improving the treatment. In 1922 Robert Sazerac and Constantin Levaditi discovered that bismuth was effective against syphilis, and this allowed doctors to alternate the toxic arsenobenzoid treatment with something less unpleasant than the older mercury preparations that had never entirely been supplanted by salvarsan. Silver salvarsan and salvarsan natrium (preparation 1206) were later developed, but the side effects remained a major drawback to a treatment that had initially promised so much.[76] Moreover, salvarsan was never quite the single dose of a chemical capable of overwhelming specific bacteria and of ridding the body of infection safely that Ehrlich had originally envisaged when he first began to talk about his quest for the 'magic bullet', and, while effective in the fight against syphilis, it proved not to be the first, but in fact the only such drug to be developed within the next two decades.

One major area in which treatment with salvarsan or bismuth had obviously failed was in any attempts to use them to reverse general paralysis of the insane. This meant that an alternative approach to chemotherapy had to be sought if there were to be any hope of treating this manifestation of tertiary syphilis. It seemed a hopeless quest. Then, on the basis of various reports of a spontaneous remission of the condition after sufferers had recovered from a fever, the Viennese neurologist Julius Wagner von Jauregg came to the conclusion that artificially induced fevers might be of benefit in inducing remissions or even cures. The opportunity to try out this theory came in the summer of 1917 when he was treating a soldier with malaria. He inoculated nine of his general paralysis patients with blood from this patient and was impressed by the improvement in their condition.[77] In 1922 he reported that 50 patients had enjoyed full remissions out of the 200 he had inoculated with malaria.[78] There was little discussion of the ethics of inoculating patients with a potentially harmful pathogen, and very quickly this malaria fever therapy spread through Europe and North America, remaining the treatment of choice in many hospitals until the late 1940s. Its inventor received the 1927 Nobel Prize for Medicine, a reflection more of the importance of the problem rather than of the originality of the solution, since in many ways it was a return to the old idea of sweating out the poison. The fight against the spirochaete continued to offer more potential for the avoidance of tertiary syphilis. If syphilis could be successfully treated in its early stages, then sufferers would not be left at risk of developing general paresis.

It was not until 1932 that there was another advance in the field of chemotherapy, one that was to have implications for the treatment of gonorrhoea though not of syphilis, which remained dependent upon Dr Ehrlich's magic bullet for its relief. Yet in many ways Gerhard Domagk's discovery of the sulphanilamide drugs was to be the direct fulfilment of Ehrlich's dreams of the potential offered by chemotherapy. His early work as a medical scientist had been dedicated to the assessment of the therapeutic potential of such metallic chemical compounds as gold, antinomy, tin and arsenic. Then in 1927 he was appointed research director of I.G. Farbenindustrie, the chemical combine that had opened a new research institute for pathological anatomy and bacteriology at Wuppertal. Since the main products of his firm were azo dyes used for colouring textiles, it made sense for Domagk to turn his attention to them and investigate the possibility that they might have an effect on streptococci, the bacteria that cause such infections as tonsillitis, scarlet fever and rheumatism. In 1932 he found that, when he administered the red dye prontosil rubrum to mice infected with haemolytic streptococci, he was able to cure them. Then his own small daughter fell seriously ill with a streptococcal infection, and, out of desperation, he gave her a dose of prontosil. It proved a risk worth taking, and she made a complete recovery. Researchers at the Pasteur Institute established that the sulphonamide molecule within the compound, rather than the dye itself, was bacteriostatic, which meant that it did not kill the bacteria but rather prevented them from growing, which gave the body's own immune system the opportunity to destroy them.[79]

Unfortunately for Domagk and his employers, prontosil could not be patented, as its active constituent sulphonamide had been synthesised as long ago as 1907. Other chemical and pharmaceutical companies were able to develop it as a drug effective against more than just streptococcal infections. The most important of these drugs was M and B 693, developed by the firm of May and Baker in 1938, which was effective against a number of bacteria, including gonococci, making it a viable treatment for gonorrhoea. However, it did not work so well on localised areas where pus had formed, and it was often found to be more efficacious to give it five days after the infection had started rather than immediately. There were also nasty side effects such as rashes and vomiting. Yet it did offer a breakthrough in the treatment of gonorrhoea. Domagk did get his reward in the form of the 1939 Nobel Prize for Medicine, but was forbidden by the Nazi government from accepting it and was even detained by the Gestapo to prevent him from going to Stockholm to collect it.[80]

The new science of bacteriology had made great advances in the early years of the twentieth century, and venereal diseases had been central to important developments in the subject and in the field of chemotherapy. Yet the long-sought-after bullet that could wipe out the scourge of syphilis had proved elusive. Syphilis was destined to remain as much of a problem in the first half of the twentieth century as it had been earlier. However, all was to change with the advent of the antibiotic age in the 1940s, but no one could have predicted that such a great advance was just round the corner.

FIVE

Fit to Fight

It was more than appropriate that a play destined to become a symbol of a new twentieth-century sexual openness by its attack on the conspiracy of silence surrounding syphilis should be suppressed by the censors when it was first written. The French dramatist Eugène Brieux had written *Les Avariés* to draw attention to the hypocrisy surrounding the subject and to chronicle the effects the disease could have on the supposedly sacred family lives of the outwardly respectable. Even though more risqué shows were openly performed at the private theatres, café-concerts and cabarets of Paris, the censor decided to ban public performances of this serious drama in which the actress Sarah Bernhardt had declared that she would happily have appeared without even seeing the text. The playwright gave a reading of his drama before a selected audience in November 1901, and the notoriety of its banning ensured that the published script was a bestseller. In March 1902, a more liberal attitude in Belgium allowed it to be performed in Brussels and Liège. The French censors relented in 1905, and the play was a hit in Paris from its first performance.[1] It enjoyed even greater success when under its English title of *Damaged Goods* the play opened on Broadway in 1913. After its rapturous New York reception, a special performance was put on in Washington to acquaint President Wilson, his cabinet and members of Congress with the social pathology of venereal disease.[2] Only in Britain did the play languish unperformed, despite an English translation with a commendatory foreword by George Bernard Shaw. Lauded in its day, the play, its purpose served in stimulating discussion of a major problem, is now forgotten.

The drama powerfully confronted the problem of sexual double standards by which sexually transmitted disease could threaten family life and make the innocent suffer. In it, Georges Dupont, a young lawyer, ignores the advice of his doctor that he should not marry on account of the syphilis he has contracted in sowing his wild oats, despite having been extremely careful and cautious in his sexual adventures. Instead he delays the marriage for a few months on the rather more respectable pretext of suspected consumption after consulting a quack who has advised him that he will be cured of his syphilis after three months. It is not long enough. His wife is infected, and hereditary syphilis is passed on to their baby daughter, whose wet-nurse is also affected, though the husband and wife show little sympathy for her plight. Georges's wife Henrietta then attempts to divorce him, but the doctor refuses to issue a certificate giving evidence of Georges's infection before the marriage, since it is not the role of the medical profession to defend a family from the consequences of a man's immorality. It is down to individuals to take personal responsibility for the consequences of their actions since 'Science is not God Almighty'. Henrietta's father is advised that he ought to have made the same searching enquiries into his future son-in-law's state of health as he did into his financial prospects. Georges, meanwhile, has been warned by the cynical doctor that he ought to have made sure that he slept with a virgin or a prostitute old enough to have gone beyond the infective stage of syphilis.[3]

For all its emphasis on personal responsibility for avoiding health risks, the play also raised the question of whether or not the modern state could afford to stand back if individuals refused to behave sensibly. The beginning of the twentieth century had been marked by anxieties over national well-being as much as over concerns about the threats to individual health. There was an almost hysterical fear of physical deterioration and racial fitness brought to the fore in Britain by reverses in the Boer War and an underlying unease that economically and militarily the country was being overtaken by an armed, vigorous and prosperous German Empire. If British forces could be defeated by a few hundred Boer farmers in 1899, there were bound to be doubts about how effectively they could stand up to the might of a well-disciplined German army. Fears of national decline were further fanned by revelations of the poor physical condition of many of the men volunteering for service in South Africa with over a quarter of volunteers at some recruiting depots being rejected as physically unfit for military service.[4] The future of the race depended upon some form of state intervention, whatever tensions might thereby arise between the principles of personal morality and public order. Concern about syphilis, moreover, tied in with fears of a differential birth rate whereby the best racial stock, that of the middle classes, was tending to marry late and have smaller families at a time when the less provident slum dwellers were continuing to breed unchecked and at a seemingly alarming rate. Syphilis could be transmitted to the next generation and was evidently endemic throughout all classes of the industrial population, making it a focus for fears of the apparently inevitable long-term physical deterioration of the British race. 'National Efficiency' was the political slogan of the time, adopted by the eugenics movement launched in October 1901 by Charles Darwin's cousin Francis Galton with his belief that only by encouraging breeding from the best stock and controlling the fertility of the worst was there any hope of progress.[5] Hereditary syphilis had no place in such ambitions for improvement of the race.

Inevitably the official response to concern about racial fitness was to set up another Royal Commission to examine the question. The 1904 Interdepartmental Committee on Physical Deterioration recommended that a commission of inquiry be set up to look into the prevalence and effects of syphilis.[6] The 1909 Royal Commission on the Poor Laws recommended that the workhouses should detain sufferers from venereal infections as being a danger to the community. One of the members of the Commission, the voluble Fabian socialist Beatrice Webb, was so concerned about the issue that, when invited to a breakfast meeting in February 1911 by Lloyd George, Chancellor of the Exchequer, at Downing Street, she could not resist raising it in the context of the new National Insurance scheme. The young civil servant William Braithwaite said that 'I felt quite awkward when Mrs Webb cornered me on syphilis', and noted that the lady had been 'at intervals comparatively sane' during the meal.[7]

Doctors were by now increasingly questioning the value of any form of regulation of prostitution in preventing the spread of venereal disease. An international medical conference held in Brussels in 1899 had criticised the state licensing of brothels and compulsory inspection of prostitutes in many countries as being of little medical value in the prevention of disease. Isolation and compulsion were no longer the most appropriate approach in a more scientific age.[8] In 1913 Ralph Johnstone, a leading British public health doctor, informed the Local Government Board that the Contagious Diseases Acts had been a failure and that it would be useless to think of reintroducing them. Instead, he advocated the adoption of the latest diagnostic and therapeutic tools now available, with the identification by Schaudinn and Hoffmann of the bacterium that causes syphilis, the development of a test for it by Wassermann and the discovery of a new treatment by Ehrlich. Although Johnstone continued to refer to the 'innocent and guilty' in mentioning patients suffering from syphilis, he did point out that it was counterproductive to stigmatise the disease; if the stigma could be removed, more people might come forward for treatment.[9]

It was one thing for a medical officer of health to make a sensible suggestion for the control of a serious social problem, but politicians were slower to act unless they were directly interested in the issue. The only way to get government action was to whip up public pressure for an official inquiry. The campaign agitating for action was spearheaded by a group of doctors led by Sir Malcolm Morris, physician and dermatologist at St Mary's Hospital, Paddington, who had been knighted in 1908 after having treated Edward VII for a skin complaint.[10] Letters from prominent venereologists were published in the newspapers, and public meetings debated the question of venereal disease as a serious social problem.[11] Resolutions calling for action were passed at the 1913 International Medical Congress held in London.[12] John Burns, president of the Local Government Board, addressed the Congress and referred to syphilis as 'one of the great cankers of humanity'.[13] The suffragette movement took up the issue, and Christabel Pankhurst cited the prevalence of syphilis and gonorrhoea as a compelling reason why women should have the vote. She argued that these two diseases were not only the result of sexual immorality on the part of prostitutes and the men who frequented them, but were also inflicted on innocent wives by men who 'would think it indelicate to utter in their hearing the words syphilis and gonorrhoea'. If women had the vote, they would be 'politically free and economically strong' enough to refuse to 'be purchasable for the base uses of vice'. Nevertheless, even Pankhurst conceded that the enfranchisement of women would not be enough on its own and stressed that the full cure for syphilis was 'Votes for Women and Chastity for Men'. If men were to exercise sexual restraint, it would be 'healthful for themselves and is imperative in the interests of the race'.[14]

As a result of the political pressure, a Royal Commission on Venereal Diseases was appointed in 1913 under the chairmanship of Lord Sydenham, a businessman and former colonial governor of Bombay. Malcolm Morris took a prominent role on the Commission, which enjoyed a strong medical presence, including Dame Mary Scharlieb of the Elizabeth Garrett Anderson Hospital, the pathologist Sir Frederick Mott, Sir Arthur Newsholme, principal medical officer to the Local Government Board, and Sir John Collis, a physician who acted as a medical examiner for insurance companies. The secretary to the Commission was James Ernest Lane, physician to St Mary's Hospital and the London Lock Hospital. The lay members, including two clergymen and two ladies from the Social Purity Campaign, had a strong moralistic bias. They were to spend several years hearing the copious evidence on the prevalence of venereal disease, the existing provision for diagnosis and treatment, and the recommendations of doctors and social reformers on the best way to combat the 'terrible peril to our Imperial race', 10 per cent of whom were estimated to suffer from syphilis and even more from gonorrhoea.[15]

Prevalent as the diseases were, the facilities available for their treatment were sparse. Despite the very considerable recent advances made in knowledge and treatment of syphilis, little had been done to take advantage of these. Wassermann testing was still far from routine. Only a third of the voluntary hospitals outside London provided the test, and very few private practitioners or poor law institutions used it. The administration of salvarsan was difficult for many doctors unused to giving intravenous injections and was also very expensive, particularly during the First World War as the supply of the drug from Germany dried up and locally produced substitutes proved costly.[16] The London Lock Hospital, in particular but like so many other hospitals, was unable as a charity to fund the costs of treatment with salvarsan or neosalvarsan and expected patients to pay £1 for each shot of the drug.[17] It was a depressing picture made worse by the ignorance and indifference of the medical profession. Many doctors 'failed to appreciate the importance of these diseases' and were 'to a large extent unfamiliar with the newer methods of diagnosis and treatment'.[18]

When it reported in March 1916, the Commission recommended that state action was essential to deal with a problem of such national significance and so damaging to the health of the race. However, any revival of the Contagious Diseases Acts, with their compulsory inspection and treatment of prostitutes suspected of having a venereal disease, was firmly ruled out. Instead a national scheme for the provision of free treatment was recommended, with county or county borough councils being made responsible for establishing the necessary pathology laboratories for diagnosis and clinics for treatment. This treatment was to be provided free of charge to the patient but the local authority would be reimbursed for 75 per cent of the cost by a grant from the Exchequer. Since venereal diseases caused a 'grave economic loss to the State', the savings to the nation from the proposed measures would 'more than counterbalance the cost'. The Commission had considered the possibility of covering venereal diseases under the 1911 National Insurance Act, itself a scheme limited to only certain occupations, but had found that many men with venereal diseases seeking treatment from their panel doctors under the Act had been denied aid because their sickness was deemed to be the result of their 'own misconduct'. It was not the way to solve the problem. For similar practical reasons of putting treatment of the disease above moral considerations, the Commission advised that no distinction should be made between the sexes, between 'good' and 'bad' women or between social classes. In order to encourage people to come forward for treatment, confidentiality was to be the cornerstone of the system, and notification of the disease was rejected, despite the advantages notification would have had for public health administrators. Instead, the Commission insisted that 'it is of the utmost importance that this institutional treatment should be available for the whole community and should be so organised that persons affected by the disease should have no hesitation in taking advantage of the facilities for treatment which are offered'.[19]

Unusually for a Royal Commission, its recommendations were swiftly followed by action implementing a national free, voluntary and confidential system for the medical treatment of venereal infections. The Local Government Board already had the power to introduce the necessary measures without the inevitable debate and delays that would have accompanied any parliamentary legislation. Under the 1875 Public Health Act it could issue permissive regulations to local authorities but could not compel them to put these regulations into force. Moreover, the 1913 Public Health Act had stressed that only in cases of emergency could the Local Government Board compel a county council to carry out any regulation issued by them. Venereal disease was accordingly declared a national emergency, a move calculated to impress public opinion and ensure that 'local authorities would undoubtedly feel compelled to move in the matter'.[20] No one challenged the declaration of a national emergency, although the county councils were concerned at being asked to pay even 25 per cent of the costs at a time when they were being urged to reduce expenditure as part of the war effort.

The Public Health (Venereal Diseases) Regulations of July 1916 instructed councils to organise schemes for the free and confidential treatment of venereal diseases through the provision of clinics, diagnostic laboratories and free supplies of salvarsan to general practitioners for the treatment of patients who preferred to see their own doctors rather than attend a public treatment centre. The emphasis was on treatment 'available to all comers, irrespective of the place of residence or means of the patient'.[21] Although the costs

An early pox sufferer
covered with pustules,
under the fatal
astrological conjunction
of 1484 believed to have
signalled the coming of
the dread disease, as
depicted by Albrecht
Durer in 1496.
(Wellcome Trust)

HIERONYMVS FRACASTORIVS

Pe. Larmessin.scul.

Girolomo Fracastoro, physician and poet, who coined the name of syphilis. *(United States National Library of Medicine)*

The preparation and administration to a patient of guaiacum: a sixteenth-century engraving, *Hyacum Et Lues Venerea*, by Philippe Galle after J. Stradanus. *(United States National Library of Medicine)*

Ioan. Stradanus invent.

J. Phl. Galæ exu.

HYACVM, ET LVES VENEREA.

6. *Grauata· morbo ab hocce membra mollia   Leuabit ista ʃorpta coctio arboris*

Treatment for syphilis in a seventeenth-century hospital in Amsterdam. *(United States National Library of Medicine)*

Syphilis the shepherd preys on a young man in the *Allegory of Youth Tempted by the Vices: Fight between Virtue and Vice (Allegorie der Jugend, die von den Lastern versucht wird: Kampf zwischen Tugend und Laster)* by Luca Giordano, 1664. *(Städel'sche Kunstinstitut, Frankfurt)*

The ravages of the French Disease captured in a waxwork tableau, the *Morbus Gallicus,* by Gaetano Zumbo, late seventeenth century. *(Photo: Saulo Bambi, Museo di Storia Naturale, Sezione di Zoologia La Specola, Universita' di Firenze, Firenze, Italy)*

Viscount Squanderfield visits the quack doctor Monsieur Pillule in search of a cure in *Marriage à la mode* (Plate 3) by William Hogarth, 1745. *(United States National Library of Medicine)*

A pioneer in venereology, the surgeon John Hunter, experimented on himself to try to prove that gonorrhoea and syphilis were different stages of the same disease. Painted by Sir Joshua Reynolds. *(United States National Library of Medicine)*

Later pioneering work in the treatment of VD: the collaboration of Paul Ehrlich and Sahachiro Hata led to the development of salvarsan, the first modern treatment for syphilis. *(Paul Ehrlich Institut, Frankfurt)*

MERCURY and his ADVOCATES DEFEATED, or VEGETABLE INTRENCHMENT.

The quack doctor Isaac Swainson promoting his 'Velno's Vegetable Syrup' and under attack by his less successful rivals and their mercury cures in *Mercury and his Advocates Defeated, or Vegetable Intrenchment* by Thomas Rowlandson, 1789. *(Wellcome Trust)*

A young man courts his sweetheart, who hides the ravages of syphilis behind the mask of a pretty young woman, 1851. *(United States National Library of Medicine)*

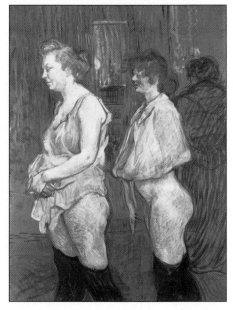

Parisian prostitutes lining up for their regular medical inspection with the 'government's penis' in *Rue des Moulins, 1894,* by Henri Toulouse-Lautrec. *(Chester Dale Collection, National Gallery of Art, Washington DC, 1963.10.69)*

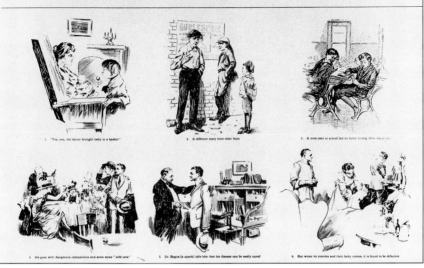

'What Wrong Impressions Did to One Boy's Life', a VD prevention poster from the early twentieth century. *(United States National Library of Medicine)*

'Friday the 13th is unlucky for syphilis', a mass rally against venereal disease in Chicago, 13 August 1937. *(United States National Library of Medicine)*

US Surgeon General Thomas Parran visiting a mobile syphilis treatment trailer established for African Americans in Brunswick, Georgia, in 1939 by future Surgeon General Leroy Burney during Parran's campaign against the 'Shadow on the Land', a public-health programme from which men in the Tuskegee Study were deliberately excluded. *(United States National Library of Medicine)*

'She May Look Clean – but . . .', a Second World War poster demonising women as sources of sexually transmitted infections. *(United States National Library of Medicine)*

of the scheme were to come entirely from public funds, the county councils were encouraged to make arrangements with the large general hospitals, many of them self-governing voluntary hospitals funded from charitable donations. The voluntary hospitals, normally resistant to any encroachment on their independence by the state, were for once happy to cooperate with the local authorities in providing clinics under the scheme, although many of them had previously been resistant to providing any statistics on the number of venereal cases they saw or their costs of treatment.[22] Faced with financial pressures resulting from the falling-off of income from charitable subscriptions and the increases in prices in wartime, they now had no choice but to consider offering state-funded services provided that, apart from regular visits from the medical inspectors of the Local Government Board, there would be no attempts at interference with the governance of the hospitals.[23] Much-valued independence could be maintained and much-needed income gained.

Even the British Medical Association, usually an opponent to any extension of state medical services that could have threatened the livelihoods and independence of the general practitioners it largely represented, was for once generally favourable to the new system on account of 'the exceptional nature of venereal diseases; the reluctance of persons affected to go to their private medical practitioner; the risk that they may go to unqualified practitioners . . . and the importance to the community of adopting all possible measures for inducing sufferers from venereal diseases to seek early and adequate treatment'.[24]

The British Medical Association was especially gratified that its battle against quack purveyors of patent medicines and dubious remedies for the pox had been supported by the Royal Commission, which had recommended not only the banning of advertisements promising quick cures for venereal diseases but also the prohibition of any treatment by unqualified practitioners. Some of these advertisements were misleading in their claims for their quack remedies, such as one cited by Arthur Newsholme that called itself 'formula 606', suggesting though not claiming that it was salvarsan and that he considered 'a particularly gross example of the kind of medication by correspondence which leads to the extensive spread of venereal diseases as the result of unsatisfactory treatment'.[25] The new venereal diseases treatment centres gave qualified doctors the opportunity to receive training in the use of the Wassermann test and the administration of salvarsan, the genuine treatment for syphilis. The 1917 Public Health (Venereal Diseases) Act went even further in restricting the administration of salvarsan to authorised trained doctors and made it a criminal offence for anyone other than a qualified doctor to offer the promise of a cure for syphilis or gonorrhoea.[26] The damage that could be done by quacks was denounced for the unnecessary suffering caused to their victims. One civil servant, 'a promising young fellow', had been 'absolutely driven to suicide by the blackmailing of a quack'. In another case, a young army officer had been treated for syphilis by a quack and 'almost driven out of his mind, thinking that he had the disease when he had really got nothing of the sort', while another officer actually had the disease, which had progressed to the secondary stage because his primary lesion had not been treated properly.[27] The only way forward for 'protecting public health' was a legal ban on 'the treatment of such diseases by unqualified persons'.[28]

At the same time as false claims about quack therapies preying upon public ignorance were being forbidden, increased emphasis was placed on education about the diseases and how they could be prevented. The Royal Commission had recommended moral instruction for the prevention of the disease, but failed to mention any practical methods of avoidance such as condoms or self-disinfection systems, known as the 'prophylactic packet', which might have been seen as condoning vice. Subsidies for such educational work about the risks of infection from sexual intercourse were given to the National Council for Combating Venereal Disease, founded in 1914 and made up largely of social purity activists worried that they might inadvertently drive young people to vice by encouraging them to seek out the meaning of such terms as 'ovary' and 'egg duct' in the Council's propaganda leaflets.[29]

The first treatment centres opened in London in January 1917, and by the end of the year there were 113 clinics in operation seeing over 29,000 new cases, with over 204,000 total attendances. By 1920 there were 190 clinics seeing 105,185 patients and recording nearly 1,500,000 total attendances. Such a rapid expansion was staggering but costly. Total spending on the scheme rose from £116,000 in 1917 to £287,000 by 1920. Yet, for all the money laid out, the quality of some of the services provided was variable. There was a shortage of suitably skilled doctors at first, and the Army Council agreed to release army medical officers for appointment to the new treatment centres where possible. Some hospitals did not even attempt to appoint qualified and experienced doctors to be in charge of the clinics.[30] Facilities for women patients were often most woeful of all. Despite the recommendation that there should be separate clinics for men and women and that women doctors should be employed in the female clinics, the sessions for women were often not at such convenient times as for men and there were few women doctors to see them. Where women were appointed to staff the clinics, they were invariably offered lower salaries than their male colleagues and were not even allowed to have charge of the female beds for inpatients.[31] St Mary's Hospital, Paddington, replied to criticisms that there were no women doctors employed when it opened its clinic hidden away in a dank basement in January 1917 with the promise that 'we should hope in time to appoint a woman practitioner' yet, when the opportunity to do so arose, appointed more male doctors.[32]

State intervention in the treatment of venereal diseases was so swiftly and successfully introduced not only because of the scale of the problem but because medical advances had now made it possible to diagnose and treat syphilis. The Contagious Diseases Acts could have had no chance of being as efficacious in the absence of any effective treatment for the disease, even had their coercive nature not aroused such opposition. Certainly, the years following the establishment of the venereal diseases treatment centres were marked by a steady decline in the incidence of syphilis, with relative death rates falling from an average of 68 per 1,000,000 men in the period 1911–20 to 35 in 1936. It is possible that this decrease in ill-health associated with syphilis might have had as much to do with rising standards of living and better general health as it did with more effective medical treatment, but without more accessible and more effective therapies it is unlikely that any great inroads could have been made against the scourge of syphilis.[35]

Gonorrhoea rates did not decline in the same way that syphilis had done, mainly because there was still no effective treatment for the disease. The mainstay of treatment remained daily urethral irrigations for men and douches and the application of caustic substances to the cervix for women. At first gonorrhoea had been seen as a more prevalent and less serious disease than syphilis. It was even considered commonplace in some circles. George V is said to have noticed that one of his courtiers appeared to be in considerable discomfort and asked one of his equerries to enquire about the problem, only to be given the discreet answer, 'the usual, Your Majesty'. Queen Mary also sent one of her ladies-in-waiting with the same enquiry and was told that the unfortunate gentleman had piles. The Queen, on hearing this, appeared surprised and commented, 'why then did the King tell me he has the clap?'[34] However, gonorrhoea was increasingly coming to be seen as a threat to the British race as serious as syphilis. Once wrongly seen as a local and mild condition affecting more men than women, gonorrhoea was now acknowledged as a major cause of puerperal disease and infertility in women.[35] The New York gynaecologist Emil Noeggerath had pointed out the dangers as early as 1876, with the staggering claim that 80 per cent of men in New York had suffered from the infection and had transmitted 'honeymoon gonorrhoea' to their innocent brides.[36] The Royal Commission on Venereal Diseases had emphasised that a 'far more serious view of gonorrhoea than has hitherto been adopted should be taken by the medical profession and the public',[37] and the National Council for Combating Venereal Disease did its utmost to change the popular impression that it was 'no worse than a cold in the head'.[38] Yet, until there was a more effective treatment for it, there was little that could be done to treat it, unlike syphilis.

Venereal disease, already brought into public prominence by the campaigns building up pressure for a national policy for the control of the problem, had further been forced to the fore by the outbreak of the First World War. The setting-up of a national treatment system had been conceived and executed as a civilian scheme and was not specifically a response to the pressures of wartime, yet the exposure of large numbers of men in the armed forces to the 'likelihood of permanent damage to the individual, infection to others, and an heritage which might stain an innocent life' raised the stakes considerably.[39] War conditions were thought to favour the spread of such infections by a heightening of sexual desire in the face of danger and death at a time when the moral climate was slacker than in peacetime. It was almost taken for granted that war led to a rise in the incidence of the diseases, but it was also realised that the threat to military efficiency posed by them should somehow be countered. How this was approached was very much conditioned by the pre-war policies towards the control of venereal diseases carried out by the belligerent states.

France, with its long tradition of licensed brothels and periodic medical inspection of prostitutes, continued with its tried and tested methods, though free venereal diseases dispensaries were also set up and a propaganda campaign warned of the dangers of syphilis.[40] The system kept prostitutes off the streets and offered reassurance that something was being done to maintain public decency. The generally static nature of trench warfare on the Western Front meant that the areas in which the troops were concentrated could be more easily policed in terms of social hygiene. If the troops frequented such *maisons de tolérances*, they were less likely to fall into bad company or contract the disease. Nevertheless, there was little to suggest that this had any real effect on controlling the transmission of syphilis and gonorrhoea, and throughout the war over one million French soldiers were admitted to hospitals for treatment.[41] The inspections were often too perfunctory to be at all effective, and the lack of any laboratory tests ensured that asymptomatic infections went unnoticed. Worst of all, the same unsterilised speculum would be used to examine each woman in the queue for inspection, sometimes numbering as many as the fifty-nine women seen in the course of an hour at Bordeaux on one occasion in 1917, which prompted an observer to comment that 'it made one fairly shudder to know that representatives of the French government were giving bills of physical soundness to women who were fairly eaten up with the disease'.[42]

Imperial Germany also had a tradition of registering prostitutes, and increased the stringency of such regulation as the war progressed and venereal disease increased. Already since the early twentieth century any woman who had sexual relations with a man to whom she was not married was in danger of being classed as an amateur prostitute and officially registered. Such women were considered to be high-risk groups, and indeed more soldiers were catching venereal diseases at home in Germany than they did abroad. In an attempt to control the spread of infection on the home front, the medical inspection of German prostitutes became the responsibility of military doctors, and in Berlin bars with hostesses were closed down.[43] Brothels in occupied parts of France and Belgium were also brought under the German system of regulation, despite the recommendation of Albert Neisser of the need for 'ruthlessly eliminating professional prostitution as well as the numerous women making themselves available for sexual intercourse in the occupied towns of the enemy'.[44] Nevertheless, the German army recognised that men, despite the numerous exhortations that it was their patriotic duty to remain chaste, would seek out sexual adventures. Officials in the Prussian War Ministry even made a distinction between younger single soldiers, whom they expected to remain chaste, and older married men, who were accustomed to sexual intercourse and could not be expected to forgo it even when separated by war from their wives.[45] In an attempt to control the situation, soldiers and prostitutes in occupied areas near the front were issued with prophylactics, and any prostitute found to be infected after one of her regular examinations would be deported or forced to undergo treatment. At the same time the War Committee for Warm Underwear, under the patronage of the Empress Auguste Viktoria and the Red Cross, sponsored the creation of jobs for women in occupied Belgium as an alternative to prostitution.[46]

The British tradition was opposed to any form of regulated vice, as the furore over the Contagious Diseases Acts had demonstrated. At first it was considered enough for Lord Kitchener to urge the men of the British Expeditionary Force to stay chaste and shun wine and women, an appeal later to be printed in each soldier's pay book as a reminder that anyone who ignored it and caused a disease would lose his pay as a forfeit during his medical treatment. Regulated brothels may have been acceptable overseas, but public opinion at home was firmly against any system that might both degrade women and encourage immorality. In wartime, contracting an avoidable disease became an unpatriotic sign of disloyalty, betrayal, selfishness and lack of moral rectitude. It ought to have been unthinkable that officialdom should condone anything that might have offended the tight moral code for which the war was being fought following the emblematic rape of Belgium by the Germans in August 1914. Nevertheless, it was equally unrealistic to declare the French *maisons de tolérances* behind the lines off limits to British troops. Had such an order been issued, soldiers would have simply sought out unregulated amateur prostitutes, who were considered an even greater danger. Yet there was an outcry from the Church, the women's movement and social purity bodies following unfounded rumours that the British army was running its own brothels in Le Havre and Cayeux-sur-Mer.[47] It was not until March 1918 that the War Office declared French brothels out of bounds for British troops, only for the French to protest that this would result in an increase in venereal disease if British soldiers flocked to unregistered prostitutes or resorted to the sexual harassment or rape of respectable French women.[48]

It was not only in France that such *maisons de tolérances* were forbidden to British troops. In Egypt British Christian and native Islamic moral purity campaigners joined forces to close all brothels, drug dens and low drinking-houses. Troops posted to Egypt had chalked up higher rates of venereal infection than elsewhere in the British Empire, especially among the Anzac forces, and the country's brothels were so popular that clients were queuing six deep to take their turns. While the local police had inherited powers from the former Ottoman rulers of Egypt to control native prostitutes, they had no control over white whores and were limited to reporting any cases of venereal disease among them to the consul general. After 1915 martial law had extended regulation to non-Egyptian women. All of them were to fall victim to the campaign against immorality. So many prostitutes, pimps and drug-dealers were arrested during the 'purification' of Alexandria and Cairo that new prisons had to be built to accommodate them all.[49]

It was also a matter of pride for the United States army to claim to be the cleanest in France and a beacon of morality and purity shining amid the corruption of the Old World after its entry into the war in 1917. The Progressive movement had long linked modern efficiency with morality and cleanliness. Soldiers were warned that 'a man who is thinking below the belt is not efficient'[50] and that 'they had to be 100% efficient to win the war'.[51] Even boys, not yet old enough to join the army, 'whether you are at school, at work or go to war in the next few years', were warned that they must make 'positive efforts . . . through self-discipline and healthy activities to put your mind and body in prime condition'.[52] The innocence of the doughboy was taken for granted and must be protected at all costs, though he might have to be reminded that 'some ignorant men hold that sexual intercourse is necessary to physical health, but this is contrary to the best medical authority'.[53]

Within eleven days of the entry of the United States into the war, President Woodrow Wilson had established the Commission on Training Camp Activities to combat the dangers of sexually transmitted infections among raw recruits. The Commission was headed by Raymond B. Fosdick, a 33-year-old Princeton-educated lawyer and social investigator who had recently revealed the extent of venereal disease among American soldiers dispatched to the Mexican border following Francisco 'Pancho' Villa's recent raid on New Mexico in March 1916.[54] Soldiers were bombarded with lectures on the dangers of sexually transmitted disease, which 'stripped the moral issue to the bone' and 'sneered at them for lacking the moral courage to fight the common tendency in modern armies' to contract venereal diseases until 'they were as pliable as putty' in the hands of their merciless lecturers, who had to be warned not to 'overstress the horrors – it sometimes creates an undesirable reaction'.[55] They were told the salutary tale of a football squad that celebrated its victory in a match by going out on the town, only for it all to end with three of them 'now six feet under the soil dead with the most loathsome of disease, syphilis'.[56]

The message was reiterated in a full-length feature film *Fit to Fight*, which followed the fortunes of five conscripts who find themselves beset by sexual temptation but handle it differently. It was hailed as 'the first time in the history of any nation that motion pictures have been used to educate an army in the perils of venereal disease'. In the film, after a visit to a brothel, the playboy among the new recruits is crippled by gonorrhoea, the worldly salesman catches syphilis because he is too late in reporting to a prophylactic station and the innocent farm boy has a syphilitic sore contracted from a kiss from a wanton woman. The womanising boxer escapes infection because he has heeded the advice of the company commander to go straight to a prophylactic station for preventative treatment but taunts the only member of the group to have kept himself chaste for refusing to visit prostitutes. The two men fight and Billy Hale, the virginal but virile college quarterback, wins and becomes a role model for his fellow doughboys of the advantages of 'clean living . . . a valuable asset to a fighter'.[57]

It was not enough to warn the soldiers of the perils of sexually transmitted infections and to promote the image of the pure and unsullied soldier without trying to eradicate the temptations themselves. Raymond Fosdick confessed that he did 'not think that we will ever absolutely eliminate the prostitute, but we do want to make it impossible for the prostitute to flaunt herself in the face of men on the streets when they are not thinking about her'.[58] In order to achieve this, the red-light districts were closed in many American cities and all houses of ill repute and saloons within five miles of military training camps were declared illegal.

It was less easy to control access to vice once the American Expeditionary Forces reached Europe. Shortly after arriving in

France, General Pershing issued his general order number 6 of 2 July 1917 setting out a series of measures, including medical inspection of troops, lectures, the setting-up of special stations for chemical prophylaxis and making it punishable by court martial for any man to contract a venereal disease. In December 1917 brothels were declared off limits, and it became compulsory to report all cases of infection.[59] All soldiers going on leave were examined for signs of infection and were re-examined on their return. They were reminded that the purpose of their leave was 'to improve your health and advance your education' not to 'sow wild oats', and that they must 'not let booze, a pretty face, a shapely ankle make you forget' that if they contracted a venereal disease they were 'guilty of a moral crime'. Above all, 'the AEF must not take European disease to America. You must go home clean.'[60] The girls back home were also warned that they must not consider that they were 'doing a patriotic duty by providing a celebration' for their returning sweethearts and that by sleeping with the soldiers they were actually 'dishonouring rather than honouring these heroes'.[61]

Exhortation, regulation and suppression were not the only ways in which attempts were made to ensure the troops went home without the dreaded disease, which no amount of educational and propaganda campaigns could halt in its progress. If the troops could not be encouraged to avoid the sources of infection, then they must be educated in the use of the technical means of preventing them. Since the beginning of the twentieth century, the Germans and Americans had been experimenting with prophylactic kits for men taking military leave. These kits contained a tube of calomel ointment for syphilis, potassium permanganate solution or tablets for gonorrhoea and cotton swabs for application to the penis. They were meant to be used immediately after sexual intercourse or as soon as practicable.[62]

The German army and navy had offered skilled disinfection by a medical orderly to their soldiers and sailors since the turn of the century. Much more popular with the troops themselves was the introduction of vending machines dispensing these prophylactic packets in the barracks, but Kaiser Wilhelm II had banned these

128

contraptions in 1912 after they had been denounced as 'an official invitation to shamelessness'. Since only the sale of prophylactics was officially banned, the German army merely removed the machines and permitted the disinfectants to be distributed free of charge on request by medical orderlies. The navy led the way after the outbreak of war by opening ablution centres in such major ports as Kiel and Wilhelmshaven, an example soon to be followed by the army. By 1917 the vending machines had reappeared in the barracks blocks.[63] The United States navy first issued calomel in 1908 and the army in 1909, but the practice had been stopped in 1915 after protests from moral purity groups, only to be reintroduced in wartime.[64]

Britain, as usual, lagged behind in sanctioning prophylactic measures in deference to opposition from the Church of England and the National Council for Combating Venereal Disease. The French, New Zealand, Australian and Canadian armies all introduced the kits in 1916, but it was 1918 before the War Office sanctioned their distribution to British troops, and even then only after the men's return to their barracks so as to avoid any charges that vice was being condoned.[65] The Canadians were sceptical about the value of the packet system and from 1916 preferred to set up their own ablution chambers in their barracks and hospitals, known as the 'Blue Lamp Depots' on account of the blue lights they displayed at night to advertise their presence.[66] The British army too had begun to establish similar ablution chambers, casuistically considering that they were for treatment once intercourse had taken place, whereas packets were issued in advance of the act, and thus were less likely to be regarded as inducements to 'unrestrained vice'.[67] In the British navy, the practice of issuing 'dreadnought packets' to sailors going ashore was believed to encourage 'the ignorant class' to 'assume that sexual indulgence is a necessity and plunge in to it dragging other hesitant youths with them'.[68]

The authorities need not have worried. Chemical prophylaxis was as unpopular with the troops as it was with the forces of morality. The ablution chambers were often installed in urinals, and disinfection had to be performed in full view of the other men.

The soldier who had engaged in risky sex and had sought treatment at a prophylactic station was first of all asked to urinate. Once he had done so, he would wash his genitals with soap and water, followed by bichloride of mercury, under the watchful gaze of an attendant, who would then inject a solution of the chemical protargol into the man's penis. The soldier had to hold this solution in his urethra and bladder for five minutes during this penile irrigation before he could expel it. After the injection, calomel ointment was rubbed on the penis, which was then wrapped in waxed paper. The unfortunate soldier would then be instructed that he should not urinate for four or five hours for the treatment to be effective.[69] It was unpleasant, painful and undignified. The system was poorly enforced and probably not particularly effective.[70] The American forces were more successful than other armies in persuading their men to use the prophylactics on offer. This was mainly because any man failing to obtain treatment could be court-martialled. Other nations were envious because 'they would not dare to do such a thing in their army'.[71] Even so, many American soldiers were so drunk or got so lost in unfamiliar French towns that they failed to find the prophylactic stations within the recommended three hours and, having missed that deadline, thought it too late to be worth bothering about. Condoms would have been a better prophylactic, but raised too many moral objections to be distributed.

The First World War introduced sexual experiences and disease to many men who would otherwise have remained ignorant. Robert Graves had a strong aversion to brothels during his service in France, motivated by a great fear of venereal disease. He considered his own abstention from sex to be unusual, though many other servicemen similarly abstained out of loyalty to their wives, fear of syphilis or just sheer exhaustion. Graves believed that most young men 'did not want to die virgins' when they knew that there was a good chance of being killed within a few weeks. Young officers were expected to live up to the image of being 'roistering blades', although many of them had to work hard at it. Graves was in command of a group of young officers, 'strictly brought-up Welsh boys of the professional classes', who had never visited a brothel nor heard of prophylactics. One of them woke up a disgusted Graves to tell him how wonderful sexual intercourse was and, when Graves hoped that he had washed himself after his experience in the brothel, replied that he had indeed washed his hands and face. For these innocents, the brothels could be a lifesaver: 'the *Drapeau Blanc* saved the lives of scores by incapacitating them for future trench service.'[72] It was a lesson not lost on the other ranks. Some of them visited brothels deliberately to get infected so that they would be sent home. Others used matchsticks to transfer the pus from the penis of an infected man to their own genitalia. If they failed to catch the diseases that terrified other men, they would bruise their penises and fake venereal discharges by injecting condensed milk into the urethra.[73]

It was not only at the Front that venereal disease posed a problem. In the laxer moral climate of wartime, 'a bad and diseased woman can do more harm than any German fleet of aircraft that has yet passed over London'.[74] Such 'women who solicit soldiers for immoral purposes' were castigated as 'disease spreaders and friends of the enemy'.[75] Nor were all of them the usual scapegoats, prostitutes. The war had increased the opportunities available to women in the workplace and given them greater freedom, which they wanted to enjoy after a day's hard work. Men on leave felt safer with such ordinary girls rather than with prostitutes, and taking them out and buying them presents was cheaper than paying a professional for sex. However, it was claimed that some soldiers 'hardly dare venture into the public thoroughfares in certain parts of London because of the temptations with which they are assailed' from the 'vile women who prey upon and poison our soldiers'.[76]

The governments of the Dominions were especially concerned about the dangers preying upon their troops, who were seen as particularly vulnerable because they were far from home and, unlike British soldiers and sailors, had no hope of relieving their sexual urges with their wives on home leave. Promiscuous women and desperate men were a combination encouraging the spread of venereal disease. Politicians pointed out that 'we have Canadian and Colonial soldiers who have come to this country quite free from these diseases, and thousands of them have been debilitated and rendered inefficient because the military authorities of this country have no power whatsoever to protect these gallant overseas kinsmen of ours'. Not doing anything to prevent this would strain the loyalty of these overseas troops to the mother country, for, 'whilst they are prepared if fate and duty decree it for the sacrifice of their sons and kinsmen on the field of battle, they deeply object to having them rendered not only ineffective but in some cases killed through these diseases which we think can and ought to be prevented'.[77] The Prime Minister of Canada and the Governor-Generals of Australia and New Zealand, seizing the opportunity to assert their independence as self-governing dominions rather than colonies, pressed the British government to take decisive action quickly, and the War Cabinet needed to keep them happy.[78]

Attempts had been made early in the war to control the situation. In some areas local authorities had limited the hours during which women could be served alcohol; and in Cardiff the military authorities had unsuccessfully pressed for a night-time curfew on women. In February 1916 the army and navy were given the power to ban convicted prostitutes and brothel-keepers from areas in which troops were stationed, a regulation that saw thirty-seven people expelled from Folkestone in one month.[79] In April 1917 these restrictions were extended to anyone convicted of offences against public order or decency who could now be removed from any area in which troops were stationed or munitions manufactured.[80] However, such action was not considered sufficient to check the problem, and on 22 March 1918 Regulation 40D under the Defence of the Realm Act came into force. This decreed that 'no woman who is suffering from venereal disease in a communicable form shall have sexual intercourse with any member of His Majesty's forces, or solicit or invite any member of His Majesty's forces to have sexual intercourse with her'.[81] The penalty was the not inconsiderable fine of £100 or six months' imprisonment.

There was an immediate outcry against Regulation 40D, which was specifically aimed at women. The National Council for Combating Venereal Disease welcomed anything that might control the growing incidence of venereal diseases; it believed that the regulation did not go far enough and should not be limited to women but 'that the knowing transmission of venereal disease should be a penal offence for all members of the community'.[82] A naval chief petty officer pointed out that women were not the only ones spreading disease and that 'sodomy in the navy is by no means as rare a practice as is believed. The guilty persons are usually long service petty officers who terrorise new and fair boys into submission.'[83] Yet nothing was done to stamp out this abuse, and the regulation not only applied solely to civilians but also did not allow for the possibility of civilian homosexual men transmitting the infection, though it might have been considered unnecessary, since homosexuality was illegal and could have been prosecuted under existing laws. Nevertheless, the fact that only women were targeted was seen as unfair and was the main criticism from such organisations as the Labour Party, the Salvation Army, the National Council for Civil Liberties and the Women's Cooperative Guild, who argued that 'men expect a certain standard of morality in their wives, and as wives we are entitled to expect the same from men'.[84]

There was also a fear that the Act might be abused. In many cases it would be impossible for a serviceman to identify which woman had given him venereal disease; by the time the symptoms manifested themselves, he might have slept with any number of women and not always when he was sober. The danger was that he might then blame the woman he 'least enjoyed or who charged the most'.[85] Completely innocent women might also be accused by disgruntled men: 'their own daughters may be the victims at any time of an unscrupulous man, who out of malice at not getting all that he wanted, could lay this fearful charge against her, and unless she submitted to a most degrading examination she would be considered guilty.'[86] The regulation was one-sided and, like previous legislation, might be considered to operate double standards. It also gave men powers over women that were open to abuse. The only way a woman could refute the charge was to be examined either by a police or prison medical officer or, at her own expense, by her own doctor. In London 396 cases were reported to the police under

Regulation 40D between February and October 1918, of whom 203 women were prosecuted and 101 convicted.[87] The majority of women arrested and treated under the regulations were professional prostitutes rather than amateurs, many of whom were engaged in war work.[88] The trials were conducted in public, with the names of the women published even if they were subsequently acquitted, but the identity of the men was withheld. As a result of pressure from critics of the regulation, the War Cabinet agreed that no names should be published until after the result of the medical examination was known.[89]

Officials in the War Office and Home Office were conscious that Regulation 40D discriminated against women but were defensive against such charges. They pointed out that the law applied only to women because men in the forces were already covered by military regulations. Soldiers were liable to two years' imprisonment with hard labour if they had contracted and concealed venereal disease, which was a greater punishment than the maximum of six months facing a civilian woman, who also had the option of paying a fine as an alternative. Soldiers could also have their pay stopped. Moreover, it was necessary for a man to appear in court against the woman accused of infecting him, whereas there was no such necessity for a woman given a disease by a man. All she need do was to report the man to his commanding officer, and this could even be done anonymously. If the soldier was medically examined and found to have a venereal infection, his accuser did not need to give evidence in court against him because 'the charges before the court martial would not be of infecting a woman . . . but of concealing venereal disease. As a matter of fact, of course, the discovery of the offence for which the soldier would be tried would arise out of the fact that he had conveyed venereal disease to a woman.'[90] Such excuses for operating double standards were neither entirely satisfactory nor convincing, but of greater cogency was the need to protect against something that caused as great a 'wastage of manpower as German poison gas'. Rather than being 'an attempt to make vice safe for men', the regulation was 'to keep the realm safe by stamping out centres of infection which injure the fighting capacity of the nation'.[91]

With the end of the war and demobilisation, Regulation 40D lapsed, although measures were taken to refer infected men to suitable medical treatment in their home areas after discharge. Confidentiality was maintained, however, by making no mention of the condition on their discharge forms.[92] The returning ex-servicemen found widespread provision for the treatment of venereal diseases at home, which encouraged patients to seek and continue treatment in a system that was free and guaranteed their privacy and confidentiality. By 1919 Britain was covered by a network of nearly 200 publicly provided 'clap clinics' patronised by over one million patients.[93] The quality of the clinics was variable. Colonel Lawrence Harrison, official adviser to the British government on venereal diseases, organised a model clinic at St Thomas's Hospital, London, headed by a specialist venereologist and offering confidential and expert treatment. The clinic offered an all-day service. Trained social workers in the form of female almoners controlled access to the clinics and ensured that patients were aware that they must continue to attend until the completion of their treatment if they were to hope for a cure and that their social circumstances would not make them default on their treatment.[94] Other services elsewhere were not so well regarded. The voluntary hospitals generally continued to remain aloof from this less respectable branch of medicine, though they were happy to accept the funding they received for providing the service. In many cases the evening part-time clinics in the teaching hospitals offered paid positions for young doctors on the first rungs of the ladder that would establish them in other specialities and ultimately gain them more prestigious positions on the hospital staff. At St Mary's Hospital, Paddington, for this reason, there was considerable opposition by the honorary medical and surgical staff to the appointment of a specialist to head the venereal diseases clinic in 1933 when the London County Council threatened to withdraw funding if the service was not brought up to scratch and extended. However, the necessary improvements were eventually introduced rather than the hospital lose the funding that came with the clinic, as well as the patients essential for teaching medical students the rudiments of venereology.[95] The poor law and municipal hospital clinics were little better. The medical officer in charge of the Dorchester Venereal Diseases Centre admitted that 'the value of the centre from the point of view of preventing the spread of disease is approximately nil', but he derived comfort from the thought that 'it is a place to which to refer cases which apply to him', any facility being better than none.[96]

Yet such clinics failed to offer any solution to the problem of congenital syphilis that was thought to have gone unrecognised among many children. The National Council for Combating Venereal Disease raised the question in 1923 of whether the prevalence of a considerable number of schoolchildren with hereditary syphilis in Plymouth was reflected across the country.[97] In Plymouth, a large number of children attended an undercover venereal diseases clinic ostensibly for their backwardness, since any mention of VD would have discouraged their parents from sending them. Many of these children were classed as 'slow learners' or backward, but were found to improve considerably and 'become quite nice children' if they were treated with mercury. Dr G.D. Kettlewell, the medical officer in charge of the clinic, believed that 'if we could get hold of these children early enough, there would be fewer stunted crippled children and adults walking around Plymouth, and there are a large number'.[98] There was a fear that feeble-minded young women were more likely to be tempted into prostitution through their helplessness and would become vectors for the transmission of further disease, with those also suffering from congenital syphilis tending to perpetuate a vicious circle.[99] In Portsmouth, another port, 'the number of suspects varies according to the social status of the school', with more cases in schools in the slum areas than in the better residential areas inhabited by the families of the superior artisans and petty non-commissioned officers,[100] but outside the naval ports the problem was not so prevalent across Britain and did not demand special measures.[101]

Little that was new was introduced in interwar Britain. The Trevethin Committee, set up in the early 1920s to investigate the best approaches to the prevention of venereal diseases, reported in May 1923 that 'medical measures alone can never operate as an absolute preventative of the disease, but their success must always depend upon the attitude towards them of the community and the co-operation of the community in securing their largest efforts'.[102] Since 'promiscuous intercourse' was still seen as the main cause of the problem, there seemed to be 'no absolute preventative except continence'.[103] All that the Committee could recommend was a campaign to educate the public about the dangers of casual sex and the employment of social workers at the venereal diseases clinics to explain to the patients that they should continue their treatment until cured and not default from attendance. There was nothing novel in the recommendations.

One method of preventing venereal disease, self-disinfection, was firmly rejected by the Trevethin Committee as not being cost-effective or efficient if self-administered. The whole issue had already split the National Council for Combating Venereal Disease. The Society for the Prevention of Venereal Disease had seceded from its parent body to advocate the supply of over-the-counter self-disinfection kits that could be sold by chemists, since 'our greatest hope of exterminating venereal disease lies in the breaking of the chain at the male end, where the handicap is distinctly in our favour'.[104] Fearing that such kits might be seen as promoting promiscuity, the National Council for Combating Venereal Disease had preferred to advertise the use of soap and water immediately after intercourse. Yet facilities for treatment outside the clinics were far from ideal. The Metropolitan Police provided prophylactic cubicles for its officers in some of their section houses 'not to assist the unfortunate patient but to prevent any real or imaginary contamination to other residents'.[105] It was not so easy for other people, as a working woman reminded the more aristocratic members of the Society for the Prevention of Venereal Disease that 'we in our larger houses could not understand the urgency of the demand and that only those who lived in one room and shared the same cup and towel could really know what the fear of infection was'.[106]

In Weimar Germany, by contrast, the availability of prophylactics was the cornerstone of a strategy against venereal disease, despite opposition from the Catholic and Protestant churches and the conservative wing of the women's movement. In 1927 all restrictions on the sale of prophylactics were removed, and vending machines became a regular fixture in public toilets. State-regulated prostitution was also abandoned and replaced by the obligatory inspection of anyone suspected of having a social disease regardless of gender and the compulsory treatment by a hospital of all sufferers.[107] In doing this, Germany was turning towards what the French, who stuck firmly to their long-established tradition of regulation, called the Scandinavian model of 'sanitary statism' based on the principle that all citizens should be subject to compulsory medical examination and treatment for venereal diseases in return for free medical care. In Sweden the *Lex Veneris* of 1918 laid down that anyone suspected of suffering from a sexually contracted infection would be examined and given free compulsory treatment. This law enshrined a tradition of medical inspections for syphilis of all inhabitants regardless of rank in particular rural areas where the disease was prevalent. Between 1812 and the abolition of internal passports for travel around Sweden in 1860, it was necessary for any traveller to be declared free of disease by the clergy, and high-risk groups such as canteen keepers, coffee boilers, costermongers and hawkers were given compulsory medical inspections every three months. In return, treatment was funded from general taxation. After 1875 more emphasis was placed on the regulation of prostitutes, but the 1918 law returned to a notion of equality in treatment between the sexes and social groups. The *Lex Veneris* also forbade the marriage of anyone found to be infected with syphilis, and made the transmission of venereal disease a criminal offence. A marriage could be dissolved if one of the partners was found to have contracted an infection as the result of infidelity.[108]

It was an extension of state powers that would have been unthinkable in Britain, where the British Social Hygiene Council, as the National Council for Combating Venereal Disease was renamed when it took on a wider remit for promoting sex education, continued to be suspicious of both compulsion and prophylaxis. Lectures and warning notices in public lavatories were acceptable in

Britain, yet a chemist could be prosecuted under the 1917 Venereal Diseases Act for circulating booklets containing advertisements for treatment and 'a number of rubber shops in London are suspected of . . . selling chemicals for the treatment of venereal disease and acting as intermediaries in the introduction of patients to unqualified men'.[109]

By the late 1930s the better of the venereal diseases clinics in Britain were staffed by doctors specialising in venereal disease rather than men marking time before moving on to careers in other specialities. No longer was venereology a branch of dermatology, a link that had once seemed logical when the external manifestation of a skin disease was the only means of diagnosis. Increasingly the new breed of venereal disease specialists looked on the illnesses as bacteriological infections that could be treated medically rather than as moral conditions to be deplored. Gerard McElligott, venereal diseases officer to the City of Stoke-on-Trent, who had studied under Colonel Harrison at St Thomas's Hospital, recommended that 'the patient be treated as a patient and not as a penitent or a prisoner' and that he or she should be treated with courtesy so as to 'create the atmosphere of a private consulting room' in the busiest of the public clinics.[110] This concern for the dignity of the patient he took with him when he was appointed director in 1933 of the venereal diseases clinic at St Mary's Hospital, with its large clientele of prostitutes in Paddington, an area 'which might be called the prostitute's paradise'. There he observed that the prostitutes were 'among the best of the patients and they were most grateful for what was done for them. They put up with more than the average shop girl, they expected to be hurt, and when this did not happen they were agreeably surprised and very grateful.'[111] The fact that this clinic was one of the few in a busy general hospital where the staff were 'kind' to all their patients, regardless of their moral status, soon got around.[112] For McElligott, venereology was the 'summation of small skills', not the least among which were kindness, tact and discretion.[113]

It was a great improvement on the days when national efficiency had been more important than humanity in the treatment of patients

139

with syphilis and gonorrhoea, and the sexuality of women was considered the greatest threat. Many venereologists prided themselves on their good humour towards both their patients and their speciality. In interwar Warsaw, one of the most prominent specialists in venereal diseases would greet each of his daughter's new boyfriends with a reference to having seen the young man in his clinic recently, a joke that may sometimes have misfired.[114] However, another war was around the corner, when the fighting fitness of many countries was once more to be tested and draconian measures might again be needed for the sake of national survival.

SIX

Tuskegee: 'Shadow on the Land'

It is not often that the President of the United States makes a public apology to any group on behalf of the federal government, let alone the victims of syphilis, unwitting participants in a medical experiment that had lasted for forty years at 'a time not so very long ago that many Americans would prefer not to remember, but we dare not forget'. Yet that was what Bill Clinton did in May 1997 to the small number of survivors of a project run by the United States Public Health Service to study the long term effects of untreated syphilis in African-American men living in rural poverty near Tuskegee, Alabama. The study had begun in 1932 and continued until 1972. Clinton stated that the men behind the 'Tuskegee Study of Untreated Syphilis in the Negro Male' had 'diminished the stature of man' because they had abandoned 'the most basic ethical precepts' and had 'forgot their pledge to heal and repair' by not offering treatment to the men being studied when they had the power to do so. For the President, 'the legacy of the study at Tuskegee has reached far and deep, in ways that hurt our progress and divide our nation. We cannot be one nation when a whole segment of our nation has no trust in America.'[1] The Tuskegee experiment had come to be seen as indicative of a profound racism in public policy and the cause of a deep-seated distrust towards medicine and public health among contemporary African Americans, a matter of great concern to the federal government under a Democratic presidency.[2] Yet, despite Clinton's rhetoric and evident concern for the subjects of the study, it was ironic that many of the doctors involved in the beginnings of the experiment were among the most progressive and dedicated medical men of their day and were instrumental in campaigns to exorcise what the surgeon

141

general Thomas Parran in the 1930s had called the 'shadow on the land'.[3] Indeed, they had been successful in reducing the ravages of syphilis in other black communities, yet had withheld adequate treatment from the men involved in the Tuskegee Study regardless of the suffering this may have caused. In this they were motivated by the search for knowledge, and what they saw as the greater good of the community overriding the rights of the individual.

The Venereal Diseases Division of the United States Public Health Service had been established in 1918 in response to fears that the high incidence of sexually transmitted diseases uncovered in wartime posed a threat to the fighting capacity of the nation. Federal funds had also been made available for the individual states to organise local treatment centres, but the end of the war made the whole issue seem less urgent, and economic problems ensured that social hygiene became a focus of cost-cutting measures. By 1926 Congress had cut all its funding of state initiatives for prevention and treatment, and the Venereal Diseases Division had been reduced to doing little other than promoting sex education laced with a heavy moralistic tone. Even such moralistic films as *Fit to Fight* were withdrawn from public release because their support for the use of chemical prophylaxis was seen as an encouragement to vice by the American Social Hygiene Association, which the Public Health Service feared to offend. The reduction in Congressional appropriations for venereal diseases work from $4,000,000 in 1920 to under $60,000 in 1926 was effectively turning the Division into a 'dying operation', causing Oliver Clarence Wenger, director of the United States Public Health Service Venereal Diseases Clinic at Hot Springs, Arkansas, to complain that 'with our present appropriations, Federal and State and private, we might just as well try to empty the Pacific Ocean with a teaspoon'.[4]

Although government support and funding for the eradication of venereal disease were at their nadir, there was some hope of greater advances being made through private funds. In 1928 a group of wealthy young philanthropists, goaded to action by having seen the impact syphilis had had among some of their friends, the gilded youth of the frenetically libidinous jazz age, established a fund to encourage laboratory and clinical research into the problem of syphilis. W. Averell Harriman alone contributed $100,000 to the fund, allowing the establishment of a Committee for Research into Syphilis, chaired by Thomas Parran, director of the Venereal Diseases Division of the Public Health Service. It was intended that this committee should be able to make sizeable grants to research scientists and venereologists, but the Wall Street Crash of 1929 was to claim the recently instituted committee among its victims, although not before it had formed the Cooperative Clinical Group made up of the directors of the leading syphilis clinics in the United States.[5] The forerunner of modern joint clinical trials conducted between different institutions, this group undertook a number of investigations into neuro-syphilis, cardiovascular syphilis and syphilis in pregnancy, as well as attempting to establish uniform methods of treatment for the disease.[6] It helped to create a climate that encouraged further clinical work, inspiring Parran to claim that, 'since World War I, there has been more scientific work accomplished and more progress made in our understanding of syphilis, both in the laboratory and in the clinic, than any other disease of equal importance'.[7]

In the late 1920s, the Rosenwald Memorial Fund, a Chicago-based philanthropic foundation set up by one of the founders of the Sears and Roebuck mail order company, turned its attention to the development of health programmes for the black people of the Southern States. The Fund had long been an active builder of schools for black Americans and now, under its innovative director of medical services, Michael M. Davis, hoped to pioneer the use of black community nurses in backward rural communities, the training of black public health doctors and the building of racially mixed hospitals in the South. Davis had sought the cooperation of the surgeon general Hugh S. Cumming for this ambitious project. Cummings was happy to appoint an adviser to the scheme but also suggested that the Rosenwald Fund might additionally consider participating in a study of the prevalence of syphilis among rural blacks as a follow-up to a recent survey of syphilis conducted by the Public Health Service on over 2,000 black workers employed by the

Delta and Pine Land Company in Bolivar County, Mississippi. A wider-scale survey could demonstrate the effectiveness of treatment and 'furnish a demonstration which will be of value in connection with similar programs in other localities and industries in which there is a high prevalence of syphilis'.[8] Davis, who, as director of the Boston Dispensary, had previously established a very successful venereal diseases clinic for working men, was interested in this proposal so long as it did not conflict with the wider aims of the Fund, and provided that employment was given to black doctors and nurses.[9]

The purpose of the new study, which began early in 1930, was to determine the practicability and effectiveness of any measures undertaken for the mass control of syphilis in areas of rural poverty. Parran, director of the Venereal Diseases Division, welcomed the opportunity to conduct syphilis control demonstrations among the black population of the South because they would not only address a serious health problem but could serve as a springboard for establishing federal leadership in the drive for the eradication of syphilis. For Oliver Clarence Wenger, who had headed the Mississippi demonstration and who was to lead the new study, the only way of breaking the cycle of inadequate treatment and reinfection that plagued ill-educated, poverty-stricken rural communities, was to test as many patients as possible for syphilis and then render as many of them non-infectious as practicable; if it proved too expensive to cure everyone with the infection, it would be better to spend what money was available on ensuring that the infection was not passed on to others. Consequently older patients, whose syphilis was no longer at an infectious stage, would not be given treatment, and younger people would be given only enough drugs to make them non-infectious but not enough to cure them. In the Rosenwald demonstrations, treatment consisted of eight or nine doses of neosalvarsan rather than the twenty considered to be adequate treatment or the seventy then considered necessary for a definite cure.[10] It was a practical solution to the problem from a dedicated worker in the public health field who, despite a paternalistic attitude to his charges and an impatience with opposition to his ideas, developed a rapport with his black patients and whose Saturday afternoon sessions taking blood samples for Wassermann testing in a crossroads country store was described by one observer as 'holding high Wassermann in the marketplace'.[11]

Six rural counties had been selected by Parran and Wenger for the syphilis control demonstration, each of them with different economic and social conditions and representing a cross section of the conditions in which black people lived in the rural South.[12] At one extreme was the prosperous Albemarle County, Virginia, where the University of Virginia at Charlottesville was the largest employer and the local African Americans were generally healthy and well educated, with access to a venereal diseases clinic and a low rate of prevalence of syphilis at 7 per cent. By contrast, the economically poorest area studied was Macon County, Alabama, with 36 per cent prevalence. The poverty shocked even such a hardened public health official as 46-year-old Wenger, who had previously served in the St Louis Public Health Department in Missouri, with the military sanitary corps in the Philippines and with the American Expeditionary Force in France. He admitted: 'I've seen what happens when the rice crop fails in the Philippines and am somewhat familiar with reports from China, but this is the first time I realized what is going on in the South at the present time.' In Macon County he saw nursing mothers surviving on corn bread and sweet potatoes, and malnourished schoolchildren lucky if they were fed on corn bread, hominy grits, molasses or salt pork, with red meat, fruit, vegetables and milk considered an unattainable luxury.[13] Most of the black population worked as cotton sharecroppers, eking out a bare living on small plots of land and living in ramshackle, poorly furnished, overcrowded shacks. Such extreme poverty was accompanied by low levels of literacy and poor educational facilities. The Tuskegee Institute had been founded in 1881 by Booker T. Washington to provide vocational and technical education for African Americans but had failed to raise more basic primary educational standards in its neighbourhood. However, its presence was one of the reasons Macon County had been selected for inclusion in the demonstration, since attached to it was the John A. Andrew Hospital, which was 'very sympathetic to the local or community needs'. There was also the Tuskegee Veterans' Hospital, staffed, like the John A. Andrew Hospital, by African Americans but which had been much criticised for its 'attitude of intellectual and professional isolation'.[14]

Macon County indeed offered great possibilities for public health initiatives that the local medical facilities had failed to seize. Yet it was clear to many observers that 'sympathetic and co-operative effort could help to make the present community more health-conscious and the present rural conditions less tenable to the people themselves'.[15] The county and state health departments were sympathetic to any such initiatives, especially the study of syphilis coupled with the 'adequate' medical treatment of all individuals found to be infected. The Alabama State Board of Health was also keen that any syphilis control programme should employ a 'Negro physician and Negro nurse' full time to work with the local people.[16] Although the hospitals in Tuskegee were staffed by African Americans, only one of the five doctors working in the community at that time was from the same ethnic background as the majority of the population they served. These local people themselves were 'as a group . . . susceptible to kindness', and indeed in the opinion of Clyde Frost, the black physician sent by the Rosenwald Fund to observe the project, 'the Negro, as found in this rural area, associates no moral or social stigmata with syphilis'. This meant that it was unlikely that anyone would conceal symptoms or refuse treatment from shame about the disease. The local landowners were also very sympathetic and saw the advantages of the syphilis control project in giving them a more efficient supply of labour. One white landowner commented: 'syphilis is the biggest problem we have with these people – it is sapping the manpower of the Negro race.'[17]

With the support of local figures and institutions of authority, the implementation of the project proved very successful. The landowners encouraged their sharecroppers to take the Wassermann test for syphilis and accept any treatment that was going. Some of them merely told their workers to report to the makeshift testing centres where the 'health doctor' had 'some government medicine to cure the blood disease', but others were more high-handed and simply gave permission for the mass testing of these people in the cotton fields in which they were working without any explanation to them of what it was about and without any thought about the need to obtain their individual consent.[18] The use of churches and schools as clinics for conducting the tests also gave a measure of official sanction and blessing, which encouraged people to come forward. As a result, many people from the more remote communities would travel for miles in all kinds of weather to be tested and treated, coming on the backs of mules, in wagons, old cars and even on foot, demonstrating 'the favour with which the opportunity was received by the people'.[19] A study of the syphilis control demonstrations by the black sociologist Charles Johnson and commissioned by the Rosenwald Fund ascribed this unquestioning eagerness to participate to 'the tradition of dependence and obedience to the orders of authority, whether these were mandatory or not'.[20] Thomas Parran preferred to believe that cooperation was not the result of deference to authority but because 'in the South . . . the Negro instinctively trusts the white man' and believed that 'the Government is a friend of his and tries to help him'.[21]

Unfortunately, doctor and patient did not always mean the same thing when they used identical phrases about the health campaign. Rather than refer to 'syphilis', the public health officials believed that it was better to use the local expression of 'bad blood' when speaking to black people, since this would be more familiar to them. Even Clyde Frost, a black doctor but not one from Alabama, assumed that 'syphilis' and 'bad blood' were one and the same when he wrote that in his dealings with the rural black sharecropper he had found that 'bad blood to him was to be expected'.[22] However, 'bad blood' was actually seen as the cause of ailments as varied as tuberculosis, pellagra, scrofula, headaches and indigestion.[23] Since ill health was prevalent in such a poor rural area, many of the people turning up at the clinics expected treatment for whatever ailed them, and could not understand why they were told that they did not have bad blood when they were so obviously sick. Dr H.L. Harris, one of the black physicians working for the Rosenwald Fund, actually wondered whether attendance at the clinics would decline if people realised that they were being tested for syphilis in particular and if it were explained to them that this was a disease transmitted through sexual intercourse.[24] The majority of the doctors involved in the programme and the subsequent long-term study of untreated syphilis did not trouble themselves with the thought that their use of a euphemism for syphilis might have confused the patient or that they might have a professional duty to explain the implications to each patient before seeking informed consent to his participation in the experiment. What mattered more to the doctor was that this was a pioneering public health project that would prove that something could be done about the problem of syphilis among poor rural African Americans. In their eagerness to test and offer limited treatment to render their patients non-infectious, they ignored the importance of education about sex and the disease for any long-term solution.

The scale of the public-health problems facing the people living in Macon County suggested to the Public Health Service officials closely connected with the Rosenwald Demonstrations that there was a need to continue the work there beyond August 1931 at the very least, and ideally to convert the syphilis control demonstrations into a comprehensive health-care programme for Macon County. Unfortunately the Alabama State Health Board had failed to contribute its full share of the costs of the original programme, and the Rosenwald Fund was reluctant to become involved in a major new undertaking in the middle of an economic depression that threatened its own income.[25] Taliaferro Clark, who had acted as adviser to the original demonstrations and had now succeeded Parran as director of the Public Health Service Venereal Diseases Division, was disappointed and complained in private that the Fund was 'more concerned with the education of the Negro than the preservation of his health', and questioned the wisdom of 'raising up generations of what we might call white-collared Negroes, with nothing to do but get into mischief'.[26] Clark was concerned that education was useless without suitable employment opportunities at the same time that the possibilities for improving the health of these people were being neglected. Rebuffed in this initiative to do something practical and offer treatment, he very soon turned to the idea of scientific research into syphilis that would be of long-term benefit. Such an approach would at least mean that something could be salvaged from the now defunct treatment programme.

The high prevalence rate of syphilis among the black population in Macon County and the fact that most of them had received little or no medical treatment for the infection made them an ideal group for a study of the natural history of the disease. Although living close to a modern and relatively well-equipped teaching hospital, the John A. Andrew Memorial Hospital attached to the Tuskegee Institute, which could be used for laboratory purposes, here were people remote from the benefits of modern medicine.[27] While doctors and scientists already knew a great deal about syphilis, Clark believed that there was more to learn, especially about how it might affect people of African descent, widely considered to be 'a notoriously syphilis-soaked race'.[28] It was commonly assumed that syphilis affected black and white people differently, but there was little real evidence to support this hypothesis. The effects of untreated syphilis in white males had already been studied among patients attending the Oslo Clinic in Norway between 1891 and 1910, and an article was published in 1929 based on this retrospective study of case histories rather than on the continuing observation of current living patients. The Oslo Study had shown that cardiovascular damage was common in patients suffering from latent syphilis but that it was rare to find neurological complications.[29] This was the opposite of the common contemporary assumption that syphilis was more likely to attack the neurological system of white men and the cardiovascular system of black men. It should have produced the conclusion that the disease affected all sufferers in similar ways, irrespective of racial differences. However, Clark saw the potential for 'making a further study of the effect of untreated syphilis on the human economy among people now living and engaged in daily pursuits'.[30]

Conscious of the need to secure the cooperation of the local medical authorities, Clark and his colleague Wenger travelled to

Alabama in September 1932 to win the support of local doctors. Officials from the State Health Board readily gave their consent to the proposed study, but insisted that some treatment should be given to anyone found to be infected. Since the experiment was expected to last only between six and eight months, it would have been unrealistic to ask for a full programme of treatment to effect a cure that would have taken more than a year. Instead it was agreed that eight doses of neosalvarsan should be given to every patient examined and found to be infected, a dosage that would have had little appreciable effect.[31] The local planters, seeing the benefits a health project could bring to their workforce, also offered their support and were 'anxious that the study, and especially the treatment, progress'.[32] However, it was even more important to have the active support and participation of the Tuskegee Institute, which enjoyed the respect and trust of the people of Macon County and had the confidence of local private doctors. Eugene H. Dibble, medical director of the Tuskegee Institute and head of the John A. Andrew Memorial Hospital, was soon persuaded to endorse the project and offer the services of his interns and nurses to help with the project, which would be of benefit for their training, together with medical facilities for making spinal punctures in sterile conditions, X-ray equipment and a ward where patients could be kept in overnight if they reacted badly to the spinal punctures.[33] The surgeon general H.S. Cumming personally wrote to the principal of the Tuskegee Institute, Dr Robert Moton, stressing the importance of the research, 'which may have a marked bearing on the treatment, or conversely, the non-necessity for treatment, of cases of latent syphilis' and 'offers an unparalleled opportunity for carrying on this piece of scientific work which probably cannot be duplicated anywhere else in the world'.[34] The implication was not only that this was an important piece of research, which would benefit black people, but also that it would also bring a degree of international prestige to those who collaborated on it rather than the disapproval and condemnation it was to evoke some four decades and more later.

With local support assured, Clark turned his attention to securing the advice of some of the foremost experts in the fields of venereal disease on establishing protocols to frame the nature of the proposed study. The Cooperative Clinical Group, formed in 1928 by Parran, offered the perfect source of peer advice. Joseph Earle Moore, a venereologist at Johns Hopkins School of Medicine in Baltimore who believed that 'syphilis in the Negro is in many respects almost a different disease from syphilis in the white',[35] was especially helpful with his suggestions. Moore recommended limiting the study to men over the age of 30, because of the difficulties of obtaining reliable information from women about the date of their infection since their early symptoms might be mild and could be mistaken for other unrelated conditions involving vaginal itching, while admitting men under 30 to the study might reduce the chances of observing the late stages of the disease and the neurological and cardiovascular complications often present in patients with longstanding infections.[36] He also warned that care should be taken in selecting 'clinical material' since 'a mere history of a penile sore would not be adequate' for diagnosing syphilis 'inasmuch as the average Negro has had as many penile sores as rabbits have offspring'.[37] Clark too was aware of the difficulties of obtaining adequate data from a poorly educated population and admitted to Paul O'Leary of the Mayo Clinic, who was also advising him on the project, that 'we have cut out for ourselves a piece of work that under ordinary conditions would be difficult but which is enormously increased in view of the lack of personal cooperation and information we are likely to obtain in the case of the class of Negroes with which we propose to deal'.[38] He did, however, concede that the plight of the men he proposed to study was not the result of any form of racial inferiority, but 'this state of affairs is due to the paucity of doctors rather than low intelligence of the Negro population in this section, depressed economic conditions, and the very common promiscuous sex relations of this population group which not only contribute to the spread of syphilis but also contribute to the prevailing indifference with regard to treatment'.[39] He hoped to effect some improvement with the research project, though treatment was not part of it. None of the medical experts consulted challenged the ethics of deliberately withholding medical treatment but considered it a valid scientific study, though Wenger predicted that 'it will either cover us with mud or glory when completed'.[40]

The study proper began on 20 October 1932 under the supervision of 35-year-old Raymond A. Vonderlehr, who had worked as a Public Health Service officer for seven years after teaching dermatology and syphilology at the Medical College of Virginia in Richmond. He was considered an expert on cardiovascular syphilis, one of the main areas of interest that the Tuskegee Study had for Clark, and was a rising star of the Public Health Service, destined to succeed Clark as director of the Venereal Diseases Division on his mentor's retirement in June 1933.[41] Superficially the programme seemed to be a continuation of the previous Rosenwald Demonstration, which had been well received by the local people. Clark admitted that 'in order to secure the cooperation of planters in this section, it was necessary to carry on the study under the guise of a demonstration and provide treatment for those cases uncovered found to be need of treatment'.[42] People turning up at treatment centres for the new investigations into 'bad blood' were given a Wassermann test and physical examination. Men found to have positive results were then invited to report for treatment at portable clinics set up in schools and churches throughout the county. Only men over the age of 25 with positive Wassermann tests who had never been treated for 'bad blood' and had been infected for more than five years were chosen for the study.[43] The offer of free treatment was vital to the success of the selection procedure, not only because the state and county health boards had insisted upon it but also because it offered an incentive for potential subjects to come forward. However, suitable patients were not as easy to find as had been expected. Of the first 300 men to be tested, only 17 per cent were infected and only 5 per cent suitable for the study.[44] This required a wider survey of the population until enough men had been found, which in turn meant even greater expenditure on neosalvarsan for treatment, prompting Clark to complain that 'it never once occurred to me that we would be called upon to treat a large part of the county as a return for the privilege of making this study'.[45] Yet he had no choice but to sanction such expenditure, as he acknowledged Vonderlehr's point that 'it would be impossible . . . to obtain the cooperation of these aged Negroes without holding out treatment in return'.[46] He also found it encouraging that 'our study should dispel the rather general belief that syphilis is a disease of small consequence to the Negro'.[47]

Late October had been chosen as the best time to begin the work, 'when the Negroes have finished cotton picking and are accessible for examination without interference with their routine work'.[48] However, bad weather was to impede the work. Heavy rain turned the roads into impassable quagmires and 'the patients refused to walk the several miles to the treatment centers under these conditions'.[49] As it was, Vonderlehr complained that 'these people have no sense of time and show up anywhere within 24 hours of the appointed time'.[50] An influenza epidemic also hindered the project and made the medical team cautious about giving treatment, so that 'we are going very slow in giving intravenous injections because of this flu situation'; 'it would be extremely unwise to give one of these ignorant patients a dose of Neo and then have him develop a flu or possibly a pneumonia'.[51]

It was also to avoid scaring off potential subjects for the study that Vonderlehr had decided against performing the spinal punctures necessary for the examination of the neurological effects of syphilis until towards the end of the initial programme. If the procedure were to go wrong, the patient could end up paralysed. Much more common was the risk of an adverse reaction, with severe headaches and stiffness in the neck and limbs. If word got out about how unpleasant the procedure could be and some of the effects of it, many men would be scared away. Clark agreed with this decision, since 'these Negroes are very ignorant and easily influenced by things that would be of minor significance in a more intelligent group'.[52] It would not just have been the men of Macon County who would have been deterred from participating in the whole study had they been given more information. So knowledge of what was really happening was withheld. At one stage the possibility of doing the tests at the patient's home was considered, which would have had the advantage of keeping their nature more secret as well as the avowed aim of reducing the 'possible dangers of transporting such patients back to their own homes over the rough country roads'.[53] However, common sense asserted itself because of the difficulty of reaching cabins a long way from the road and only accessible by foot; there might not even be a suitable bed or table on which to perform the procedure, so overall it would be safer done in a hospital.[54] Letters were sent to men who had been examined previously and were considered suitable for inclusion in the study, reminding them that 'some time ago you were given a thorough examination and since that time we hope you have gotten a great deal of treatment for bad blood'. Patients were then given an appointment to meet the nurse working with Dr Vonderlehr, who would take them to the Tuskegee Institute Hospital for 'free treatment'. The men were warned to 'remember this is your last chance for special free treatment. Be sure to meet your nurse.'[55] Nothing was said about the spinal puncture until arrival at hospital. Some of the men even claimed to have been told by Eugene Dibble that they were receiving a shot of neosalvarsan when the needle was injected into the spinal fluid. For all of them it was unpleasant and painful, if not terrifying, and made them suspicious of the seemingly sympathetic doctors they had by now come to trust.[56]

The study was scheduled to be wound up by the end of May 1933, but Vonderlehr was keen to extend it. Ignoring the fact that the men had received some treatment, however meagre and inadequate, which meant that the infection could not be considered to have been left to follow its natural course, he suggested that, 'should these cases be followed over a period of some 5 or 10 years, many interesting facts would be learned regarding the complications of untreated syphilis'. So far as he was concerned, if these men had 'received only mercury', they 'may still be considered untreated in the modern sense of therapy'.[57] Clark was sympathetic but stated, 'these are very trying times and the spirit of uncertainty abides in all of us', so he did not hold out much hope of continuing the study in the face of severe federal financial problems.[58] He retired a few months later and was succeeded as director of the Venereal Diseases

Division by Vonderlehr, who was now in a position to ensure that the study would be continued. By mid-July he could confidently state that 'everyone is agreed that the proper procedure is the continuance of the observation of the Negro man used in the study with the idea of bringing them to autopsy'.[59] No longer was he talking of a limited period for the study, but was assuming that it would continue indefinitely until the men involved had died. What was forgotten was the plight of the men themselves, condemned to suffer the complications of syphilis without receiving treatment that could have helped them. In 1933 there was no money to treat the men anyway, but it was possible that there might be funding for treatment in the future. Yet Vonderlehr was not a callous, unfeeling man, and actually cared about his charges, even if the demands of scientific knowledge and the greater good overcame any other considerations. One of his colleagues from Tuskegee said on his departure from Macon County that 'no man has ever given service here with more dignity and cooperation nor left a finer impression than did Dr Vonderlehr'.[60]

Someone else had also made a big impression on everyone with whom she had come into contact during the gruelling nine months that Vonderlehr had devoted to the Tuskegee Study, and she was destined to play a longlasting, central role at the heart of the continuation of the project. Nurse Eunice Rivers was the 34-year-old night supervisor of nurses at the John A. Andrew Hospital when Eugene Dibble selected her to work alongside Vonderlehr as special scientific assistant. She had trained as a nurse at the Tuskegee Institute and worked in the field of public health for the Alabama State Health, which she had enjoyed, but had lost this job as a result of budget cuts in 1931. She was lucky to get another job at John A. Andrew quickly, but hated night nursing and admitted that, when she was offered work on the syphilis project, she would have accepted anything to get off night duty.[61] She soon proved indispensable to Vonderlehr and Wenger, both on account of her willingness to do anything that was needed, however menial, and because of the rapport that she as a black woman built up with the men in the study. Vonderlehr praised her for being 'untiring in her

155

efforts to bring in cases for our study, and it is really due to her that the number of defaulters has been kept down'.[62] Now he hoped to make her the continuing contact point between the study and its subjects, although his colleague Wenger would have preferred to save money by asking the local doctors to keep an eye on the progress of the patients.[63] However, Nurse Rivers was appointed at a salary of $1,000 a year, and the Tuskegee Institute was asked if it could provide her with a room in return for her working part time there, since it could not afford to supplement her salary by even $50.[64] It was an arrangement that suited Nurse Rivers.

The idea was that the nurse would now act as the follow-up worker for the study, maintaining yearly contact with most of the men but keeping in closer touch with any of her patients who might show signs of complications or who were likely to die within the year. Her role was also to persuade the families of any dead patient to agree that an autopsy could be performed. Meanwhile, a Public Health Service officer would visit Macon County once a year to check up on Nurse Rivers's work, examine the more advanced cases and give a placebo form of treatment to any men who requested it.[65] So 200 men free from syphilis were now selected to form a control group against which the 411 men with 'untreated syphilis' could be compared.[66] There were problems in finding the correct terminology to describe these men when it came to explaining to them why they were receiving free treatment: it would be impossible to state 'free treatment for bad blood', since 'the controls are not syphilitic and have been told that their blood is normal'.[67] No one thought of explaining to any of the men involved what was actually going on. John Heller, a graduate from Emory University in 1929 and friend and classmate of Murray Smith, the health officer for Macon County with whom he was to cooperate closely on the experiment, was the first officer sent to conduct the annual follow-up study in October 1933.[68] He was described by Vonderlehr as 'an unusually intelligent young physician who has a clinical turn of mind'.[69] He returned the following year when Nurse Rivers commented that 'Dr Heller's visit . . . renewed the interest of the patients.'[70] It was an event that established a pattern and offered good experience of practical field work to generations of young Public Health Service doctors, many of whom were, like Heller, who succeeded Vonderlehr as director of the Venereal Diseases Division in 1943, to go on to senior positions in the service. In the 1960s, as the men involved in the study got older and the local agricultural calendar no longer mattered, the annual visits or round-ups were changed from the winter to the summer so that the men and doctors would have better weather.[71] By now the experiment was so long established that no one questioned it or the ethics behind it; everyone looked on it as part of the routine round of duties.

As the young doctors came and went, some of them sympathetic to their patients and others harsh and condescending, Eunice Rivers remained the fixed point of contact for the men being studied. They all considered themselves privileged to receive the welfare benefits arising from being members of what they referred to as 'Nurse Rivers's Lodge'. After her retirement in 1965, she continued to help with the annual round-ups of patients to the end of the study. As the years went by, they came to look on her as a friend and to rely on her help. When one of her patients, John Waggoner, was ill, his neighbour immediately contacted her and she at once agreed to visit him every day and get him into hospital if he did not improve under her care.[72] She would eat with the families of her patients, tend their ailments and attend the funerals of the men who died. It was this empathy that made her so persuasive in getting the families of the dead men to agree to the distressing idea of an autopsy being performed, which might otherwise have been repugnant to them, especially when they were grieving. She herself was squeamish about the autopsies but believed it her duty as a professional woman to overcome her personal feelings. In the first twenty years of the experiment, she obtained permission from all but one of the 145 families she approached. Often they gave her the opening she required by asking what the dead man had died from and worrying that they might themselves have caught the same disease, which allowed her to suggest that the best way of finding out would be to allow a post-mortem examination. Otherwise, she had no scruples about broaching the subject herself and was helped with this when, in 1935, the Public Health Service began to offer burial grants to families agreeing to an autopsy.[73]

Rivers saw herself very much as charged with looking after her patients and also their families, so long as they did not receive any treatment for syphilis. Never once did she challenge the instructions of her superiors. When only neosalvarsan and bismuth were available for treatment, she accepted that it might be safer and less painful for her men not to be treated with them. However, that did not prevent her from administering these drugs to other sufferers when she acted as assistant to a black doctor, William H. Perry, sent by the Rosenwald Fund to Macon County in 1937 to resume for a few months the abandoned syphilis control programme. This role enabled her to ensure that none of the men in the study was treated if he sought it. It was her surveillance that prevented any of her patients receiving treatment in the rapid treatment clinics set up by the Public Health Service in the late 1930s and early 1940s, a monitoring aided by the connivance of local doctors and hospitals.[74] This was in violation of Alabama's public health legislation and the 1943 Henderson Act which required that cases of venereal disease be promptly reported and treated, but the subjects of the Tuskegee Study were left outside the law. Vonderlehr was even able to ensure that none of the younger men liable for call-up during the Second World War would receive the compulsory treatment doled out to other draftees found to be syphilitic.[75] By this time penicillin was available and much safer than earlier treatments, but the men were still prevented from benefiting from it. By now Nurse Rivers was so involved in the programme that she did not even bother to rationalise why it was being denied to her patients when it could have helped them. The study had become her life and she was convinced she was helping her patients as part of it, especially when they received regular health examinations and better medical care than their neighbours who were not involved.[76]

The Tuskegee experiment would have continued until the last subject died, so deeply entrenched was it in the ethos and routine of the Public Health Service. As the men involved got older, it became a study not only of syphilis but also of the ageing process.

Even revelations about Nazi medical experiments in concentration camps did not provoke much discussion of the ethics of continuing the study, until 1966, when Peter Buxtun, a young psychiatric social worker working with the Public Health Service on venereal diseases in San Francisco, began to challenge the morality of refusing treatment to the sick as part of a scientific study. Buxtun, who had switched to the study of law, became increasingly concerned about the racial implications of the experiment following urban race riots in the late 1960s and again challenged his former employers about the ethics of what they were doing in 1969. The Center for Disease Control in Atlanta considered his concerns and, with the support of the Macon County Medical Society, reaffirmed the value of the study and the need to upgrade it scientifically now that Nurse Rivers was unable to monitor the local situation.[77] Buxtun subsequently took his story to the press, and an article by the journalist Jean Heller in the *Washington Star* caused an outcry.[78] The day after this article appeared, an inquiry was set up, which concluded that the Tuskegee experiment was 'ethically unjustified' and that even the knowledge gained from it was meagre compared with the risks that it posed for its subjects. Moreover, the subjects, although they had consented to be examined and treated, had never been told about the study or its purpose, and this lack of information had prevented them from making an informed decision on whether to be involved or not. Indeed, they were never given any opportunity to quit the study, and adequate treatment had been withheld from them, most significantly when penicillin had become available. In November 1972 the Tuskegee Study was suspended.[79] The next year, following a lawsuit filed by the National Association for the Advancement of Colored People, the United States government agreed to give free medical treatment and burial to all survivors of the experiment and their wives and children, who might have been infected as a result of the study.[80]

It was ironic that at the same time as the Tuskegee Study was in its early days of implementation and development, renewed vigour was being applied to a campaign to encourage people to come forward and be treated, spearheaded by the very same people who were sanctioning the withholding of treatment in the relative

159

isolation of Macon County. The appointment of Thomas Parran as surgeon general in 1936 marked the beginning of a national campaign to get people to seek out testing and treatment for syphilis. Parran, born in 1892 on a Maryland farm and a graduate of Georgetown University, was an expert in venereal disease. He had entered the Public Health Service in 1917, and by 1926 had been appointed director of the Venereal Diseases Division. Frustrated by the lack of funding for the control of syphilis and gonorrhoea control, a situation made worse following the impact of the Wall Street Crash, in 1930 he had accepted an invitation from Franklin D. Roosevelt, then governor of New York, to become health commissioner for the State of New York. Now appointed surgeon general by his friend President Roosevelt, he was in a position to bring syphilis to national attention.[81]

Parran's first step was to break the taboo surrounding the discussion of venereal disease, since 'first and foremost among American handicaps to progress against syphilis is the widespread belief that nice people don't talk about syphilis, nice people don't have syphilis and nice people shouldn't do anything about those who have syphilis'.[82] In articles and his bestselling book of 1937, *Shadow on the Land: Syphilis*, he went to great lengths to make his point and emphasise that 'syphilis does a hundred times as much damage as poliomyelitis, yet we can cure most of it. We still do not know how to cure poliomyelitis, only how to mitigate it.'[83] What he proposed was a five-point programme to control syphilis. The first step was to find cases through free diagnostic centres offering confidential blood tests. In order to reach high-risk groups, such as the young, he proposed 'Wassermann dragnets', a systematic trawl among these populations, administering hundreds of tests at one time. Prompt therapy would be offered to anyone found to have the disease. Their contacts would then be traced and offered treatment. He also proposed to introduce mandatory blood tests and treatment in the early stages of pregnancy to halt the transmission of hereditary syphilis. The final element in his programme was public education.[84] None of it was new, but it generated public demand for concerted action against the disease.

Roosevelt supported his friend the surgeon general in his campaign against syphilis and became the first American president directly to address the issue when he sent a message to a conference on venereal disease control in January 1937 linking it with his New Deal concern about 'conserving the resources of the country by all appropriate means'. Parran's campaign would improve the health of American citizens and reduce the costs to the community of dealing with the ravages of the disease. *Time*, in an allusion to the recent abdication crisis in Britain, commented that he had 'matched Edward VIII in making sexual conduct a matter for unembarrassed adult discussion' and that 'no President had ever said or written so frankly'.[85] Less enamoured of Roosevelt were outraged moralists who protested against Parran's proposals 'whereby clean and thrifty citizens are to be heavily taxed for the fancy treatment of pauper syphilitics'. Eleanor Roosevelt was accused of having invited 'white and colored prostitutes' to tea in the White House, and it was alleged that 'never under any other President have such gestures been made for the syphilitic vote'.[86]

Syphilis was not a subject that the politicians could ignore, and in May 1938 Congress passed the National Venereal Disease Control Act, sponsored by Senator Robert LaFollette of Wisconsin and Congressman Alfred Bulwinkle of North Carolina. Syphilis was a national problem demanding a federal solution, since, according to LaFollette, the 'germ that causes syphilis does not respect state lines', nor 'does it take into consideration the financial ability of states or communities'.[87] The Act provided for federal grants to be given to state boards of health for the development of measures to control the spread of venereal disease. These would be controlled by the Public Health Service, which would set up diagnostic clinics and train staff. Money was also allocated for research.[88] At Brunswick in Georgia, one of Parran's young protégés, himself destined to be a future surgeon general in the 1950s, Leroy Edgar Burney played a major role in helping to establish the very first Public Health Service mobile venereal disease clinic. Using a mobile trailer, the clinic was able to reach remote communities where many African Americans hitherto had had no real access to treatment facilities.[89] Similar initiatives were introduced throughout the country.

The states themselves were introducing marriage laws requiring blood tests and physical examination for all prospective brides and grooms. Connecticut led the way in 1935 with a law that withheld marriage licences if either of the parties was discovered to be infected until they were found to be non-infectious. After the law was passed, it became popular for Connecticut couples to have weekend weddings across the state border in New York until that state passed its own marriage law. When that law came into effect in July 1938, there was a 41 per cent decrease in the number of marriages celebrated, and in nearby New Jersey there was concern that premarital legislation could lead to an increase in the number of common-law marriages and illegitimate births.[90]

States and cities also pursued syphilis control programmes based on the screening and treatment of infected individuals, nowhere more vigorously than in Chicago. The Chicago Syphilis Control Program had been inaugurated in January 1937 following a national conference on venereal diseases held in Washington DC, and prided itself on being 'the first attempt to control syphilis in a large urban population by the combined efforts of federal, state and local agencies'.[91] Mayor Edward E. Kelly had convened a meeting of representatives of the labour movement, philanthropic organisations, medicine, the business world and the churches of Chicago to gain the widest possible support for a campaign in which 'we in Chicago must take the leadership and do our share in controlling and overcoming these scourges of modern civilization'. With their progressive faith in the efficiency of large-scale enterprise, these civic, business, labour and religious leaders had no doubt that 'what science and public cooperation have done in combating other diseases can be repeated in this case and to a greater degree'.[92] The objective of the programme was to determine how prevalent syphilis was in Chicago and to ensure that everyone diagnosed with it should be given appropriate medical treatment. Social workers would encourage patients identified through the screening sessions to reveal the names of their sexual contacts, who would be tracked down and treated as a result of what unflagging field caseworkers termed 'shoe-leather epidemiology'. Educational and legal measures, such as the 1937 State of Illinois Marriage Law requiring premarital certificates confirming freedom from venereal disease, which was an 'effective weapon' in the control program, were also considered essential if new infections were to be prevented.[93] It was an ambitious project but, with cooperation between different groups, not an impossible one.

With advice from Oliver Wenger, the Public Health Service officer who had played such a prominent role in the early stages of the Tuskegee Study, and with federal funding obtained under the New Deal Social Security Act and from the Works Progress Administration, the mass campaign was launched with a mailout of more than one million questionnaires to local residents offering free blood tests. Banners proclaiming that 'Friday the thirteenth is an unlucky day for syphilis' were borne aloft in a syphilis parade from the Chicago Loop to City Hall on 13 August 1937; meanwhile, an aeroplane circled overhead trailing an anti-syphilis message. Newspapers and the radio publicised the free blood tests. The *Chicago Tribune*, which assigned special reporters to cover the campaign, took the lead in publicising what was being done and 'broke the taboo of the press' through its publication of the 'frank straightforward facts'.[94] A specially written play by Arnold Sundgaard entitled *Spirochete*, dramatising the history of syphilis from the days of Columbus to the problems it caused in contemporary Chicago, was commissioned for the Federal Theater Project.[95] Theatregoers were invited to have a free Wassermann test in the foyer during the interval. Wenger believed that 'this play will do more than any other one factor to arouse public opinion in syphilis control'.[96]

Such publicity engendered tremendous demand for testing, which severely strained the existing clinic and laboratory facilities and encouraged an expansion of what was available. At the height of the campaign, 10,000–12,000 people were being tested every day in what Parran had called a 'Wassermann dragnet', a term that had a particular resonance in Chicago, where police dragnets had been effected against organised gangster crime. The aim was to get as many people as possible in for testing and, if necessary, treatment.

Even high-school students were tested, not so much because anyone expected to uncover many cases of syphilis but from the consideration that 'every boy or girl who submits to a blood test feels the prick of the needle, which they will forever associate with syphilis and . . . be less apt to expose themselves to infection'.[97] The University of Chicago introduced compulsory blood tests for new students in 1939 and anyone found to be infected was offered treatment by the student health service, while the students themselves at Northwestern University took the initiative in promoting voluntary testing.[98] Chicago's industrialists and businessmen were just as keen to encourage their employees to come forward for screening and offered workplace facilities, but were less happy at being criticised for dismissing anyone revealed to be infected.[99] It could be bad for business if it were known that syphilitics were being employed, as laundry firms discovered when the *Chicago Daily News* published an article in which laundry workers headed the list of infected domestic staff; as a result of this bad publicity, the Chicago Laundry Association withdrew from the Syphilis Control Program.[100] The large department stores were worried that Herman N. Bundesen, the commissioner of the Chicago Board of Health, might 'use the results of the test against them for his own political purposes . . . and give adverse publicity to the findings of any company that he did not particularly like'.[101] Meanwhile, the unions were suspicious of company doctors carrying out the tests in case they used the results to discriminate against workers in ways that might 'certainly prevent their advancement and possibly mean their divorce from the payroll'.[102] However, despite such hiccups, over 31 per cent of the population of Chicago received Wassermann tests between 1937 and 1940, and the dragnet uncovered and provided free treatment to more than 56,000 sufferers.[103]

The African-American people of Chicago in particular benefited from the Control Program. Health-care facilities for them were totally inadequate and rates of infection were high. Indeed, more than 60 per cent of the cases of syphilis uncovered and treated were from Chicago wards with high black populations. Such statistics reinforced the 'unfortunate emphasis which has been given to the syphilis problem in the Negro in Chicago'.[104] Indeed, 'a special effort was made to reach underprivileged groups', which had included seeking the support of prominent black physicians to win over the trust of people who might otherwise have mistrusted official interference in their lives.[105] Yet it was black parents who had been more responsive than white to suggestions that their children be tested at school and proved generally positive in their attitude towards a project they could see as valuable. It was also notable that there was a lower rate of infection among young black people in Chicago than in similar age groups in the Deep South, which indicated to Wenger, who had worked with African Americans in both areas, 'the relation of syphilis incidence to economic status and free treatment facilities'.[106] This was a conclusion that tied in with the findings of Taliaferro Clark during a survey of venereal disease in Baltimore in 1930, where the lower incidence of syphilis among the white population reflected their greater level of access to treatment facilities that offered the possibility of controlling the problem.[107] Parran was even more emphatic in condemning newspaper reports that there were 'eight colored syphilitics to every one among whites' and informed the editor of the *Chicago Tribune* that 'the spirochete of syphilis is no respecter of the size of one's bank balance or the pigment of one's skin'.[108] In contrast to the situation in Alabama for the people involved in the Tuskegee Study, there was already a better educated, more prosperous black population in Chicago whose sexual health was improved considerably with better testing and treatment centres.

The Chicago Program was a success, but it had its critics. Mayor Kelly, who had helped to launch it, was concerned that Parran's emphasis on the fight against venereal diseases was at the expense of other public-health issues of equal importance and that 'the dramatic highlights of syphilis, and the attendant publicity, have thrown into the dim background the civic and economic disasters of tuberculosis'.[109] Others criticised the campaign for fostering a climate of fear about syphilis that might prove counterproductive.

Ben Reitman, a 'clap doctor' working with the prostitutes and down-and-outs among the poorest of Chicago, was especially critical of sensationalist headlines, which he called 'scareheads' and which he feared might lead to paranoia about sexuality as well as venereal disease and arouse hostility to anyone with the disease, potentially driving it underground once more.[110] Even Raymond Vonderlehr considered that some doctors and scientists, with their 'melodramatic and somewhat obscene descriptions . . . may be the cause of the loss of public interest in the present campaign'.[111]

Yet sensational headlines sold newspapers, and the syphilis scares made for good copy. Reports that the notorious Chicago gangster Al Capone, now incarcerated in Alcatraz, had gone mad as a result of tertiary syphilis dominated the newspapers in February 1938, overshadowing the news that free testing centres were to be opened as part of the Control Program. His fellow prisoners had spread the news that 'Capone's cuttin' up dolls' in his cell.[112] Capone had run brothels in his mobster days, and that was enough to convince the public that he had caught the infection from the prostitutes he controlled. His doctors denied that his mental breakdown had been due to syphilis, more concerned that his public image might suffer from the taint of syphilis rather than from the crimes of tax evasion, gangsterism, extortion and murder, of which he was undoubtedly guilty.

Parran was not worried about the stigmatisation of syphilis nor about stoking up syphilis phobias with his crusade. So far as he was concerned, the main task was to stop the spread of the disease. People might become neurotic with fear of the disease, but 'syphilophobia never killed anyone, never brought a handicapped child into the world, never infected an innocent person'.[113]

It was from a real desire to do something about a serious social problem and to help people suffering from syphilis that Parran and his colleagues in the US Public Health Service were so active throughout the 1930s. In the case of the Chicago Control Program and other such initiatives, they were able to make a great improvement to the lives of many people. In Macon County, they set out with the best of intentions, as befitted some of the most progressive-minded doctors of their time, but things went horribly wrong and an iniquity was perpetuated for many years, long after the money and other resources were there that could have put an end to it. In the attempt to disperse one shadow over the land, another much more dishonourable and shameful darkness was brought into being that in time overshadowed all else.

SEVEN

The 'Best Military Advantage'

The air-raid sirens sounded almost immediately after Prime Minister Neville Chamberlain had announced to a nation listening to the wireless on Sunday 3 September 1939 that the country was now at war with Germany. It surprised no one, as almost universally it had been assumed that the United Kingdom would be assailed by an air attack just as soon as war had been declared; it was taken for granted that the bomber would always win through. Equally expected was a syphilis Blitzkrieg, for, as Arthur McNalty, the Chief Medical Officer, had earlier stated on the day that Germany had attacked Poland, 'it is well known that a state of war favours the spread of venereal diseases and is an important cause of the wastage of manpower'.[1] War and syphilis seem fated to be yoked together in a marriage of circumstances. Where there are young men away from home and a consequent loosening of morals, venereal disease is rarely far away amid 'a lack of self-control . . . favoured by the excitement of war conditions'.[2] From the start, with the experience of the First World War still relatively fresh, the battle against syphilis and gonorrhoea was seen as important to the war effort, among both the troops and the equally essential war workers upon whom national survival would so soon depend.

The predicted upsurge in venereal infections very soon became a reality as the war caused social dislocation. The problems were exacerbated as people moved from the towns with their venereal diseases clinics to munitions factories, army camps and aerodromes in country districts where facilities were inadequate to cope with the demand from a sudden population increase. In these areas there was an urgent need for the expansion of VD services. One expedient

168

suggested was the setting-up of mobile units in some parts of the country.[3] These had been proposed at the time of the 1938 Munich Crisis, when the very real threat of war had concentrated minds on planning for the coming conflict, but financial constraints meant that the hoped-for fleet of twenty vans never materialised. As the Battle of France was lost across the English Channel and the Battle of Britain was won in the skies, the rise in infection rates caused official alarm, but it was not until October 1940 that the Ministry of Health was given its funding. The return of the British Expeditionary Force from Dunkirk had placed enormous strains on local health authorities, many of them ill equipped to deal with the upsurge in venereal disease in their areas. The Treasury was at last persuaded to fund the mobile service to deal with the problem.[4]

It was not only in rural areas that the problems posed by wartime promiscuity raised alarm. Prostitutes, nicknamed 'Piccadilly Warriors', were much more visible in Central London in the blackout than they had been before the war. In Soho two members of the Public Morality Council were solicited at midnight by thirty-five women within little more than one hundred yards. Even at 4 a.m. there were still seven women peddling their wares. In the darkness of the blackout, the police paid them little attention unless they were involved, as they frequently were, in fights between their customers.[5] Even the Blitz did not have a serious effect on prostitution and perhaps even added for the customers a certain frisson of risk of death from bombs to the lure of the socially frowned upon. Even those prostitutes who did leave London at the height of the bombing had returned by 1942.[6] In many areas they were becoming 'more bold', behaviour that was viewed as 'an unavoidable consequence of the blackout'.[7] At St Mary's Hospital in the heart of the red-light district near Paddington Station, student nurses would amuse themselves when they had any free moments during the day by watching the rapid turnover of business among the prostitutes in the rooms above the shops opposite the hospital.[8] There were fears that this increase in infection might be linked to organised crime, although most moral crusaders, such as members of the National Vigilance Association, preferred to blame it on 'nasty young men' among the refugee troops from France, Poland and the other countries of occupied Europe who were now based in the capital.[9] Syphilophobia and xenophobia formed an unsavoury alliance in seeking scapegoats.

Anxiety over the wartime incidence of venereal diseases resulted in a national campaign in 1942 to increase public awareness of their dangers and how the diseases could be avoided and treated. This breached the taboo on mentioning such things in the press and on the radio, but propriety ensured that euphemisms and scientific terminology were used rather than the more popularly understood terms such as 'the pox' and 'the clap'.[10] Soldiers were warned by posters of the dangers posed by loose women, being humorously reminded 'that's Phyllis' if they were to see a provocatively dressed siren passing by.[11] Such posters were displayed in railway stations and public conveniences, where their warnings might be considered to be most timely.[12] Smaller advertisements were placed in the newspapers on such subjects as 'ten plain facts about venereal diseases'.[13]

Cinemas, the staple of mass wartime entertainment, offered an even greater audience for the anti-VD message. In 1943 the Ministry of Information produced a 20-minute documentary, *Subject for Discussion*, which drew attention to the dangers and consequences of syphilis.[14] However, even more likely to be heeded were feature films at a time when such dramas as *Mrs Miniver* and *In Which We Serve* were great morale-boosters at home and effective propaganda abroad. Hollywood magnificently rose to the challenge and was ready to break the taboos about mentioning what had once been unmentionable, although sometimes the approach of the major studios remained coy. In 1940 the story of Ehrlich and his quest for a magic bullet effective against the disease, which was so terrible in its effects that it could blight entire families, was filmed by Warner Brothers at the height of Thomas Parran's campaign against syphilis. In *Dr Ehrlich's Magic Bullet*, the eponymous hero was played by Edward G. Robinson, more usually cast in the role of a gangster, as a dedicated and far-sighted doctor fighting against hypocrisy to advance the progress of medicine. The film was timely and popular but was not an explicit warning about the disease. Another American film made in 1942, *Social Enemy No. 1*, was to serve a more open propagandist role. When released in Britain in 1943, it was prefaced with a short introduction by the Minister of Health, pointing out that there were differences between Britain and the United States in the treatment available for venereal diseases.[15]

Social Enemy No. 1 was billed as being 'not for the prurient minded or for the sordid sensation seeker' but as 'a picture with a great moral lesson'. The film's likeable young hero, Bill Thorne, a worker in a Midwestern defence plant, is tempted by, and contracts syphilis from, a prostitute brought into town by a gangster seeking to profit from the newly opened munitions factory. Bitterly regretting his folly, Bill pays a fortune for a quack remedy and marries his sweetheart Betty. Meanwhile the newly appointed health commissioner for the town, Dr Cavanagh, played by Leon Ames, appropriately for an actor typecast in fatherly roles, starts up a campaign to rid the town of vice and persuades Betty to take a Wassermann test as an example to all the munitions girls. The test proves positive and Bill, realising that he has been duped, confronts and kills the quack doctor who sold him the false cure. He is arrested for the crime but refuses to reveal his motives from a desire to protect his wife and their baby from the disgrace that revealing their infection from syphilis would bring them. Only when Dr Cavanagh is called to give evidence does Bill reveal why he killed the impostor. He is acquitted and reunited with Betty. The melodramatic plot was hailed as depicting 'the greatest social evil that besets our country at the present time' and for encouraging a situation where 'by society's frank admission of the existence of the scourge, we have automatically robbed it of its most potent weapon – secrecy'.[16]

It was appropriate that American movies should be used in the propaganda campaign about the menace of venereal diseases, since the entry of the United States into the world war in December 1941 and the arrival of American GIs in Britain from the spring of 1942 onwards had brought to a head concerns over the problem of venereal disease. With their own husbands and boyfriends serving overseas, many lonely young women living or working in the areas in which American troops were stationed were easily seduced by the better-paid, better-fed and more glamorous young men from a country they associated with the excitement of the movies. In East Anglia, more women were observed in the bars frequented by wealthy American and Canadian troops drinking the more expensive spirits rather than the local beer. This fascination of the foreigner for young women was enhanced by the generosity of these young men with more than spam, chewing gum, Hershey bars, cigarettes and nylons, and by their money, which allowed them 'rapidly to skim the top off the market'.[17]

However, the United States army and air force were more concerned about their soldiers and airmen being at the mercy of sexually voracious British women. Most American troops on leave tended to congregate in London, and many of them, 'in the holiday spirit', proved 'susceptible to urgent solicitation' from professional prostitutes working in the Piccadilly area, the source of between a third and a half of all infections among Americans stationed in the United Kingdom.[18] There were calls from the American military headquarters for prostitutes to be cleared from all the main streets of the principal cities and for their removal from the vicinity of American Red Cross hostels, where their presence especially caused 'something like disgust'. The Foreign Office was sympathetic to such demands, since open prostitution was having 'a really damaging effect on American opinion about this country'.[19] A Joint Committee on Venereal Disease was formed under the auspices of the Ministry of Health for consultation with the American and Canadian military authorities, but soon became bogged down in a discussion over prostitution that prevented it from having much effect.[20]

It was not only prostitutes who were causing the problems for the Americans. Just as dangerous to the increasing number of American troops in London were 'young girls out for a good time'.[21] Taking a break from their arduous war work in munitions factories, as land girls or in the women's forces, these young women, already released from parental control as a result of wartime conditions, wanted a bit of fun and were attracted by fit, healthy young Americans who were 'comparatively rich' and had 'little to do' on leave far from home. The outcome of such encounters was perhaps inevitable, as 'the acquaintance between American soldiers and good time girls, which started with a desire for companionship on the part of the soldiers and for a good time on the part of the girls, frequently led to intercourse and venereal disease'.[22] All the blame for such natural and comprehensible encounters was heaped on the women concerned; the soldiers were viewed as innocent victims: 'young inexperienced men who had probably never spent much time in a large city' for whom 'it was natural that they would form an easy prey to the less desirable characters in London'. Only reluctantly was it conceded that 'many of the United States soldiers over here tended to show a lack of self-control and restraint'.[23] Although the women, not the GIs, were seen as the root of the problem, the police could take no action against them because they were not common prostitutes and they did not accost the men they consorted with.[24]

The scale of the problem of sexually transmitted diseases demanded that something should be done for the sake of maintaining national efficiency in wartime. In November 1943 a new regulation was added to the 1939 Defence of the Realm Act to permit the compulsory tracing of contacts and treatment of anyone found to be infected. Phyllis, the syphilis-bearing vamp of the anti-venereal poster campaign, had come under the surveillance of Dora, the wartime regulations that restricted the freedom of the individual for the sake of national defence. Regulation 33B under the Defence Regulation Act laid down that doctors treating any patient with syphilis or gonorrhoea should notify the medical officer of health for the county or county borough, together with details of any sexual contacts from whom the sufferer might have contracted the disease or to whom it might have been passed. If the patient refused to reveal names and addresses of sexual contacts or refused to have treatment on a voluntary basis, the medical officer of health could enforce compulsory treatment if he had received two or more notifications about any one individual.[25] Although the general basis of treatment remained voluntary, confidential and free, the new element of compulsion, albeit only when persuasion had failed, was a new departure that many doctors deplored. Nevertheless, the regulation was declared to be of national importance in that it was 'to bring under medical care those infected persons who have shown themselves unresponsive to education, work or to methods of treatment and who, owing to this refusal to undertake treatment, remain a constant source of danger to the health of the community and a drain on the man-power and woman-power of the nation in its war effort'.[26]

Such a scheme of compulsory notification and treatment had been widely advocated before the war, but compulsion was regarded as an unacceptable infringement of individual liberty and notification a threat to the anonymity upon which the existing system of clinics was based. Most doctors considered that it was more effective to have a voluntary system, where treatment was sought at an early stage by the patient and the case could be followed up more easily. Any compulsory system of notification might deter people from seeking treatment until it was unavoidable, just as servicemen, who had deductions made from their pay if they reported sick with a venereal infection, were likely to cover up their disease or resort to private medical practitioners.[27] Many peacetime clinics had appointed social workers to investigate the home conditions of their patients and to a limited extent trace contacts. In 1925 a successful experiment in the port of Rotterdam had suggested the feasibility of an extension of the system of tracing contacts, and this was to be the basis of a new programme of contact tracing introduced by John Charles, Medical Officer of Health for Newcastle upon Tyne in 1943. The Newcastle Venereal Diseases Clinic covered a wide area encompassing Northumberland, County Durham and the county boroughs of Newcastle upon Tyne and Gateshead. All patients presenting themselves at the clinic were questioned in depth about their recent sexual partners, their names, addresses, physical descriptions, workplaces and favourite haunts such as pubs, clubs and cafes. The patient would then be given a contact slip with details of the clinic to give to their sexual partners in the hope that they could encourage them to attend for treatment. If the contact did not attend within a certain time, social workers or health visitors would telephone them, visit their homes, their places of work and their leisure haunts.[28] This 'Tyneside System' not only ensured that anyone likely to be infected was made aware of the available treatment facilities but actively persuaded contacts to agree to treatment. Regulation 33B made the methods compulsory. In 1944 throughout Britain, 8,339 contacts were notified, of whom it proved possible to trace only 3,696 and only 2,858 could be persuaded to accept treatment. That year 82 people who had refused treatment were prosecuted, and 827 were forced to have treatment after two or more of their sexual partners had named them as contacts. Although Regulation 33B avoided the furore over the notorious First World War Regulation 40D by applying equally to both sexes, it was still women who were more likely to be pursued under it.[29] The regulation continued in force until 1947, but the machinery for contact tracing remained in place, with confidentiality and persuasion rather than the ultimate sanction of compulsion as the cornerstone.

The American military authorities had felt frustrated by the emphasis on confidentiality in the British approach to contact tracing of suspected carriers before Regulation 33B came into force and by the lack of prophylactic treatment centres in London. The British attitude was that 'any general encouragement of the use of prophylactic packets for the prevention of venereal disease by the civilian population would definitely be undesirable in tending to encourage a false sense of security', although there was no objection to making sheaths and chemical preventatives available on request to British servicemen.[30] However, the Americans were allowed to set up disinfection stations under American Red Cross supervision in Piccadilly, near the Rainbow Club for American servicemen, and close to mainline railway stations in London, but there were frequent complaints that they were poorly signposted.[31] It was not only in wartime Britain that such facilities were difficult to find. In Chicago in 1942 the 'safety-first station' at the Chicago and Northwestern Railroad Station was a case in point. It took over 15 minutes for anyone following the confusing signs to reach it; not surprisingly the 'young medical student . . . on the job' at that particular facility reported that 'he had very little business'.[32]

In the United States even before Pearl Harbor and entry into the world war, there had been a concern that 'again, as we are faced with the necessity of building up our national defence, venereal disease comes to the fore as a major factor determining the efficiency of armed and industrial defence forces'. There was a determination not to repeat the mistake made after the First World War when investment in the control of sexually transmitted infections was wasted and 'the first successful steps towards reducing the toll of syphilis and gonorrhea were nullified'.[33] Much of the approach to protecting against a resurgence of infection if war came remained traditional. As in the First World War, measures were taken to prohibit prostitution, 'a great saboteur of the defence effort',[34] in the vicinity of military bases, and in July 1941 an Act introduced by Representative Andrew J. May made vice activities near military installations a federal offence.[35] There was also concern about the '48,000 young men, otherwise able to serve their country, who are not exercising the privilege of free citizenship because of syphilis' and the urgent need to give them compulsory treatment when they were being drafted into the forces.[36] For the surgeon general Thomas Parran, progress was not rapid enough; in 1941 he and the head of the Public Health Service Venereal Diseases Division, Raymond Vonderlehr, launched an attack on the military failure to grapple with the problem in a book entitled *Plain Words about Venereal Disease*,[37] a work that was critical enough to have merited a court martial if Parran had been surgeon general of one of the armed forces rather than a civilian official of the federal government.[38]

Once the United States was at war, the dispute between Parran and the military authorities was subsumed in the more important task of implementing a programme to deal with the threat posed by sexually transmitted infections. As in the First World War, efforts were made to provide soldiers with wholesome educational and recreational diversions from alcohol and sex, including lectures, sporting activities, movies and organised entertainments. A propaganda and educational campaign in the training camps pointed out the grave implications of catching an infection. Posters and leaflets reminded men that it was unpatriotic to become infected and that the spread of venereal diseases was helping the enemy. VD was portrayed as a woman, being shown arm in arm with Adolf Hitler and the Emperor Hirohito, yet being 'the worst of the three'. Loose women and casual pickups were depicted as representing a 'booby trap', while even the woman 'who may look clean' might be carrying infection.[39] Men were issued with a pamphlet on *Sex, Hygiene and Venereal Disease*, whose message was reinforced by a one-reel film. However, such educational programmes were not as effective as venereal diseases specialists had hoped, mainly because of a lack of funds and the 'difficulty of arousing enough interest from the higher officers to lead to their devoting their interest to this teaching problem at least equal to the interest accorded such problems as teaching the use of weapons, self-protection and hand-to-hand combat'.[40]

Recognising the limits of sex education in encouraging continence, the armed forces were compelled to take measures to provide the troops with more effective protective measures. Adopting the motto 'if you can't say "no", take a pro', the military authorities provided condoms and established prophylactic treatment stations. Packs containing three condoms and a small tube of lubricating jelly were available for 10 cents on military bases, and, when women took over the role of selling them and sales went down, condom vending machines were installed in canteens.[41] Condoms were classed as essential medical supplies and given priority access to rubber for their manufacture.[42] Since the Japanese invasion of the Far East, rubber had been a scarce commodity in great demand for war industry, and its use for protective sheaths indicated the importance given to the control of sexually transmitted diseases. That did not stop servicemen complaining about 'general-issue' condoms that burst at the all-important moment or that were 'so damn thick you can't enjoy yourself'.[43] Nevertheless, men were encouraged to take them with them on leave, albeit 'with the warning that if the men are foolish enough to have sexual intercourse with commercialised or clandestine prostitutes they will sooner or later be infected with a venereal disease but that the proper use of prophylactic agents will lessen the chance of such infections being acquired'.[44]

At the same time that servicemen were being warned to take precautions, there was a clampdown on prostitution close to military camps. Enforcement of the May Act was entrusted to the Social Protection Division under its director Eliot Ness, renowned for his war, as one of the 'untouchables', against gangsterism in Chicago and for having subsequently cracked down on vice and organised crime as Director of Public Safety in Cleveland, Ohio. Ness, no stranger to the delights of nightclubs, now rallied the support of police chiefs, mayors and city managers in his new crusade against prostitution. He persuaded the National Cab Association to agree that the driving licences of taxi drivers found to be pimping for prostitutes should be revoked.[45] His opponents argued that the repression of prostitution would force men to look elsewhere for sexual release and encourage homosexuality, seduction of virtuous girls and rape as alternative outlets of passion. Having taken on Al Capone in his time, Ness took such criticism in his stride and pointed out that, 'despite the alarums and dire prophecies of many critics of repression who were either honestly misinformed or whose financial interests were at stake, the more than 300 communities which clamped down on prostitution have not experienced great crime waves, or increases in rape cases'.[46]

It may have been repression all the way in the United States, but in continental Europe longstanding traditions of regulation assumed new importance. The French had set up their *maisons de tolérance*, licensed brothels, on the outbreak of war in 1939. Inevitably, during the tedious, drawn-out months of inaction of the Phoney War, bored young soldiers of the British Expeditionary Force had sought amusement where they could, either with the Polish immigrant labourers of Northern France, the 'unemployed shop-girl' or in brothels, much to the indignation of the purity lobby at home in Britain.[47] The French had no scruples about their own soldiers using these brothels, and arranged for their inspection by army medical officers who could be relied upon to be more thorough than some of their civilian counterparts had been at the beginning of the war. The demands of national defence also brought in more draconian powers of state regulation. A statutory order of 29 November 1939 made it

178

compulsory for doctors to notify the authorities of all cases of venereal disease, forbade breastfeeding by any woman with syphilis and enforced the compulsory treatment of prostitutes. After the fall of France, the right-wing and Roman Catholic Vichy regime reinforced these measures as part of its policy of the moral regeneration of France. In 1942 premarital medical examinations were made compulsory, to be followed by legislation making it a criminal offence to refuse treatment for syphilis and fining doctors if they did not trace contacts. For the national good, medical confidentiality was to be breached.[48] Prostitution too was to be more tightly controlled, with the licensing of places for soliciting as well as of regular brothels and the complete segregation of infected prostitutes under special surveillance in cordoned-off sections of venereal disease hospital wards. Yet in Vichy France, syphilis continued to be a problem, causing some of Marshall Pétain's supporters to call for the complete abolition of prostitution if the new watchwords of 'Travail, Famille, Patrie' ('work, family, country') were to have any meaning in the new morally regenerated nation.[49]

In the occupied zone of France, as indeed in all the countries that they conquered, the Germans maintained a system of regulated brothels. By late 1942 the *Wehrmacht* was running about 500 establishments exclusively for the use of the occupying armies. These brothels were staffed by women from all over Europe, many of them forced into prostitution by their military occupiers. Each prostitute employed carried a card to show that she was free of disease. Male nurses were posted at the foot of the staircase to record the names of the soldiers and the prostitutes they were frequenting. In the rooms of the brothel were notices reminding the men to use condoms and to disinfect themselves with potassium permanganate and calomel ointment after their encounter. Sexual intercourse was seen as essential for morale and for stopping frustrated soldiers from turning to what were seen as such unnatural forms of vice as homosexuality.[50]

Yet the German Führer had a profound fear of syphilis. Despite allegations that he had been infected by a Jewish prostitute in

Vienna in 1908, the evidence for Adolf Hitler having suffered from syphilis is all based on hearsay. Nevertheless, it was a subject significant enough to be included in his political testament and racist manifesto *Mein Kampf*. One of the major failures of Weimar democracy in his eyes had been its inability to deal with the scourge of syphilis that had infected Germany while the political establishment had given way to 'total capitulation'. In this view all attempts to treat the infection had been futile because what was needed was the elimination of its cause. For a demagogue like Hitler, there could be only one simple cause, in this case what he termed 'the prostitution of love', which he linked to the 'jewification of our spiritual life', which would sooner or later destroy the German people. Uneducated fear of syphilis and of contamination of the blood was combined with the crudest anti-Semitism and a fear that the Aryan bloodline would be racially contaminated unless both could be cleansed. It was especially galling that the most effective treatment for the disease he so dreaded should be salvarsan, dismissed by him as 'a remedy of questionable character', which had been developed by the undeniably Jewish Paul Ehrlich, who had been in his own time equally unquestionably a great German scientist.[51] Ironically, the best available treatment throughout the reign of terror of the Third Reich for one of his fears remained something developed by a member of an ethnic group he hated, and there was nothing that Nazi ideology could do to change that.[52]

Hitler's pathological fears of racial degeneracy linked to syphilitic infection were paralleled by changes in the way that venereal diseases were regarded generally. Resort to prostitutes as a rite of passage, with the attendant risk of becoming venereally diseased, was no longer widely regarded as a sign of virility. Anglo-American propaganda contrasted the 'wanton promiscuity' of the Axis Powers with the greater purity and self-discipline of their own ideal of the good citizen and soldier. Men infected with syphilis were depicted as unpatriotic, bad comrades and inadequate personalities. Rather than being the reckless, dashing blade of the past, the sufferer from syphilis was coming to be seen by doctors and psychiatrists as neurotic, unstable, self-centred and something of a wimp, likely to put personal comfort before his duty to country and comrades.[53] The manly soldier or civilian was now the one who had the self-control and good sense to take precautions against catching something nasty. It was 'the man to whom reason does not appeal – the rather stupid sensual fellow who indulges most of his appetites' who was most likely to betray his comrades by getting himself infected.[54] Soldiers were reminded that 'you were transported thousands of miles to fight the Germans or help your comrades to do so'; if they were incapacitated by venereal disease they were 'not only useless . . . but are doing about as much as you can to prolong the war'. They were even told, not altogether convincingly, that 'a man can endure the hardships of war better if he does not go with a woman'.[55] Good morale in a military unit was correlated with a low incidence of infection.[56]

Yet, despite all this medical emphasis on the inadequacy of the syphilitic, there still remained some idea that sexual recklessness had some glamour attached to it, and a devil-may-care attitude towards the risks of infection was alluring. This was nowhere more apparent than in the air force, where 'the glamour of being a flying man . . . appeals so much to the ladies', though even there it was admitted that the most efficient flight crews and units had the lowest incidence of disease and any rises were as much due to the fact that, as the war had gone on, 'the portals of recruiting have been opened wide to all and sundry'.[57] Even the medical officers treating these airmen were not always above temptation or reproach. At the RAF Infectious Diseases Hospital at Halton, the officer in charge, Gerard McElligott, would shout at bedraggled, unshaven, unkempt officers slinking back to their quarters after a night on the tiles, 'Rover, Rover, Rover, you naughty dog! Where have you been since we let you out yesterday?'[58]

The ideal fighting man might have kept himself pure, but that did not stop the real serviceman from contracting a venereal disease. Appeals to chastity as a patriotic duty were never likely to go very far in changing young men's sexual behaviour. What mattered more was whether or not there were any ready opportunities for sexual intercourse. Where troops were stationed close to large towns, there were always plenty of prostitutes and casual pickups to keep them satisfied. India and, after 1943, Italy had the highest rates VD rates, with 70–80 men infected per 1,000 by the end of the war. When they were on active duty in remote areas such as the jungles of Burma, opportunities were fewer and sexually transmitted infections less of a problem.[59] Where prostitution was a problem in overseas areas where troops were stationed, the military authorities, despite all the rhetoric about being superior to the enemy in not condoning the evil, had no scruples about trying to bring it under military and medical control by whatever means possible. In Egypt that at first meant the inspection of brothels and a crackdown on the activities of streetwalkers.[60] Such official toleration of prostitution was criticised for encouraging the notion that the brothels were safe, whereas in addition to the risks of contracting syphilis or gonorrhoea there was also the danger of catching typhus at a time when this was rampant among the local population. However, it was for political reasons that the notorious Berka military brothel was placed out of bounds to servicemen in December 1942 following a fight there between British, Australian and New Zealand troops; against a background of rising anti-British sentiment in Egypt, it was essential to stress the moral superiority of the imperial power.[61]

During the Italian Campaign of 1943–4, the question of regulating or repressing prostitution in military areas also became a major issue at a time when many British soldiers were being infected not only in the brothels of Naples but also by casual sexual encounters on 'the doorstep', some of the men being seduced by 'having bottles of wine thrust into their hands in broad daylight by these harpies or their agents'.[62] At first the American military authorities had accepted the situation and had permitted tolerated brothels to service their troops, but when infection rates soared they put these houses off limits to their troops and took measures to suppress clandestine prostitution, which reduced the scale of the problem.[63] The British military authorities were quick to appreciate this lesson and oppose the use of licensed prostitution for their own troops.[64] Instead, they preferred to clamp down on vice.

The military police were made 'VD conscious', and combined United States army, British army and Royal Air Force 'vice or morality squads' were established. Such squads expected cooperation from the Italian authorities but found, when working with four 'underfed and badly clothed' agents of the Squadra Buon Costume in Rome, that, 'like all Italian police, they are unwilling to devote themselves whole-heartedly to this work'.[65] Prostitution had been regulated in the Kingdom of Italy since Prime Minister Camillo Cavour had introduced the relevant legislation in 1860 to safeguard the health of the Italian people, and the system was considered to offer a relatively safe initiation for young men to their sexual careers as Latin lovers. Mussolini's fascist regime, with its emphasis on traditional male dominance in the household, had strengthened the regulatory system.[66] Since resort to brothels was seen as the norm among young Italian males, the Rome policemen would have seen no reason why young Allied soldiers should not enjoy what was on offer too.

In view of the difficulties of keeping the troops away from the pleasures of the flesh, coercion and sanctions offered an alternative means of dealing with this problem. It was a crime under British military law for a diseased man not to report his illness, but if he did so he could be punished with the loss of pay: 'the man who incurs venereal disease is in the same category as the man who intentionally wounds himself in order to avoid service and the man who gets drunk and so by his action renders himself unfit for duty'.[67] Soldiers were fined 1s 6d for each day they were in hospital and forfeited any increases in pay they might have expected for length of service. Non-commissioned officers and tradesmen were punished with loss of rank and privileges, which in some cases could mean a reduction in pay of between 6d and 9d per day.[68] At least they were spared the threat of court martial for self-inflicted wounds, even though the financial deterrent was not seen as altogether effective. The British army was also considered to be backward in being almost the only modern armed service to retain such financial penalties as a deterrent.[69] In the American army, the regulations withholding pay from soldiers with venereal disease had been rescinded in September 1944, following a bitter debate between the moralists and the pragmatists in the course of which it was revealed that some pilots were endangering themselves and others by continuing to fly while receiving clandestine treatment that affected their coordination and reaction times.[70]

In Britain, too, such financial punishment was considered counterproductive in that it only led to concealment.[71] Rather men were urged that, 'if you so lack self control that you can not keep away from diseased women, most of whom will have taken hundreds of men of many nationalities before taking you, at least use the precautions which the army offers you'.[72] These included the provision of condoms, although few men bothered to wear them.[73] Gerard McElligott, adviser on venereal diseases to the RAF, considered the condom to be 'a two-edged sword' anyway, since it could 'easily engender a false sense of security and, like the schoolboy's half-crown, is apt to burn a hole in the pocket until it is used'.[74] Chemical prophylaxis was the other precaution on offer, but take-up of it was also low, fewer than one soldier in 20 who had become infected having bothered with any form of personal disinfection.[75] Ablution rooms where such procedures were carried out were far from inviting for their patrons. Having urinated in gushes, the unfortunate soldier would then wash his penis, scrotum and lower abdomen, sponging them with potassium permanganate and perchloride of mercury. An orderly next injected another disinfectant into the urethra and a calomel cream was rubbed into the genitals.[76] It was not surprising that few men visited such Green Cross stations, leaving medical officers with the unpleasant task of finding the early stages of infection through regular 'free-from-infection' check-ups. The soldiers would be paraded with their trousers unbuttoned, ready to drop them when the medical officer approached to inspect them with his hand for signs of infection, though he often used a stick to lift up the penis to look for sores underneath.[77]

The failure to control the spread of disease had serious consequences in the Central Mediterranean theatre of war in 1943 and 1944 during the North African and Italian campaigns.

Within two months of the invasion of North Africa, 30 out of every 1,000 troops were contracting venereal infections. In some units a tenth of the soldiers were incapacitated by syphilis or gonorrhoea. More men were out of action from gonorrhoea than were incapacitated by wounds. Only malaria had a greater effect on military manpower.[78] Moreover, gonorrhoea was showing signs of becoming resistant to the sulphonamide drugs.[79] Clearly something had to be done, and, as luck would have it, there was a new wonder-drug being tested out on some of the wounded in North Africa at that time. Professor Howard Florey of the Sir William Dunn School of Pathology at the University of Oxford and Hugh Cairns, consulting neurosurgeon to the army, had begun clinical trials in May 1943 on the effects of penicillin, which Florey had been instrumental in developing, on battlefield wounds. In August they tried it on ten cases of gonorrhoea with amazing results. Penicillin could cure cases of gonorrhoea within twelve hours of treatment. Here seemed to be the answer to the prayers of the War Office. Florey and Cairns were adamant that penicillin should be used only for cases that would advance knowledge of its capabilities.[80] The issue was simpler for the War Office. If the scarce drug were to be used on gonorrhoea, the manpower crisis might be solved, whereas if it were used on wounds, there would still be a lengthy period in which healing and rehabilitation took place, even after the infection had cleared, before the troops could return to their units. At the same time there was a concern about the political reaction if it ever got out that penicillin was being used to treat sexually acquired infections rather than the wounds of war heroes. General L.T. Poole, Director of Pathology at the Army Medical Department, referred the matter to the prime minister, Winston Churchill, who decreed, scrawling across the memorandum in green ink, that 'this valuable drug must on no account be wasted. It must be used to the best military advantage.'[81] It was an enigmatic pronouncement capable of differing interpretations. Should it be used on severe battlefield casualties, for more minor wounds and infections, which might heal when the infection had cleared, or to treat cases of VD among the armed forces? The military authorities considered the various options and decided that the treatment of venereal cases was the best strategic use of the drug. These soldiers could be got back into action much more quickly, in more ways than one!

This godsend, penicillin, had been discovered by the 47-year-old Scottish bacteriologist Alexander Fleming at St Mary's Hospital, London, in 1928, but it was not until 1941 that it was effectively brought into systemic clinical use as a result of the work of a research team at the Sir William Dunn School of Pathology at the University of Oxford. Venereal disease had been an almost constant motif running through Fleming's career, so there was a certain appropriateness that penicillin was to be so important in the treatment of syphilis and gonorrhoea. His involvement went back to 1909 when Paul Ehrlich, during a visit to London to lecture on chemotherapy, gave a sample of his then new drug salvarsan to his friend Almroth Wright, head of the Inoculation Department at St Mary's Hospital. Wright, Fleming's great mentor, was primarily an immunologist with little sympathy for any form of chemotherapy. He handed over the sample to his junior colleague Alexander Fleming, who was to have great success in injecting salvarsan into patients at a time when few doctors knew much about intravenous injections. This skill was to enable him to build up a successful private practice administering salvarsan to wealthy patients in the years leading up to the First World War, and led to an honorary post as pathologist to the London Lock Hospital. Fleming and his colleague Leonard Colebrook published a note in the *Lancet* on the use of salvarsan and were for a time the only doctors in England to use it to any great extent.[82] Among Fleming's patients were fellow volunteer soldiers in the London Scottish Regiment, of which he was a keen member in his spare time. These young men, clerks, lawyers and other professionals who had exchanged their city suits for the swirl of the kilt, were to nickname him 'Private 606' in reference to Ehrlich's compound 606, and the artist Ronald Gray caricatured him as *Private 606* in his regimental kilt, his trademark cigarette drooping from his lip, and armed with a syringe in place of a rifle and with another syringe tucked into his stocking.[83] He had been involved in the clinical tests in the wards of the Inoculation

Department on Kharsivan, the generic substitute for salvarsan developed in First World War Britain. Then, when St Mary's was planning to open its venereal diseases clinic in 1917, Fleming returned from military service to help set it up.[84] In the 1930s he looked at the effect of the sulphonamides on gonorrhoea.[85] His interest in the *Treponema* bacteria continued throughout his life, and now in the 1940s he turned to an investigation with the gynaecologist Jack Suchet of the effect of penicillin on venereal diseases.[86]

It was above all with penicillin that Fleming made his impact on venereal diseases, although he had by no means set out to do so. His observation on 3 September 1928 of a chance contamination of a culture plate of *Staphylococcus aureus* by the fungus *Penicillium notatum*, in which something produced by the mould was stopping the growth of bacteria, triggered the process that led to the birth of the antibiotic age in medicine. An observant and meticulous worker, despite his reputation for not working in the tidiest of laboratories, Fleming noticed something that others might have missed and asked himself the questions his scientific training had prepared him for. Had he not investigated further and not published his findings, nothing else could have followed. However, Fleming was working very much in the nineteenth-century tradition of the lone researcher, ideal for following up his chance observation, but not such a useful approach if the discovery were to be developed for clinical use. What was required was a greater range of expertise, knowledge and experience than one man could possibly have. Only multidisciplinary teamwork could offer that. Working with two young research assistants whose knowledge of chemistry was only a little greater than his, he found it impossible to stabilise the penicillin, which meant that it soon lost any power to do any good, or purify it sufficiently so that it would be safe to use.[87] Yet he did point out the therapeutic potential of penicillin if these problems could be overcome.[88]

It was only when a team at the Sir William Dunn School of Pathology led by Howard Florey began work on penicillin in 1939 that there was some hope of surmounting the difficulties that

Fleming had found. The 1945 Nobel Prize for Medicine was jointly awarded to Fleming, for the initial discovery, and to Florey and Ernst Chain, the German-Jewish biochemist on the Oxford team, for the development of penicillin. It was a fair division of the honours so far as it went, but behind them was a larger research group. Indeed the key to their success lay in the fact that they were working together as a multidisciplinary team, whereas Fleming had essentially been working alone. By 1941 they had used penicillin successfully on a patient. However, in wartime, munitions came before medicine, and the facilities were not available for mass production. Florey and one of his colleagues from Oxford, Norman Heatley, went to America to get production going in the New World for the aid of the Old, but it was only after Pearl Harbor and the entry of the United States into the war that American industry showed any real sense of urgency in beginning penicillin production, and even then American production was primarily geared to American needs. Britain was left to get on with production for itself, and rose to the challenge but mainly for military use.[89] By sanctioning its use for preventing the mass incapacitation of men with gonorrhoea, Churchill ensured that penicillin would play a vital part in the war effort.

The great breakthrough in establishing the remarkable impact that penicillin had on syphilis had been made by John Mahoney, director of the United States Marine Hospital and Venereal Disease Research Laboratory at Staten Island, New York, in June 1943. He and his colleagues were studying the effect of penicillin derived from mould grown in their own laboratory on sulphonamide-resistant strains of gonorrhoea. Not really expecting any great results, they decided to try it out on lesions in rabbits infected with syphilis. In March 1943 Mahoney had already unsuccessfully tried penicillin on the bacteria causing the infection in a test tube. Harry Eagle at Johns Hopkins University School of Medicine had also shown that penicillin was useless against the spirochaetes *in vitro*,[90] so it was with no great hope that Mahoney's colleague Richard Arnold had injected a large dose of penicillin into a syphilitic rabbit, but Mahoney insisted that the experiment should go ahead. A few hours later, Arnold returned to check the condition of the diseased animal and to his surprise found that most of the spirochaetes had disappeared from its ulcers. His chief was equally surprised and later commented that 'we very nearly missed the boat'.[91] At once he and his team repeated the experiment on other rabbits and, over and over again, found that the infection cleared up within some twelve hours. This encouraged them to use properly manufactured penicillin on a patient, confident that at long last they might have truly found Paul Ehrlich's magic bullet against syphilis. Their first patient was a young sailor only recently infected with syphilis who volunteered to take part in the experiment. Every four hours for the next eight days he had 25,000 units of penicillin intramuscularly injected into him, a total of 1,200,000 units. After only four hours, there was very little trace of the spirochaetes in his blood or ulcer and by the fifteenth day of his treatment Wassermann tests showed him to be free of the disease. Within four months of receiving his first injection of penicillin, the young man was found to be completely free from infection and could be declared cured. Three other young men were treated in exactly the same way and cured just as quickly.[92]

Despite such encouraging results, Mahoney remained cautious in warning that a much longer observation of patients would be needed to make sure that none of them relapsed, since syphilis had a tendency to recur after periods of remission from the symptoms. However, he and his colleagues as well as other doctors reported good follow-up results, which confirmed the promise offered by penicillin.[93] The Public Health Service studied the effects of penicillin on patients in the Coast Guard but rejected any massive use on merchant seamen, because 'the study has been largely experimental and in order to evaluate the results the selected cases must be among patients who can be followed'.[94]

Meanwhile, the value of penicillin in the treatment of tertiary neurosyphilis was being studied simultaneously but separately by Joseph Earle Moore at Johns Hopkins and by John H. Stokes in Philadelphia.[95] Moore, however, cautioned that 'we are still learning how to use this drug. We don't know yet, and it is going to be some time before we are sure.'[96] In his view it would take two years of further investigations of the effects of penicillin to be sure of its value in the treatment of the disease, and 'to supply a million units of penicillin devoted to experimentation in syphilis, whether clinical or experimental, will probably mean the death of a member of the Armed Forces whose life might have been saved by it'.[97] However, many of his colleagues, especially 'officers of the United States Army and Navy . . . expressed the desire to have the investigations of penicillin in early and in late, especially neurosyphilis, expanded as rapidly as possible in order that the Army and Navy might obtain the maximum amount of information concerning the usefulness of penicillin in syphilis within the shortest possible period of time'.[98] Mahoney, in the quest to know more, was as enthusiastic as the military doctors about committing resources to the investigation of the effects of penicillin, and was keen to study the effects of it on latent syphilis with an experiment involving long-term federal prisoners who had not been exposed to any other forms of treatment during their years in prison.[99] However, the Federal Bureau of Prisons was less enthusiastic about such an experiment and pointed out that it would be difficult to procure sufficient cases for the study, since most prisoners would have been exposed to treatment before being arrested and sentenced.[100]

The Allied invasion of Sicily in July 1943, the precursor of the long-awaited Second Front in Europe, intensified the demand for penicillin. Venereal infections were rife and rising. In 1943, 27 soldiers out of every 1,000 admitted to hospitals were suffering from venereal diseases in Italy. In 1944, this rate had risen to 51 per 1,000 and in 1945 to 64 per 1,000. Men, clearly, were failing to take precautions.[101] This put enormous pressure on hospital beds, and after 1944 only the most seriously affected were hospitalised, the others being treated by special mobile VD-treatment teams.[102] By this time, the use of the sulphonamide drugs for gonorrhoea had been phased out and replaced by penicillin, which was now the normal treatment. After a fairly painful series of intramuscular injections over a period of twenty-four hours, the discharge could be 'turned off like a tap'. Syphilis too could now effectively be treated in about eight days with intramuscular injections of penicillin, compared with the 40–50 days needed with the old treatment with arsenical drugs and bismuth.[103] The depletion of troops by the old scourges of the wounds of Venus was at last checked in Naples and Italy where it had seemingly all begun 450 years earlier.

By June 1944 penicillin had been adopted as the drug of choice for the treatment of early syphilis by the American armed forces; the British services soon followed their example.[104] However, the authorities remained reticent about any publicity concerning the use of penicillin against syphilis and gonorrhoea and, because of 'certain conditions that exist at present, it is requested that no public announcement be made that we are instituting such treatment as routine'. With penicillin still in short supply, there were fears of a public outcry if it were known that it was being used on men with a sexually transmitted infection; anyone administering it was warned that 'you are expected and requested to exercise discretion as to its use'.[105] At the same time, 'to meet the demand for originality of thought and experimentation', investigators were being given more freedom to use up to 20 per cent of the penicillin allocated to them 'for whatever individual study in whatever field of syphilis he prefers' on the understanding that 'it may not be used in other diseases than syphilis, nor for the treatment of purely distress cases, private or otherwise'.[106]

With successful cures guaranteed in 90–97 per cent of cases of early syphilis, penicillin played a major part in reducing the number of servicemen out of action because of the infection and in doing so made a great contribution to the Allied victory. Had there not been an effective treatment now available, the British and American armies would have been severely incapacitated. Gerard McElligott, for one, was convinced that 'the decision to use it in early syphilis in the Forces on active service was completely justifiable . . . many thousands of man hours were saved for the war effort'.[107] By early 1945 it was also available for civilian cases of syphilis.[108] Victory in war was seemingly paralleled by victory over venereal disease, but syphilis proved a more resilient foe than the Third Reich and was destined to strike back.

EIGHT

'No Medicine for Regret':
Complacency and Resurgence

With the end of the Second World War, it seemed as if the scourge of syphilis had at long last been conquered after holding sway for over 450 years. Professor George Joakimoglou of the University of Athens declared in 1952 that the advent of the antibiotic age had 'caused much distress . . . many doctors used to specialise in VD. This brought them much wealth and a luxurious life. After the advent of penicillin the whole branch is practically demolished and its previously successful practitioners have to turn to another speciality.'[1] The venereologists may have lost income and a sense of challenge with the widespread availability of antibiotics that could cure sexually transmitted diseases easily, but the bacteria had even less cause to be happy. No longer did syphilis and gonorrhoea hold the terrors they had done just a few years earlier, especially now that syphilis could be effectively cleared up in its earlier stages and its long-term complications became increasingly rare. In Britain in 1954 the total number of syphilis cases fell nationally from 17,675 to 808 in only one year.[2] In the United States, the number of cases of primary and secondary syphilis reached an all-time low of 3.9 per 100,000 and of the always more prevalent gonorrhoea to 127.4 per 100,000.[3] John Mahoney commented that 'their importance as public health entities, based upon their ability to produce human suffering, definitely has changed' and suggested that heart disease, cancer, arthritis and mental health were much more important medical problems not so easily solved.[4] John Charles, the Chief Medical Officer in the United Kingdom, was not so sanguine and warned in 1953 that, since sexual promiscuity was as rife in peacetime as it

192

ever had been in wartime, the venereal peril would always be lurking.[5]

Certainly, without penicillin, there was a danger of a major epidemic of sexually transmitted infections amid the social dislocation at the end of the Second World War. In the Germany of Year Zero, many desperate and displaced young women turned to 'hunger prostitution' in their struggle for survival. In return for sex with members of the occupying forces, they gained food, shelter and a certain measure of protection.[6] They also spread venereal disease. The occupying military authorities already forbade fraternisation with the former enemy, but this was a policy they could not easily enforce. In Hamburg, where venereal disease and prostitution had become a major problem within weeks of the occupation of the port by the British army, raids on bars, cafes, restaurants, tram and bus stops, and railway stations hauled in any woman found in the company of a man who was not her husband for a forcible examination for signs of disease. Women found to be both persistent offenders and prostitutes were deprived of their freedom and sent to a reformatory under a practice begun under National Socialism whereby a woman with a venereal infection was judged incapable of managing her own affairs and could be stripped of her civil rights and institutionalised indefinitely for the protection of the state. Käthe Petersen, who had been appointed by the Nazis in 1934 to head the Pflegeamt, the department in charge of the rehabilitation of prostitutes, was allowed to stay in office and given complete authority over her 'wards', so great was the anxiety to control the problem.[7] While German women were punished for spreading disease, British soldiers were merely reminded that 'a happy and successful family life as husbands and fathers in the years to come could have its best and most sure foundation on a life of self-control and fair living in the days of their youth'.[8]

Yet it was penicillin not social control that was to be crucial in preventing the spread of disease. At first, in the unforgiving mood of the post-war occupation, there had been great opposition to allowing defeated Germany access to the benefits of antibiotics. However, the practical necessity of safeguarding the troops stationed there from gonorrhoea and syphilis and preventing them from bringing them back to austerity-weary Britain, together with newly emerging ultra-virulent strains of the streptococcus bacterium, and so causing an epidemic, produced a change of heart, and penicillin was exported to Germany.[9] As ever, disease knew no political or ethnic boundaries, and, with greater movement between countries, public health issues in one place affected those in another. The American forces were also concerned about the possibility of a major epidemic of venereal diseases as discipline among their men loosened during demobilisation, and 'bobby soxers', as the new generation of teenage American girls were dubbed, made eyes at the men coming out of uniform; it was recognised that it was penicillin that had averted such a catastrophe.[10]

Antibiotics now meant that old solutions to the prevention of venereal diseases no longer seemed appropriate to the new age. Even France, long the bastion of the regulation and inspection of prostitution, despite its dubious efficacy in controlling the spread of such diseases, passed a law doing away with the regulated brothels. The Marthe Richard Law of 13 April 1946 removed surveillance of venereal diseases from the police, but responsibility for tracking down and treating infected prostitutes was now given to the French health authorities. Prostitutes continued to be discriminated against by such a system of recording their sexual health and it was not until 1960 that full regulation of prostitutes finally came to an end. Meanwhile further legislation in 1948 had reorganised the venereal diseases dispensaries set up in the interwar period and made it compulsory for anyone with a venereal disease to receive treatment until he or she was no longer contagious.[11]

In Italy, too, optimism about the decline of venereal diseases and the growing awareness that the rights of women were being infringed by regulated prostitution provoked a struggle to abolish closed houses led by the socialist member of parliament Lina Merlin. However, the brothel keepers themselves organised opposition to her bill, first proposed in 1948, and received some support from venereologists, who argued that, if compulsory medical examinations were abolished as well as regulated brothels, there would be an increase in the incidence of infection and also of sexual crimes committed by men denied a safe outlet for their urges in the brothels. The venereologists would also lose their lucrative jobs in the public administration of regulation, although that was rarely mentioned. Moreover, many of the male members of the Italian parliament had themselves enjoyed their own sexual initiations in licensed brothels. It was not until 1958 that Merlin's Act was passed, although there were frequent calls for the reintroduction of the system in later years.[12] By contrast, in Franco's Spain, where brothels had been regulated on the model of the French system since the mid nineteenth century, the brothels were officially suppressed in 1956 in an excess of traditional morality rather than from any recognition of the rights of the women concerned.[13]

The quick cure that penicillin offered for syphilis and gonorrhoea raised many concerns about the impact it would have on sexual customs and practices, especially when other traditional forms of control over promiscuity and protection against the spread of sexually transmitted infections were all passing into history. At a time when there were optimistic predictions that these diseases might be eradicated, the Spanish physician Martinez Alonso warned that 'the wages of sin are now negligible. A few shots of penicillin put you on your feet in no time (or in whatever position you may want) and you can start all over again. If the road back from sin is paved with nothing more lethal or painful than a few million units of Sir Alexander's discovery, why not indulge?'[14] If the disease was no longer such a health threat, then it no longer posed a moral deterrent. Public health slogans, in a bid to counteract this effect, offered the reminder that 'VD can be cured but there's no medicine for regret'.[15]

By the mid-1950s, such appeals to traditional moral assumptions could not prevent a resurgence in the incidence of sexually transmitted infections as the post-war decline went into reverse. In 1955 figures for the treatment of gonorrhoea began to rise again in Britain and by 1962 had passed the levels they had reached in 1939. Gonorrhoea had quickly developed resistance to penicillin, just as it had earlier done with the sulphonamides.[16] Syphilis still seemed controllable with penicillin in conjunction with a policy of contact tracing, but here too rates of infection were on the rise. The causes of such increases in infection were seen as immigration, homosexuality and promiscuity among the young.[17]

Venereal diseases were still viewed as threats to family life and linked to the perceived breakdown in society. In the 1950s rock and roll music was linked with juvenile delinquency and was denounced as 'a communicable disease', a metaphor tying it in with promiscuity and venereal infections.[18] Although there is little evidence to connect venereal diseases with such youth cults as rock and roll, teddy boys, and mods and rockers, the teenager was a threat to the moral code of the older generation. The longstanding view that venereal disease was a just retribution for sin had now been replaced by a view of it as a penalty of ignorance in the young. Sexual adventures were seen as part of the new consumer culture open to all in an age of affluence. This aspect of the consumer culture was exemplified by such magazines as *Playboy*, in which to its critics 'real sex is something that goes with the best scotch, twenty-seven dollar sunglasses and platinum-tipped shoelaces'.[19] Instant gratification in fashionable accessories and in sex went unashamedly hand in hand. Some young men did not even bother to hide their infections, such as the Eton schoolboy who turned up at a Windsor clinic suffering from *tinea cruris*, ringworm in his crotch, in full school uniform.[20] Much of the post-war moral panic about venereal disease, however, focused on the perceived promiscuity of young women haunting cafés, pubs, cinemas and dance halls. In Glasgow in the 1960s, it was the traditional bastion of working-class culture, the public house, where most of the pickups took place that led to casual sex and infection.[21] Although it was generally working-class women who were blamed for spreading disease, one man in a 1960 Granada television documentary on the burgeoning health hazard claimed to have been infected by a debutante.[22]

Women were traditionally vilified as the vectors for the transmission of syphilis and gonorrhoea rather than men, but from the 1950s onwards homosexual men also came to be seen as bearing responsibility for increasing numbers of infections. In part this was a recognition that homosexuality actually existed. Although gay men had acquired infections since the first appearance of syphilis, it was not until 1948 that British venereologists began to write about 'the problem of the homosexual with venereal disease'.[23] By the mid-1950s, 60 per cent of new syphilitic infections in some parts of London were reported among homosexual men, especially in the West End, where 'cottaging' in the public lavatories of Covent Garden, Piccadilly, Jermyn Street and Waterloo Station offered gay men the possibility of clandestine coupling and anonymity.[24] This was at a time when homosexual activity was a criminal offence in the United Kingdom. Jim Jefferiss, who specialised in the treatment of gay men, found that many of his patients were unwilling to have their sexual lives investigated and their partners traced in order to be offered treatment because they were 'still felons in the eyes of the law' and he believed that 'a change in the law would make effective contact tracing possible and so would help in the control of venereal disease'.[25] The 1957 Wolfenden Report on Homosexual Offences and Prostitution ushered in a more liberal climate, but it was only after much debate in parliament and the press over the next decade that such activity was partly decriminalised in 1967. In the meantime, gay men were increasingly patronising VD clinics and were prepared to give details of their sexual partners so that their contacts could be traced and offered treatment.[26] The gay rights movement of the late 1960s and 1970s was accompanied by greater sexual liberation among homosexual men, for whom infection was little more than a nuisance that went with their more active sex lives. It was not only in the United States and Britain that gay men were becoming more noticeable. Even in the Soviet Union, where the very existence of homosexuality had been denied, 'there is now almost a competition to record the largest chains of homosexual transmission'.[27] As these men formed vocal campaigning groups to assert their rights, many of them were equally bold in demanding good treatment. The venereologist Dick Willcox, whose prolific writings on his speciality had led to him being dubbed 'the Enid Blyton of Venereology',[28] found nothing unusual in being publicly confronted in the late 1960s by a homosexual barrister complaining volubly about having been kept waiting for half an hour to have treatment for his rectal gonorrhoea.[29]

Older generations of venereologists, however, were not always as sympathetic to their gay patients as they were courteous to the prostitutes who attended their clinics. The stigmatisation of patients with sexually transmitted diseases continued, despite attempts by doctors and nurses to seem more understanding.[30] At St Mary's Hospital, Paddington, G.L.M. McElligott, the director of the Special Clinic, was known for his kindness to the local streetwalkers but would chase any male patient who admitted to having had intercourse with another man from his consulting room with the threat of eternal damnation. However, the clinic staff would suggest to the unlucky man that he return to the clinic when one of McElligott's colleagues, Jim Jefferiss, was seeing patients. Less strait-laced and censorious in such matters than his chief, Jefferiss not only became the consultant of choice for gay men in the Special Clinic in Paddington, but also built up a thriving private practice.[31]

Homosexuality was not the only social change of the 1950s and 1960s to impact on the resurgence of venereal diseases. Immigration raised concerns about the import of infections by the waves of African, West Indian and Asian people arriving in Britain from the Commonwealth and reveals much about the racial assumptions of the doctors treating them. In 1950 Robert Lees, the VD medical officer for Leeds, drew attention to the 'acute problem' posed by 'the coloured men who spread venereal disease' in London and the larger ports. He assumed that these men came from communities with high infection rates and that 'they certainly had not the moral or social training which would enable them to live as decent members of a civilized society, and that they were badly assimilated into the community'.[32] In the mid-1950s a quarter of all men with gonorrhoea were immigrants from the West Indies, compared with just under half the cases coming from white Englishmen and a quarter from men infected abroad.[33] The fact that many of their female contacts were white, British-born teenagers raised concern about such interracial sexual relationships, which had first surfaced during the Second World War, when there had been similar anxieties about white women and black GIs having sex. Then the response of the Americans had been to consider segregating black units from the British population, which did not always share the discriminatory attitudes of their allies, and to keep the good-time girls away from the troops.[34] Now there seemed to be a similar problem of sexually uncontrollable young women attracted to black immigrants, far from home and lonely until their wives and families could join them. Compared with the wartime response, there was a greater awareness of race-relations issues, especially after the Notting Hill race riots of 1958, and no attempts were made to control the spread of infection among Afro-Caribbean immigrants by coercion. Instead, the existing clinics opened their doors willingly to the newcomers, though whether or not there was racial discrimination depended on the ingrained attitudes of the staff treating them.

Female sexuality rather than race was at the heart of the debate over the control of sexually transmitted infection in the heat of the sexual revolution of the 1960s and 1970s, just as it had always been. Permissiveness and promiscuity now centred on the contraceptive pill and the sexual liberation it offered. The first oral contraceptive for women, Enovid, went on sale in May 1960. It offered the promise of an end to worries about unwanted pregnancies, and of a woman having the same sexual freedom as a man, potentially abolishing the old double standards of sexuality and morality. By 1962 the pill was being widely used, although some women were all too aware that it had actually shifted the onus for birth control from the man to the woman. It also increased the risk for both partners of contracting a venereal disease by making the condom superfluous when the woman was taking the pill. The sheath had originally been developed as protection against the pox rather than as a contraceptive device. It had become much more popular in the interwar periods when technical improvements had made it more reliable and comfortable to use. The first latex condoms, known as 'Dreadnoughts', had gone on sale in the late 1920s, marketed as 'the strongest, thinnest and silkiest protectives in the world'. In 1932 the London Rubber Company, which had long sold imported German sheaths in barber shops, launched the Durex company to manufacture these 'durable, reliable and excellent' condoms in Britain. In the mid-1930s it was producing 2,000,000 a year and in 1945, thanks to British and American military orders, 36,000,000.[35] The latex version had been a big improvement on the washable and reusable 'rubbers' manufactured by the same firm that produced Mackintosh raincoats, using vulcanised rubber developed in 1844 by Charles Goodyear, which in themselves had been an improvement on the linen sheaths previously used.[36] Now the pill and other forms of female contraception made the sheath seem redundant and so meant that 'safer sex' was not always secure against infection, however much it might have been effective in preventing pregnancy.

Nevertheless, it was widely felt that increasing use of the pill had dramatically changed patterns of sexual behaviour by promoting greater promiscuity and disease. Dick Willcox noticed that 'the women now come in droves, sometimes three abreast, almost as if under the influence of Women's Liberation, they demand the right to have as much VD as the men'.[37] Robert Morton, President of the Medical Society for the Study of Venereal Diseases, denounced the pill as being 'the most dangerous of the polluting pesticides' and its use as 'more calamitous than anything precipitated by thalidomide', referring to the drug prescribed against morning sickness for many pregnant women which had resulted in the birth of malformed babies.[38] Teenage girls, in particular, were seen as being encouraged to be irresponsible with their 'anti-social urges' towards promiscuity, making them 'the female equivalent of the skinhead in his bovver boots'.[39] Such were the perceptions of many venereologists, but the reality was that women who relied on the pill for contraception were no more promiscuous nor at greater risk of contracting an infection than women who used other forms of birth control or none at all.[40]

In Roman Catholic countries, contraception continued to be officially frowned upon. In Italy, following the Concordat with the Vatican of 1929, the Fascists had introduced laws prohibiting the sale and use of contraceptives yet had allowed the manufacture of condoms to continue because they were considered essential as a protection against sexually transmitted diseases. Such a use of condoms came to be associated with prostitution and immorality, a prejudice that persisted long after the repeal in 1971 of laws against the promotion of birth control and also after Roman Catholicism had ceased to be the state religion in 1984. Even today, cool young Italian men, well aware of the health risks of unprotected sex but eager to cut 'la bella figura', refuse to use condoms from a belief that their use can diminish sexual pleasure, that it ruins the romantic atmosphere and that it detracts from their sophisticated image and from the persistent belief that sexually transmitted infection is almost exclusively transmitted by prostitutes.[41] For many devout Catholics, the use of condoms is also unacceptable as preventatives against infection because of their potential contraceptive use. Liberal Catholics ignored the teachings of their Church on the subject, but the attitude of the Vatican towards anything that smacked of contraception remains strong today, despite overpopulation in the developing world being an impediment to social progress and millions dying of AIDS, for whom the use of contraceptive condoms might be an answer.

Meanwhile, the social stigma everywhere remained a bar to investment in combating venereal disease. Venereology, always a neglected and undervalued service, had been in grave danger of being run down entirely in the euphoria following the realisation that penicillin could be so effective in treating sexual transmitted diseases, although the reduction in such services was in turn to contribute to the resurgence of the diseases. In 1960, in a comment rare for the time by a patient on her treatment, a prostitute blamed her infection with syphilis on placing too much faith in her regular hospital check-ups.[42] The falling incidence of infection and the resulting perceived lack of any clinical challenge posed by the specialty made it a much less attractive career path for doctors. Penicillin had reduced the level of technical skill needed to treat syphilis and gonorrhoea, so that general practitioners rather than specialists could just as easily give the injections. Although, in Britain, the transfer of the special clinics from local authority control to the new National Health Service in 1948 had raised the status of the VD specialist to the level of other hospital consultants, fewer doctors entered the speciality and more clinics were being closed.[43] By 1955 there were only ninety-three consultants left in the speciality, many of them rapidly approaching retirement, and only nine senior registrars in training as venereologists.[44] Not only were staffing levels dwindling and approaching critical levels, but the clinics were housed in sub-standard, overcrowded buildings with variable laboratory facilities, perhaps because there were no votes for the politicians in the treatment of venereal disease and money was being spent on research into more emotive medical problems such as cancer.[45]

Despite being a growth industry as infection rates rose, venereology as a speciality still remained uninviting to new entrants. Not only was there a shortage of doctors, but it was also hard to recruit nurses, technicians and clerks. The Medical Society for the Study of Venereal Diseases warned in 1976 that 'failure to provide resources could quickly destroy all the advances and gains of the last sixty years and result in a recrudescence of sexually transmitted diseases'.[46] It was only with reluctance that clinics were refurbished and rehoused in new buildings by hospital boards of governors when absolutely necessary. When a new special clinic was built at St Mary's Hospital, Paddington, in 1971 to replace one 'which already carries an individual outpatient load exceeded in only few places outside of Bombay or Calcutta', it was remarked that 'St Mary's would be the largest teaching hospital attached to a VD clinic', something that it could not be expected to be proud of but that it would just have to accept.[47] Elsewhere, more government money was made available not only for new buildings but also for an increase in staffing levels. In order to make the speciality more attractive and of higher academic and clinical status, greater emphasis was placed on research, with the first chair in genitourinary medicine being established at the Middlesex Hospital Medical School in 1979. Despite these initiatives, the staffing problem remained acute and more and more posts were filled by 'overseas' doctors.[48]

It was not only in Britain that the advent of antibiotic therapy had downgraded sexually transmitted infections in the priorities of the public health authorities, which often increasingly relied on old ideas despite changing circumstances. In the United States, federal expenditure was progressively reduced for venereal disease control and new approaches, such as the screening of higher-risk populations like college students, teenagers and homosexuals, were rarely undertaken. There was also a reluctance to promote the use of condoms. Meanwhile the tracing of contacts also became more difficult as patients were reluctant to reveal details of their sexual activities to older-style epidemiologists and social workers, who still adopted a moralistic tone when interviewing them. It was not until 1972 that the Public Health Service woke up to the need for a specific programme to control the disease for the first time since Thomas Parran's campaign of the 1930s. Yet funding for research into venereal diseases from the National Institutes of Health remained small.[49]

Despite the rising rates of infection and the potential importance of education as a comparatively cheap weapon in the fight against disease, the old stigma attached to syphilis and gonorrhoea meant that it was an unmentionable subject in respectable circles. If in the early 1950s a mention of the star Lucille Ball's very visible pregnancy on the popular television comedy series *I Love Lucy* could be considered risqué, it was not surprising that the taboo against the mention of venereal diseases on TV, this increasingly ubiquitous form of home entertainment, was not to be breached.[50] In 1964 the producers and writers of the widely watched medical drama *Dr Kildare* planned to air an episode in which a high-school student contracted an anti-social disease. The NBC television company refused to allow the story to be filmed, since it would have to contain language and a discussion of sexual intercourse deemed unsuitable and inappropriate for television.[51] In 1960s Britain, the subject of venereal disease and warnings to avoid it did not feature in television drama, though hard-hitting documentaries were more courageous in tackling the subject, especially the ground-breaking *World in Action*.[52] Yet, as a mass medium, television could have had a role in educating people about the dangers of unprotected sex both in dramas for more adult audiences and through advertising.

Not until the 1980s, as a result of a new and very different venereal peril, was the potential of television for educating about sexually transmitted infections used, with a controversial campaign aimed at encouraging the use of condoms and the practice of safe sex. Even then there was criticism from the moral majority about the airing of such subjects on television and possibly encouraging vice.

Indeed, only with the appearance of AIDS in the 1980s did sexually transmitted infections once again take centre stage as a major medical problem, but at the expense of upstaging syphilis. Between 1978 and 1987 syphilis had declined from more than 2,500 cases a year in Britain to fewer than 200, and the incidence of gonorrhoea had more than halved to about 20,000 cases.[53] However, cases of chlamydia and genital herpes had become a much more serious cause for public concern and infection. So distressing did the incurability of herpes seem to sufferers that for many it was seen as heralding the end of an individual's sex life. For women, this incurable infection was linked with cervical cancer and risks to their children if they became infected during pregnancy. Although its long-term problems were probably less than those of untreated syphilis, genital herpes was widely believed to be more dangerous than syphilis.[54] Where once syphilis might have been evoked in fiction as the most horrific of diseases, Scott Turow in his 1990 novel *The Burden of Proof* was to use shame over a longstanding infection with genital herpes as the motive for the suicide of the wife of the main character, which acts as the springboard for the plot of the novel.[55] Herpes, though, aroused far less fear than AIDS was to do.

Rumours were rife in the years between 1979 and 1981 of a strange syndrome affecting the gay communities of Los Angeles, San Francisco and New York, in which young men were being struck down with an especially malignant form of Kaposi's sarcoma, a cancer that usually affected older people. The disease was accompanied by an unusual form of pneumonia. Before they had become ill, all the men affected had seen their immune systems break down. By 1982 there were over 200 cases in the United States, and similar symptoms were being reported among European gay men. In this early stage it was only homosexual men who were being struck down; the press dubbed it the 'gay plague', a name that deliberately summoned up connotations of divine punishment for sexual transgressions. Doctors preferred to call it 'Acquired Immunity Deficiency Syndrome' or AIDS, and it was this term that came into widespread use in 1982. However, very soon the infection had spread to intravenous drug users, which also bolstered its associations with sin and stigmatised its victims, just as the pox had been stigmatised because of its sexual associations.[56] In the United States, Haitian immigrants were singled out as scapegoats and blamed for having brought the disease to North America. While moralists ascribed their infection to the results of poor hygiene, drug abuse and even voodoo, epidemiologists soon established that AIDS had only become so prevalent in Haiti because of widespread sex tourism.[57] Ironically, Haiti is one of the places from which syphilis may have first passed to Europe with Columbus's sailors.

At first, in another echo of the pox, very little was known about the new disease or how it was spread. Researchers suspected that a virus caused it. Two research teams, one based in France and the other in the United States, separately began to investigate. Early in 1983 the Paris-based team led by Luc Montagnier at the Pasteur Institute claimed to have identified the organism causing the syndrome but did not publish its findings until May 1983. At the same time, researchers at the National Cancer Institute led by Robert Gallo in Washington DC made a similar claim. National rivalries were keen in the bitter dispute to claim the credit for the discovery. Gallo and his team also developed a diagnostic test for the virus, only to have their patents disputed in court by the French. At last in 1986 it was recognised that the two organisms were identical, a virus christened the 'Human Immunodeficiency Virus' or HIV, which deactivated the immune system. However, this was not before the struggle for prestige, scientific recognition and monetary reward had brought nothing but acrimony for scientists in an area where cooperation could have led to better results.[58]

By now, it was not only homosexual men and drug addicts who were contracting the disease. A group of heterosexual haemophiliacs were diagnosed with AIDS in 1982, suggesting that it might be transmitted through blood and blood products as well as semen. Sufferers from haemophilia who had thought that the clotting agent Factor VIII was an answer to their condition were now afraid that they would either succumb to AIDS or have the treatment with Factor VIII withheld at the risk of shortening their lives. Their worries were to be relieved once blood products began to be routinely heat-treated. With the development of a diagnostic test for HIV, it became possible to screen blood donors. However, this did not prevent the growth of hysteria about the infection, fuelled by the rapid spread of AIDS among the partners of bisexual men, drug users and haemophiliacs. Prostitutes in Europe and America were found to have the infection. Several cases affecting babies were reported. There were calls for mandatory testing of high-risk groups and compulsory treatment. Sufferers from AIDS lost their jobs and homes, and children who were either innocently infected or even whose parents had AIDS were expelled from their schools.[59] There were scares about the danger of surgeons contracting AIDS in the operating theatre and of patients catching it from HIV-infected doctors.[60] The politician Edwina Curry advised businessmen that their best protection against sexually transmitted infections when travelling abroad was to take their wives with them.[61] The bathhouses of San Francisco and New York, mostly frequented by gay men, were closed, just as their counterparts in Renaissance Europe had been suppressed from fear of the pox.[62] In 1987 the United States made infection with HIV grounds for refusing entry to immigrants, as a result of which in the early 1990s a group of Haitian refugees were detained for two years in the naval facility at Guantanamo Bay, Cuba, that was later to become notorious as the detention centre for Al-Qaeda and Taliban prisoners from the 2002 war in Afghanistan.[63] It was all very reminiscent of the initial reactions to the pox.

In highly developed Western societies, the millions of cases of AIDS initially predicted never materialised, partly as a result of a sex hygiene campaign that popularised safe sex and the use of condoms, aimed at not only the highly organised gay community but also at heterosexuals. This use of condoms had its effect on preventing the spread of syphilis and other infections. It was also realised that AIDS was more likely to be a chronic condition that could take years to develop into the full-blown disease. A further breakthrough came with the development of the drug azidothymidine (AZT), also marketed as Retrovir, which prolonged the latent period of the virus, stopped patients from losing weight and improved their general well-being.[64]

It was all very different in the developing world. In Africa, AIDS was a mass killer, affecting heterosexual men and women – and capable of being transmitted to children in the womb – as well as gay men and women. Retrospective diagnosis of patients showed that people had been dying from it since the 1960s. There was also some evidence that the HIV virus had jumped the species barrier and was descended from retroviruses found in some chimpanzees and macaques, possibly transmitted to humans through the consumption of bush meat. This 'African hypothesis' had its critics, who dismissed it as little more than racist speculation about Africa as the 'dark continent' spawning disease. European doctors were accused of exaggerating the extent of AIDS in Africa. Sadly they had underestimated the extent of the infection.[65]

All this emphasis on AIDS and HIV took the spotlight off syphilis. Much of the interest in combating the new disease was the result of a strong vocal lobby from the articulate gay communities of Europe and North America. This activity did, however, have the advantage for syphilis and the other sexually transmitted infections of channelling funding towards what had been badly neglected medical services. This was not only the result of the campaigning and support groups established by the victims of AIDS, their partners and friends, but in the United Kingdom was also pushed by a small number of STD specialists, infectious-diseases doctors, virologists and immunologists, the 'samurai of AIDS' as they were to be dubbed, working in London teaching hospitals that had seen the first influx of AIDS patients. Money was poured into the improvement of services, allowing for improved facilities in the special clinics.[66] AIDS offered new scientific and clinical challenges and prestigious research projects that could attract talented young doctors to the once-neglected speciality. For the dedicated researcher there was the challenge of working in new fields and of possibly making a breakthrough that would be of benefit to millions of people. St Mary's Hospital, Paddington, became a major centre for the study and treatment of AIDS when in 1981, after hearing of this strange new disease affecting American gay communities, the consultant in genitourinary medicine Willie Harris joined forces with the immunologist Tony Pinching to begin investigating the causes of the new disease and its immunological effects. A young registrar, Jonathan Weber, was given the responsibility for tracking the lifestyles and habits of the gay men enrolled for the study, while Pinching concentrated on studying their immunological profiles. At first none of the men displayed any of the signs of AIDS that were so familiar in US sufferers, but their blood samples showed many abnormalities in their immune systems and an inability to fight disease. Within weeks of beginning the project, the research team in the Praed Street Clinic at St Mary's was seeing cases of AIDS, which gave an added urgency to their work. Yet at first the Medical Research Council refused to fund a study of a disease not yet reported in Britain, and it was only through the foresight of the Wellcome Trust in providing funding that the work got under way. Pinching soon found himself involved in the public campaign to raise awareness of AIDS, promote safe sex and to destigmatise the condition.[67] Very soon the British government was pouring money into the investigation and treatment of AIDS. The treatment of syphilis, gonorrhoea and herpes benefited from this increased funding and improved staffing levels. It could not last: when the predicted AIDS epidemic failed to materialise, there was a return to the old policy of benign neglect of the Cinderella medical services dealing with sexually transmitted infections.[68]

Since the end of the Second World War, the incidence of sexually transmitted infection has peaked and troughed on numerous occasions. At the beginning of the twenty-first century these diseases are on the rise again. Although by now syphilis is considered 'an uncommon disease' in the United Kingdom, a number of outbreaks of the disease since 1996 has resulted in sharp rises in incidence in young men and women. An outbreak in Bristol was associated with commercial sex workers and cocaine users. Other outbreaks in London, Brighton and Manchester were linked to homosexual groups, with many of the reported cases also testing positive for HIV. In all these cases the rise was linked with people with a large number of sexual partners, who spread the infection. It was also associated with a growth in the number of opportunities in these highly metropolitan areas for casual sexual contacts in such 'sexual marketplaces' as saunas, 'cruising grounds' and Internet chat rooms. The increase in international travel also increased opportunities for casual sex and disease.[69] It was little wonder that smart-suited businessmen and women, fashionably dressed young people, casual backpackers and a variety of male and female sex workers should be found waiting for the opening of GUM (genitourinary medicine) clinics on their way to work or after a night on the town. As William Osler had said of syphilis a century ago, sexually transmissible infection 'is common in the community and is no respecter of age, sex or station in life'.[70]

Today, more than five centuries after it made its explosive first impact on Western Europe, syphilis continues to pose a social and health problem that all the best efforts cannot eradicate. Penicillin had seemed to offer the apparently elusive magic bullet that would make the scourge of the pox a thing of the past. It merely ameliorated its effects. Periodically, the disease appears to be in its last throes. The next thing is that the newspapers are full of dire reports of its resurgence. A fifteen-fold rise in syphilis between 1998 and 2003 has been blamed on young men failing to wear condoms when having sex after binge-drinking sessions and ignoring messages about having safe sex. It is predicted that the number of young people with the disease will rise by 50 per cent in the three-year period beginning in 2005 as part of a continuing crisis in sexual health.[71] Young people now consider their generation to be 'a lot more sexually aware' than their elders; yet a 23-year-old man working in the retail sector could say that 'because we aren't getting married young, people are having different sexual partners so . . . there is a lot of pressure to perform', without displaying any awareness that such sexual behaviour can lead to disease if precautions are not taken.[72] So long as such carefree and casual, if not careless, attitudes to sex persist, syphilis can be assured of a certain future. After all these years and despite coming close to its own death, there is still life in the pox and it seems destined to go on and on, its story continuing to encompass all human life. It may be the cause of bitter rue, but any mourning for its own death is still a long way off.

Notes

Preface and Acknowledgements

1. W. Osler, 'Internal Medicine as a Vocation', in *Aequanimitas: With Other Addresses to Medical Students, Nurses and Practitioners of Medicine* (1932), p. 133.
2. D. Hayden, *Pox: Genius, Madness and the Mysteries of Syphilis* (2003).
3. W. Osler, *The Quotable Osler* (2003), p. 146.
4. J. Arrizabalaga, J. Henderson and R. French, *The Great Pox* (1997), p. 126.

Chapter One

1. J. Burckhardt, *Civilization of the Renaissance in Italy* (1990); J. Hale, *Civilization of Europe in the Renaissance* (1993).
2. A. Benivieni, *De Abditis Nonnulis ac Mirandis Morborum et Sanationum Causis*, Paris, 1528, fo. 12ᵛ; Nicolo Leoniceno, *Libellus de Epidemia quam Vulgo Morbum Gallicum Vocant*, Venice, 1497, sigs d. iʳ⁻ᵛ; A. Corradi, 'Nuovi Documenti per la Storia delle Malattier Veneree in Italia della fine dell Quatrocento alla metà della Cinquecento', *Annali Universali di Medicina e Chirugia*, 269/808 (1884), 289–386.
3. Marcellus Cumanus, cited in C.G. Gruner (ed.), *Aphrodisiacus sive de Lue Venerea* (1789), p. 2.
4. G. Ongaro, 'Medicine,' in P. Del Negro (ed.), *The University of Padua* (2001), pp. 162–3.
5. A. Benedetti, *Anatomice sive Historia Corporis Humani*, Venice, 1497, quoted in C. Quétel, *History of Syphilis* (1990), p. 10. See also A. Benedetti, *Diario de Bello Carolino*, Padua, 1496.
6. Quétel, *History of Syphilis*, p. 10.
7. F. Guicciardini, *The History of Italy* (1984), p. 108.
8. Treponemes are responsible for causing four different diseases in humans. *Treponema carateum* is responsible for producing pinta, a skin disease found in Central and South America. *Treponema pallidum* has three different subspecies that all cause different infections. Yaws, which affects the skin and bones, is found in rural settings in the humid tropics and is caused by *Treponema pallidum pertenue*. Similar to yaws is endemic syphilis, produced by *Treponema pallidum endemicum*, which is restricted to warm, arid

211

climates. Non-venereal syphilis is called *bejel* in North Africa, the Middle East and the Eastern Mediterranean, where it is transferred among children often by sharing drinking vessels. Most serious of all is venereal syphilis caused by *Treponema pallidum* subspecies *pallidum*, which can affect any tissues of the body and is not restricted to any one climatic zone. Despite producing very different diseases, these four treponemes are very difficult to differentiate; they produce the same reactions to blood tests and are all susceptible to penicillin. They obviously share a common origin but have evolved differently. See P.L. Perine, 'Non-Venereal Endemic Treponematoses: Yaws, Endemic Syphilis (Bejel) and Pinta', in J.G.G. Ledingham and D.A. Warrell (eds), *Oxford Concise Textbook of Medicine* (2000), pp. 1677–80.

9. D.J.M. Wright and G.W. Conska, 'Syphilis', in Ledingham and Warrell (eds), *Oxford Concise Textbook of Medicine*, pp. 1680–6.

10. W. Osler, 'Internal Medicine as a Vocation', p. 133.

11. W. Osler, 'The Campaign against Syphilis', *Lancet*, 1 (1917), 789.

12. Wright and Conska, 'Syphilis', pp. 1684–5.

13. R. Diaz de Isla, *Tractado Contra el Mal Serpentino* (1539); see also 'Tractado contra el Mal Serpentino: que vulgamente en España es llamado Bubas', in I. Bloch, *Der Ursprung der Syphilis* (1901–2), vol. 1, pp. 306–7.

14. See C. Columbus, *The Four Voyages of Christopher Columbus* (1969), pp. 139, 156; H. Thomas, *Rivers of Gold* (2004), pp. 155, 167.

15. A.W. Crosby, *The Columban Exchange* (1972).

16. F. Guerra, 'Aztec Medicine', *Medical History*, 10/4 (1966), 320.

17. C. Roberts and M. Cox, *Health and Disease in Britain* (2003), pp. 272–4. In the 1994 excavation of a medieval friary in Hull, there seemed to be evidence that 60 per cent of the skeletons earlier than the late fifteenth century in the cemetery showed bone changes in the leg compatible with syphilis, a high incidence of disease, but which it has been suggested may be associated more with nutritional or febrile diseases confined within a small and poor community rather than arising from syphilitic infection. See R.S. Morton and S. Raschid, 'The Syphilis Enigma: The Riddle Resolved?', *Sexually Transmitted Infections*, 77 (2001), 322–4.

18. E.H. Hudson, *Non-Venereal Syphilis* (1958); C.J. Hackett, 'On the Origin of the Human Treponematosis', *Bulletin of the World Health Organisation*, 29 (1963), 7–41; H.H. Scott, 'The Influence of the Slave Trade in the Spread of Tropical Diseases', *Transcripts of Royal Society of*

Tropical Medicine and Hygiene, 38 (1943), 169.

19. K. Manchester, *The Archaeology of Disease* (1982), p. 49; S. Zivanovic, *Ancient Disease: The Elements of Palaeopathology* (1982), pp. 232–4.

20. T. Sydenham, 'History and Cure of the French Pox', in *Works* (1729), p. 248.

21. H. Miller, *Secrets of the Dead* (2000), pp. 183–4.

22. D. Barlow, '*Neisseria gonorrhoea*', in Ledingham and Warrell (eds), *Oxford Concise Textbook of Medicine*, pp. 1599–602.

23. W. Osler, 'The Anti-Venereal Campaign', *Transactions of the Medical Society of London*, 11 (1917), 290.

24. B. Halioua and B. Ziskind, *Medicine in the Days of the Pharaohs* (2005), p. 177. Bruno Halioua believes that gonorrhoea was prevalent in ancient Egypt and ancient Israel (personal communication to the author, 2005). There is no palaeopathological evidence of syphilis from this period.

25. Leviticus, 15: 2–33.

26. See Hippocrates, 'Epidemics III', *Hippocratic Writings* (1978), pp. 121–2, 138; *ibid.*, 'Aphorisms', 3: 21, p. 215; Galen, *Selected Works*, tr. P.N. Singer (1997), 202–89.

27. J. Fabricius, *Syphilis in Shakespeare's England* (1994), pp. 122–3.

28. Corradi, 'Nuovi Documenti', p. 361.

29. B. Zambotti, 'Diario', ed. G. Pardi, in *Rerum Italicarum Scriptores*, 24/7 (1934–7), 267.

30. S. dei Conti da Foligno, *Le Storie de suoi Tempi* (1883), vol. 2, p. 272.

31. *Ibid.*, p. 273.

32. F. Materrazo, 'Cronaca della Città di Perugia', in A. Fabretti (ed.), *Archivo Storico Italiano*, ser. 1, 16/2 (1851), 32–6.

33. 'Cronica Bianchi' in A. Corradi, 'Nuovi Documenti', p. 344.

34. The painting is in Kupferstichkabinett, Kunstmuseum, Basle. See Hale, *The Civilization of Europe in the Renaissance*, p. 554.

35. R.S. Morton, *Venereal Diseases* (1974), pp. 24–5.

36. *Ibid.*, p. 556.

37. T. di Silvestro, 'Diario', ed. L. Fumi, *Rerum Italicarum Scriptores*, Bologna, 15/5 (1925), 69.

38. *Ibid.*, 101.

39. L. Landucci, *Diario* (1883), p. 141.

40. S. dei Conti da Foligno, *Le Storie*, vol. 2, p. 272; Arrizabalaga, Henderson and French, *The Great Pox*, p. 28.

41. G. Torella, *Tractatus* (1497), fos c4^v–d2^v.

42. J. Cattaneo, *Opus de Morbo Gallico*, Genoa, 1522, c.12^r.

43. F. Bacon, *Works* (1857–74), vol. 2, pp. 347–8.

44. D. MacCulloch, *Reformation* (2003), pp. 94–5.

45. J. Calvin, sermon 157 on Deuteronomy 28: 25–9, *Opera omnia quae supersunt* (1863), p. 404.

46. M. Harrison, *Disease and the Modern World* (2004), p. 37.

47. P.A. Russell, 'Syphilis', *Archive for Reformation History*, 80 (1989), 294.

48. J. Grünpeck, *Tractus de Pestilentia Scorra sive mala de Franzos* (1496).

49. *Ibid.*, chapter 10; Arrizabalaga, Henderson and French, *The Great Pox*, pp. 107–12.

50. G. Pico della Mirandola, *Disputationes adversus Astrologiam Divinatricem* (1496), ed. E. Garin (1946), vol. 1, pp. 60–6.

51. M. Sanudo, *I Diarii* (1879), vol. 1, pp. 233–4; Giovanni Portoveneri, 'Memoriale' in *Archivo Storico Italiano*, ser. 1, 6/12 (1845), 338.

52. Materrazo, 'Cronaca', 36.

53. F. Cartwright and M. Biddiss, *Disease and History* (2004), p. 56.

54. Arrizabalaga, Henderson and French, *The Great Pox*, p. 35.

55. Quétel, *History of Syphilis*, pp. 12, 24–5.

56. J.D. Comrie, *History of Scottish Medicine* (1932), vol. 1, p. 200.

57. Harrison, *Disease and the Modern World*, p. 38.

58. M. de Montaigne, *Journal de Voyage en Italie par la Suisse et l'Allemagne en 1580 et 1581* (1942), p. 10.

59. G. Torella, *Dialogus de Dolore cum Tractatu de Ulceribus in Pudendagra Evenire Solitis* (1500), sig. d4ᵛ.

60. MacCulloch, *Reformation*, p. 632.

61. *Troilus and Cressida*, 5. 10.55–7.

62. 'Goosey, Goosey, Gander, whither shall I wander? Upstairs and downstairs and in my lady's chamber.' The words of the nursery rhyme might be seen to have a double meaning that could be applicable to syphilis, but Iona and Peter Opie do not record the rhyme before the late eighteenth century: I. and P. Opie (ed.), *The Oxford Dictionary of Nursery Rhymes* (1997), pp. 223–6.

63. Fabricius, *Syphilis in Shakespeare's England*, pp. 60–2.

64. J.F. Larkin and P.L. Hughes (eds), *Tudor Royal Proclamations* (1964), vol. 1, pp. 365–6.

65. N. Orme, 'The Reformation and the Red Light', *History Today*, 37 (March 1987), 36–41.

66. Piero di Marco Parenti, 'Istorie', in A. Corradi, 'Nuovi Documenti', p. 342.

67. D. Gentilcore, *Healers and Healing* (1998), pp. 126–8.

68. MacCulloch, *Reformation*, p. 631.

69. Arrizabalaga, Henderson and French, *The Great Pox*, pp. 173–6.

70. *Ibid.*, p. 172.

71. W. Clowes, *A Brief and Necessary Treatise Touching the Cure of the Disease Now Usually Called* Lues Venerea, *by Unctions and Other Approved Ways of Curing* (1596, repr. 1945), pp. 151–2.

72. Dürer, who had sketched a syphilitic man on the first appearance of the disease, also painted St Job with skin eruptions in a painting now at the Städel Gallery, Frankfurt.

73. Job 2: 7–8, 7: 5, 19: 17–20, 30: 30.

74. Arrizabalaga, Henderson and French, *The Great Pox*, p. 52; P. Moroni, 'Origins and Development of Bologna's Dermatological School', *Acta Dermatovenerologica Alpina, Pannonica et Edriatica*, 10/2 (2001), 1–7.

75. M. Pelling, 'Appearance and Reality: Barber-Surgeons, the Body and

Venereal Disease in Early Modern London', in A.L. Beier and R. Finlay (eds), *The Making of the Modern Metropolis* (1986), pp. 97, 106.

76. M.B. Honeybourne, 'The Leper Hospitals of the London Area', *Transactions of the London and Middlesex Archaeological Society*, 21/1 (1963), 3–61.

77. See Galen, *Selected Works*, pp. 202–89.

78. K. Schellig, *In Pustulas Malus Morbum quem Malum de Francia Vulgus Appelat que sunt de Genere Fornicarum* (1495–6).

79. Leoniceno, *Libellus de Epidemica quam Vulgo Morbum Gallicum Vocant* (1497), sig. a3ᵛ.

80. Hippocrates, 'Epidemics III', pp. 121–2, 138; 'Aphorisms', 3: 21, p. 215.

81. Leoniceno, *Libellus de Epidemica*, sigs d2ᵛ–d3ʳ.

82. Pliny the Elder, *Natural History* (1991), 26: 1–4, pp. 244–5.

83. Cited in A. Tosti, *Storie all' Ombra del Malfrancese* (1992), p. 56.

84. Torella, *Tractatus*, sigs c3ᵛ, d2ʳ, e2ʳ, f3ʳ; *Dialogus*, sig. e2ʳ.

85. Clowes, *A Brief and Necessary Treatise*, pp. 160–1.

86. R.S. Munger, 'Guaiacum, the Holy Tree from the New World', *Journal of the History of Medicine*, 4 (1949), 202.

87. U. von Hutten, *De Guaiaci Medicina et Morbo Gallico* (1519), sig. a4ᵛ, b1ᵛ, d3ʳ.

88. U. von Hutten, *Of the Wood Called Guaiacum that Healeth the French Pockes and the Palsy, Lepree, Dropsy, Fallying Evil and other Diseases*, tr. T. Paynel (1536), p. 15.

89. Von Hutten, *De Guaiaci Medicina et Morbo Gallico*, sigs c1ʳ, d4ᵛ, c3ʳ.

90. See R. Jütte, 'Syphilis and Confinement in Early Modern German Hospitals for Syphilitics', in N. Finizsch and R. Jütte (eds), *The Prerogative of Confinement* (1995). One native of Augsburg, Hans Holbein the Younger, drew a head and shoulder portrait of a young man with his head covered with the pustules of syphilis in 1523, now in the Fogg Art Gallery, Harvard University Museums, Cambridge, Massachusetts.

91. B. Cellini, *Autobiography* (1998), pp. 101, 103–4.

92. J. de Béthencourt, *Nova Penitentialsi Quadragesima, nec non Purgatorium in Morbum Gallicum sive Venereum* (1527), sig. ovʳ–oviʳ.

93. A. Arber, *Herbals, their Origin and Evolution: A Chapter in the History of Botany* (1953), p. 255.

94. C. Webster, 'Alchemical and Paracelsian Medicine', in Charles Webster (ed.), *Health, Medicine and Mortality* (1979), pp. 301–34.

95. Paracelsus, *Vom Ursprung und Herkommen der Franzosen sant der Recepten Heilung* (1529).

96. W. Pagnel, *Paracelsus: An Introduction to Philosophical Medicine in the Era of the Renaissance* (1958), p. 24. See also A.G. Debus, *The Chemical Philosophy: Paracelsian Science and Medicine in the Sixteenth and Seventeenth Centuries* (1977).

97. M. Lindemann, *Medicine and Society in Early Modern Europe* (1997), p. 57.
98. J. Fernel, *Universa Medicina* (1643), pp. 433–43.
99. G. Fracastoro, *De Contagione et Contagiosis Morbis* (1930).
100. C. Kidwell, *Pietro Bembo: Lover, Linguist, Cardinal* (2004).
101. G. Fracastoro, *Syphilis* (1984), p. 102.
102. Ovid, *Metamorphoses*, 4: 1–415.
103. *Ibid.*, 6: 190.
104. Fracastoro, *Syphilis*, pp. 76–82.
105. *Ibid.*, pp. 86–100.
106. Fracastoro, *Syphilis*, pp. 56–8.
107. *Ibid.*, p. 131, note on lines 1: 409–11.
108. *Ibid.*, p. 7.
109. F. Lopez de Villalobos, *Summario de la Medicina en Romance Trovado Con Un Tratado Sobre Las Pestiferas Bubas* (1498).
110. G. Fracastoro, *De Contagione* (1930), p. 130.

Chapter Two

1. A.G. Carmichael, 'Syphilis and the Columban Exchange: Was the New Disease really New?', in M.G. Maques and J. Cules (eds), *The Great Maritime Discoveries and World Health* (1991), pp. 187–90.
2. J. Grant, *Natural and Political Observations Made Upon the Bills of Mortality* (1662), p. 24. This underreporting continued well in to the twentieth century. In 1916 the Medical Officer of Health for Essex noted that 'the number of deaths due to syphilis is impossible to ascertain, as syphilis as a cause of death is rarely given on the death certificate', London Borough of Redbridge Local Studies and Archives, Report of Medical Officer of Health for Essex, 1916, p. 34.
3. F. Rabelais, *The Histories of Gargantua and Pantagruel* (1955), p. 268.
4. Cartwright and Biddiss, *Disease and History*, p. 55.
5. The portrait of Battista Fiera by Lorenzo Costa is in the National Gallery, London.
6. Arrizabalaga, Henderson and French, *The Great Pox*, p. 32.
7. *Ibid.*, pp. 44–9.
8. M. Hollingsworth, *The Cardinal's Hat* (2004), p. 16.
9. G. Vasari, *Lives of the Painters, Sculptors and Architects* (1996), vol. 1, p. 747.
10. Torella, *Tractatus*, sigs c4ᵛ–d1ʳ.
11. P. Pintor, *Tractatus de Morbo Foedo et Occulto his Temporibus Affligente* (1500), sig. e1ᵛ.
12. A.S. McNalty, *Henry VIII, a Difficult Patient* (1952), p. 159; J.J. Scarisbrick, *Henry VIII* (1968), p. 625.
13. A. Yanov, *The Origins of Autocracy: Ivan the Terrible in Russian History* (1981).
14. R.S. Morton, 'Some Early Aspects of Syphilis in Scotland', *British Journal of Venereal Diseases*, 38 (1962), 179.
15. See Fabricius, *Syphilis in Shakespeare's England* for analysis of this.
16. *2 Henry IV*, I. ii. 229–32.
17. Rabelais, *The Histories of Gargantua and Pantagruel*, p. 167.

18. James I & VI, *A Counterblast to Tobacco* (1604), sig. b2ᵛ.

19. Quétel, *History of Syphilis*, p. 63; A. Seiler-Baldinger, 'The Pharmacy of the Rain Forests', in R. Pötzsch (ed.), *The Pharmacy: Windows on History* (1996), pp. 45–59.

20. C.R. Hill and R.E.A. Drey, *Drug Jars* (1980), p. 28.

21. W. Buchan, *Observations Concerning the Prevention and Cure of the Venereal Disease* (1796), pp. xvi–xvii; A.P. Luff, *Textbook of Forensic Medicine and Toxicology* (1895), p. 255.

22. B.O. Rogers, 'A Chronological History of Cosmetic Surgery', *Bulletin of the New York Academy of Medicine*, 47 (1971), 265–302.

23. N. Massa, *Liber de Morbo Gallico* (1532).

24. G. Falloppio, *De Morbo Gallico* (1563).

25. Letter to Dr Sydenham from Dr Henry Parham in T. Sydenham, *Works* (1729), p. 244.

26. T. Sydenham, 'History and Cure of the French Pox', in *Works* (1729), pp. 246–7.

27. S. Pepys, *The Shorter Pepys* (1985), 19 September 1664, pp. 426–7.

28. *Ibid.*, 19 March 1665, pp. 476–7.

29. *Ibid.*, 15 January 1665, p. 463.

30. *Ibid.*, 13 July 1667, p. 807.

31. *Ibid.*, 6 April 1668, pp. 901–2.

32. C. Goldsworthy, *The Satyr* (2001).

33. W. Wycherley, *The Country Wife* (1675), in R.G. Lawrence (ed.), *Restoration Plays* (1992), pp. 11–104.

34. C. Tomalin, *Samuel Pepys* (2003), pp. 205–14; L. Stone, *The Family, Sex and Marriage* (1978), pp. 341–50.

35. Pepys, *Shorter Pepys*, 13, 14, 15–16 March 1664, pp. 363–5.

36. E.L. Zimmermann, 'Was Fracastoro the First to Describe Alopecia Syphilitica?', *Janus*, 39 (1935), 105–26.

37. C. Mörgeli, *The Museum of the History of Medicine of the University of Zurich* (1994), p. 88.

38. Sydenham, 'History and Cure of the French Pox', p. 262.

39. *Ibid.*, pp. 252–5.

40. *Ibid.*, pp. 263–4.

41. J. Astruc, *De Morbis Venereis* (1736).

42. N. Andry, *De la Génération des Vers dans le Corps de l'Homme* (1700); A. Deidier, *Dissertation Médicinale sur les Maladies Vénériennes* (1735).

43. P.-J. Barthez, *Nouveaux Eléments de la Science de l'Homme* (1778).

44. J. Hunter, *A Treatise on the Venereal Disease* (1787).

45. G. Morgagni, *De Sedibus et Causis Morborum* (1761).

46. One of the first medical texts to use the word syphilis was D. Turner, *Syphilis: A Practical Dissertation on the Venereal Disease* (1727).

47. e.g. J. Gautier D'Argoty, *Exposition Anatomique des Maux Vénériens sur les Parties de l'Homme et les Remèdes les Plus Usités* (1773).

48. The best collection of anatomical waxworks is at La Specola in Florence, although some models from the collection of comparative anatomical specimens and microscopic preparations are held

in the Pathology and Anatomy Institute of the University of Florence, and models of abnormal births can be seen at the Museum of the History of Science in Florence. The best and most complete collection of copies of the La Specola waxes, commissioned by the Emperor Joseph II, brother of the Grand Duke Peter Leopold of Tuscany, can be seen at the Josephinum in Vienna.

49. B. Lanza *et al.*, *Le Cere Anatomiche della Specola* (1997), pp. 73–5, 79, 235; M. von Düring, G. Didi-Huberman and M. Poggessi, *Encyclopaedia Anatomica: A Complete Collection of Anatomical Waxes* (2004), pp. 20–7, 65.

50. G. Swarzenski, 'Un Quadro di Luca Giordano in Francoforte sul Meno', *Bolletino d'Arte* (July 1922), 17–21; R. Wrebenwein, 'Luca Giordano: Kampf der Tugend gegen das Laster', *Entdecklungen in Hessener Museen* (1985), pp. 218–21.

51. J.F. Conway, 'Syphilis and Bronzino's London Allegory', *Journal of the Warburg and Courtauld Institutes*, 45 (1986), 250–5; R. Bolton, *A Brief History of Painting* (2004), pp. 56–7.

52. John Hunter's patients treated for sexual transmitted infections included prostitutes and their clients, servants and their masters, military officers and rank and file soldiers, husbands and wives, clergymen, surgeons and clergymen, J. Hunter, *Case Books* (1993), pp. 252, 260–1, 266, 267, 269.

53. Hester Thrale, cited in J. Peakman, *Lascivious Bodies* (2004), pp. 21–2.

54. Ned Ward, cited in *ibid.*, p. 20.

55. Lord Chesterfield, *Letters to his Son* (1992), p. 213.

56. Richard Lassels, *The Voyage of Italy* (1670), quoted in B. Redford, *Venice and the Grand Tour* (1996), p. 21.

57. Redford, *ibid.*, pp. 118–20.

58. J. Black, *Italy and the Grand Tour* (2003), pp. 118–21.

59. F. Murray, *Memoirs of the Celebrated Miss Fanny Murray* (1759), p. 113.

60. D. Defoe, *Roxana* (1996), p. 336.

61. L.E. Merians, *The Secret Malady* (1996), p. 149.

62. Peakman, *Lascivious Bodies*, p. 24.

63. J. Marten, *Venereal Disease* (1704), p. 68.

64. See L. Moore (ed.), *Con Men and Cutpurses* (2001), pp. 175–7.

65. P. Martin, *Life of James Boswell* (1999), p. 75.

66. J. Boswell, *The Essential Boswell* (2003), 14 December 1762, p. 15.

67. *Ibid.*, 19 January 1763, p. 33.

68. *Ibid.*, 20 January 1763, p. 33.

69. *Ibid.*, 20 January 1763, p. 36.

70. *Ibid.*, 20 January 1763, pp. 34–6.

71. *Ibid.*, 22 January 1763, pp. 37–8.

72. *Ibid.*, 25 March 1763, p. 45.

73. *Ibid.*, 31 March 1763, pp. 45–6.

74. *Ibid.*, 8 March 1767, p. 129.

75. *Ibid.*, 28 December 1776, p. 224.

76. G. Casanova, *Histoire de Ma Vie* (1993), vol. 3, p. 637.

77. *Ibid.*, vol. 1, p. 139.

78. *Ibid.*, vol. 2, p. 365.

79. *Ibid.*, vol. 10, p. 329.

80. Stone, *The Family, Sex and Marriage*, pp. 334, 380.

81. J.-J. Rousseau, *Émile* (1911), p. 299.
82. Genesis 38: 9.
83. S.A.A.D. Tissot, *Onanism* (1756), p. 152.
84. S. Watts, *Epidemics and History* (1997), p. 144.
85. D. Turner, *Syphilis: A Practical Dissertation on the Venereal Disease* (1727).
86. R. Porter, *Quacks* (2003), pp. 212–13.
87. BL, C112, collection of 185 advertisements, fo. 9, 2.
88. *Ibid.*, fo. 9, 93.
89. BL, 551, collection of 231 advertisements, a.32, 14.
90. BL C112, fo. 9, 42.
91. *Ibid.*, fo. 9, 7.
92. *Ibid.*, fo. 9, 159.
93. *Ibid.*, fo. 9, 81.
94. James Gillray, 'Voluptuary under the Horrors of Indigestion', 1792.
95. William Hogarth, *Marriage à la Mode*, plate 3, 1745.
96. William Hogarth, *Harlot's Progress*, plate 5, 1732.
97. R. Porter, *Bodies Politic* (2001), pp. 14–17.
98. R. Lamont-Brown, *Royal Poxes and Potions* (2001), pp. 57, 270.
99. P. Ziegler, *King William IV* (1971), p. 51. William IV as Duke of Clarence would have got such a pure girl had he married Catherine Tylney-Long, the fabulously wealthy heiress whom he wooed but lost to the greater charms of the Duke of Wellington's dissolute but handsome wastrel nephew William Wellesley-Pole. Ironically, the successful wooer was to be suspected of having suffered from syphilis himself and to have passed it on as their only inheritance to his sons by Catherine, whose fortune he had squandered. T. Couzens, *Hand of Fate* (2001), pp. 108, 177.
100. Voltaire, *Candide* (1968), p. 62.
101. *Ibid.*, pp. 63–4.

Chapter Three

1. T. Zeldin, *France 1848–1945: Taste and Corruption* (1980), p. 86.
2. J. Harvey, *Men in Black* (1995); T. Edwards, *Men in the Mirror* (1997), pp. 18–22.
3. A. Mearns, *The Bitter Cry of Outcast London*, in P. Keating (ed.), *Into Unknown England* (1976), p. 99.
4. *Ibid.*, p. 98.
5. W. Booth, *In Darkest England and the Way Out* (1890), p. 51.
6. *Ibid.*, p. 54.
7. *Ibid.*, p. 53.
8. K. Hughes, *The Short Life and Long Times of Mrs Beeton* (2005), p. 319.
9. T.J. Wyke, 'The Manchester and Salford Lock Hospital 1818–1917', *Medical History*, 19 (1975), 75.
10. M.W. Adler, 'The Terrible Peril', *British Medical Journal*, 281 (1980), 206.
11. *Ibid.*, 206.
12. A.E. Clarke-Kennedy, *London Pride* (1979), pp. 24, 31.
13. e.g. Glasgow (1805), Newcastle (1813), Manchester (1819), Liverpool (1834), Leeds (1842), Bristol (1870) and Brighton (1881).

See H. Richardson (ed.), *English Hospitals 1660–1948* (1998), pp. 118–20.

14. J. Bettley, 'Post Voluptatem Misericordia: The Rise and Fall of the London Lock Hospitals', *London Journal*, 10/2 (1984), 167–75; D.I. Williams, *The London Lock* (1999), pp. 12–14.
15. *Ibid.*, p. 27.
16. *Ibid.*, p. 21.
17. *Ibid.*, pp. 38, 57–8.
18. TNA: PRO CO 273/203, Max F. Simon to Colonial Secretary, 17 April 1895.
19. *Ibid.*, memorandum from Edward Fairfield, 24 May 1895.
20. Williams, *The London Lock*, p. 68. The majority of the male patients at the same time were bachelors aged around 30 and employed as clerks, small tradesmen or labourers.
21. Quétel, *History of Syphilis*, pp. 103–5.
22. N. Restif de la Bretonne, *La Pornographe* (1769), p. 45.
23. A.J.B. Parent-Duchâtelet, *De la prostitution dans la ville de Paris* (1836), vol. 2, pp. 93–5.
24. R. Thomson, P.D. Cate and M.W. Chaplin, *Toulouse-Lautrec and Montmartre* (2005), pp. 208, 223. The painting, *Medical Inspection (Rue des Moulins)*, 1894, is in the National Gallery, Washington DC.
25. T. Zeldin, *France 1848–1945: Ambition and Love* (1979), pp. 307–8.
26. Parent-Duchâtelet, *De la Prostitution*, vol. 2, p. 338.
27. *Ibid.*, pp. 275, 283.
28. TNA: PRO ADM 116/26, contagious diseases acts in force in foreign countries, 1881.
29. W. Acton, 'Observations on Venereal Disease', *Lancet*, 2 (1846), 369.
30. W. Acton, *Prostitution Considered* (1857).
31. Royal Commission on the Health of the Army, PP, 1857, XVIII, 15.
32. TNA: PRO WO 33/17A, 'Report of Committee to Enquire into the Treatment and Prevention of Venereal Diseases in the Army and Navy', 1864, p. 149.
33. TNA: PRO WO 33/12, 'Report of the Committee to Enquire into the Prevalence of Venereal Diseases in the Army and Navy', 1862.
34. 'Editorial', *Lancet*, 2 (1862), 465.
35. TNA: PRO WO 33/12, evidence of Dr W.C. Maclean in 'Report of the Committee to Enquire into the Prevalence of Venereal Diseases in the Army and Navy', 1862.
36. *Daily News*, 2 July 1864.
37. 'Venereal Disease in the Army and Navy', *Lancet*, 1 (1864), 327–9.
38. Portsmouth, Plymouth, Woolwich, Chatham, Sheerness, Aldershot, Colchester, Shorncliffe, Curragh, Cork and Queenstown.
39. *An Act for the Prevention of Contagious Diseases at Certain Naval and Military Stations*, 29 July 1864, 27 & 28 Vic. c.85.
40. *An Act to amend the Contagious Diseases Act 1866*, 11 August 1869, 32 & 33 Vic. c.96; the additional towns were Dover, Gravesend, Maidstone, Windsor, Dartmouth, Southampton, Winchester.

41. 'Editorial', *Lancet*, 2 (1864), 101.
42. H. Markham, 'Editorial', *British Medical Journal*, 2 (1864), 425.
43. TNA: PRO WO 33/17A, 'Report of Committee to Enquire into the Treatment and Prevention of Venereal Diseases in the Army and Navy', 1864, p. 141.
44. *Ibid.*, pp. 143–7.
45. *Ibid.*, p. 144.
46. *Ibid.*, p. 149.
47. *Ibid.*, p. 151.
48. Zeldin, *France 1848–1945: Ambition and Love*, p. 306.
49. Thomas Wakely quoted in T. Fisher, *Prostitution and the Victorians* (1997), p. 71.
50. 'Report of Epidemiological Society', *Lancet*, 1 (1865), 235.
51. 'International Medical Congress', *British Medical Journal*, 2 (1867), 212.
52. *British Medical Journal*, 2 (1867), 527, 560, 582, 591.
53. B. Hill, *Syphilis and Local Contagious Disorders* (1868).
54. B. Hill, 'The Venereal Disease among Prostitutes in London', *British Medical Journal*, 2 (1868), 505–6.
55. TNA: PRO WO 33/17A, 'Report of Committee to Enquire into the Treatment and Prevention of Venereal Diseases in the Army and Navy', 1864, p. 142.
56. Report of the Royal Commission upon the Administration and Operation of the Contagious Diseases Act, C. 408, 19, 1871, recommendations, 48.
57. 'Report of the Committee on Venereal Disease in the Army and Navy', *Lancet*, 1 (1867), 184.
58. 'Health Sanitary Commission', PP, 1867, 32: 10.
59. J.R. Walkowitz, *Prostitution and Victorian Society* (1980), pp. 137–47; P. McHugh, *Prostitution and Victorian Social Reform* (1980), pp. 259–62.
60. *Daily News*, 31 December 1869.
61. T. Fisher, *Prostitution and the Victorians* (1997), pp. 100–2.
62. Report of the Royal Commission upon the Administration and Operation of the Contagious Diseases Act, C. 408, 19, 1871, evidence of Josephine Butler, Q. 12, 869–78.
63. *Ibid.*, Q. 12, 683, 12, 905–15.
64. *Ibid.*, recommendations, 48–53.
65. Hansard, 278 (20 April 1883), cols 749–857.
66. *Ibid.*, 303 (16 March 1886), col. 645.
67. F.B. Smith, 'The Contagious Diseases Acts Reconsidered', *Social History of Medicine*, 3/2 (1990), 197–215.
68. A. Patterson, 'Statistics of Glasgow Lock Hospital since its foundation in 1805, with Remarks on the Contagious Diseases Acts and on Syphilis', *Glasgow Medical Journal*, 18 (1882), 414–15.
69. TNA: PRO HO 45/9511/17273A, memorial from JPs of Devonport, Aldershot, Greenwich, Winchester, Portsmouth, Maidstone, Windsor, Canterbury and Gravesend, June 1884.
70. The detention of British women against their will in continental brothels after being lured abroad by promises of marriage or offers of employment.

71. P. Levine, 'Venereal Disease, Prostitution and the Politics of Empire: The Case of British India', *Journal of the History of Sexuality*, 4 (1994), 579–602.

72. E.B. Turner, 'The History of the Fight against Venereal Disease', *Science Progress*, 11·(1917), 83–8.

73. Final Report of the Commissioners, Royal Commission on Venereal Diseases, Cd. 8189, 1916, 188.

74. R. Darby, 'Where Doctors Differ: The Debate on Circumcision as a Protection against Syphilis, 1855–1914', *Social History of Medicine*, 16/1 (2003), 57–78.

75. F.B. Smith, *The People's Health* (1979), p. 303.

76. P. Levine, *Prostitution, Race and Politics: Policing Venereal Disease in the British Empire* (2003).

77. J. Joyce, *Ulysses* (1998), p. 311.

78. B. Stoker, *Dracula* (1993), p. 41.

79. *Ibid.*, p. 104.

80. L. and M. Hutcheon, *Opera: Desire, Disease, Death* (1996).

81. L. Daudet, *Devant la douleur* (1915).

82. R. Schain, *The Legend of Nietzsche's Syphilis* (2001), p. 50.

83. *Ibid.*, pp. 73–4.

84. Letter from Maupassant to Robert Pinchon, 2 March 1877, quoted in Quétel, *History of Syphilis*, pp. 128–9.

85. Quétel, *History of Syphilis*, p. 128.

86. G. de Maupassant, *Boule de Suif* (1984), p. 650.

87. L. Murat, *La Maison du Docteur Blanche* (2001), pp. 327–51.

88. H. de Balzac, *La Cousine Bette* (1984), p. 190.

89. F. MacCarthy, *Byron: Life and Legend* (2002), pp. 134, 335.

90. R. Gittings, *John Keats* (1968), pp. 155–8.

91. M.M. Platts, 'Some Medical Syndromes Encountered in Nineteenth-Century French Literature', *Journal of Medical Ethics*, 27 (2001), 83.

92. C. Pichois and J. Ziegler, *Baudelaire* (1991), p. 98.

93. *Ibid.*, pp. 340–62.

94. I.F. Walther, *Gauguin* (2004), pp. 72–95.

95. O. Wilde, *Complete Works* (1966), p. 167.

96. G. Leroux, *The Phantom of the Opera* (1993), p. 9.

97. S.L. Gilman, *Health and Illness* (1995), pp. 67–70.

98. S. Prideaux, *Edvard Munch: Behind the Scream* (2005), p. 173.

99. Williams, *The London Lock*, p. 110.

100. R.F. Foster, *Lord Randolph Churchill* (1981), p. 218, has suggested that the onset of general paralysis may have been the result of multiple sclerosis or a brain tumour, though it was widely believed that tertiary syphilis hastened his death.

101. This was a view reflected in feminist fiction of the period. See E. Liggins, 'Writing against the "Husband–Fiend": Syphilis and Male Sexual Vice in the New Woman Novel', *Women's Writing*, 7/2 (2000), 175–95.

102. H. Ibsen, *Four Plays* (1981), pp. 89–164.

Chapter Four

1. A. Pope, 'The Second Satire of Dr Donne Versified', l. 47, in *Alexander Pope: A Critical Edition of the Major Works* (1993), p. 359.
2. W. Moore, *The Knife Man* (2004).
3. J. Hunter, 'A Treatise on the Venereal Disease', in *The Works of John Hunter* (1835), vol. 2, pp. 417–19.
4. I.J. Hunter, 'Syphilis in the Illness of John Hunter', *Journal of the History of Medicine and Allied Sciences*, 8 (1953), 249–62; G. Qvist, 'John Hunter's Alleged Syphilis', *Annals of The Royal College of Surgeons of England*, 59 (1977), 205–9; P.J. Weimerskirch and G.W. Richter, 'Hunter and Venereal Disease', *The Lancet*, 1 (1979), 503–4; D.J.M. Wright, 'John Hunter and Venereal Disease', *Annals of the Royal College of Surgeons of England*, 63 (1981), 198–202; Simon Chaplin, Curator of the Hunterian Museum and an expert on John Hunter, states: 'On balance, I think it is probable that Hunter did carry out the experiment on himself' (personal communication to the author, 29 September 2004).
5. J. Foot, '[Review of] Observations on the New Opinions of John Hunter in His Late Treatise on Venereal Disease', *Monthly Review* (September 1788), 302–3; see also J. Foot, *The Life of John Hunter* (1794).
6. T. Brand, *Strictures in Vindication of Some of the Doctrines Misrepresented by Mr Foot in His Two Pamphlets Entitled, 'Observations upon the New Opinions of John Hunter in His Late Treatise on the Venereal Disease'* (1787); C.B. Trye, *A Review of Jesse Foote's Observations on the New Opinions of John Hunter, in His Late Treatise on the Venereal Disease* (1787); H.D. Clutterbuck, *Remarks on Some of the Opinions of the Late Mr John Hunter Respecting the Venereal Disease* (1799); J. Adams, 'Defence of Mr Hunter', *Medical and Physical Journal*, 8 (1802), 12–17; P.A.O. Mahon, *Important Researches upon the Existence, Nature, and Communication of Venereal Infection in Pregnant Women, New-Born Infants and Nurses* (1808).
7. B. Bell, *A Treatise on Gonorrhoea Virulenta and Lues Venerea* (1797).
8. M. Kelly, 'Swediaur: The Vicious Anti-Hunterian Rheumatovenerologist', *Medical History*, 11 (1967), 170–4.
9. P. Labarthe, *Nos médecines contemporaines* (1868), p. 44.
10. P. Ricord, *Lettres sur la Syphilis* (1851), pp. 5–6.
11. P. Ricord, *Traité pratique des maladies veneriennes* (1838), p. 78.
12. *Ibid.*, p. 77.
13. *Ibid.*, p. 101–34.
14. *Ibid.*, p. 134.
15. J. Rollet, 'Études cliniques sur la chancre produit par la contagion de syphilis secondaire, et spécialement sur la chancre de mamelon et de la bouche', *Archives générales de*

médecine, 13 (1859), 129–44, 306–22, 397–417.

16. J.A. Auzias-Turenne, *La Syphilisation* (1878), pp. 5–167.

17. *Ibid.*, pp. 43–5, 118–20, 152–4, 353–6.

18. *Ibid.*, p. 328.

19. See Chapter Six for the story of the Tuskegee experiment in which treatment was withheld from African Americans from 1932 until 1972 to trace the effects of untreated syphilis, without the consent or knowledge of the men concerned.

20. A. Dracobly, 'Ethics and Experimentation on Human Subjects in Mid-Nineteenth-Century France: The Story of the 1859 Syphilis Experiments', *Bulletin of the History of Medicine*, 77/2 (2003), 332–66.

21. A. Fournier, *Traité de la syphilis* (1899, 1901).

22. A. Fournier, *L'Hérédité syphilitique* (1891).

23. A. Fournier, *Leçons sur la syphilis tertiare* (1875).

24. Quétel, *History of Syphilis* (1990), pp. 160–4.

25. J. Hatcher, *Founders of Medical Laboratory Science* (1978), p. 105.

26. Fournier, *L'Hérédité syphilitique*.

27. Williams, *The London Lock*, p. 100.

28. A. Fournier, *Syphilis et Mariage* (1880).

29. A. Fournier, *Prophylaxie de la syphilis* (1903).

30. S. Freud, *On Sexuality: Three Essays on the Theory of Sexuality and Other Works* (1991), p. 161.

31. S. Freud, 'Fragment of an Analysis of a Case of Hysteria', in *The Freud Reader* (1995), p. 214.

32. 'Case of Obsessional Neurosis', in *ibid.*, p. 331.

33. 'Anxiety and Instinctual Life', in *ibid.*, p. 779.

34. R. Koch, 'Die Aetiologie der Tuberkulose', *Mittheilungen aus dem Kaiserlichen Gesundheitsamte*, 2 (1884), 1–88.

35. A. Neisser, 'Über eine der Gonorrhoe eigentumliche Micrococcenform', *Centralblatt für die Medicinischen Wissenschaften*, 17 (1879), 497–800.

36. E. von Bumm, *Der Mikro-Organismus der Gonorrhoischen Schleimhaut-Erkrankungen 'Gonococcus-Neisser': Nacht Untersuchungen beim Weibe und an der Conjunctiva der Neugeboren* (1885).

37. K.F. Kipple (ed.), *The Cambridge Historical Dictionary of Disease* (2003), p. 152.

38. F.R. Schaudinn and P.E. Hoffmann, 'Vorläufiger Bericht über das Verkommen von Spirochaeten in Syphilischen Krankheitsprodukten und bei Papillomen', *Arbeiten aus dem Kaiserlichen Gesundheitsamte*, 22/2 (1905), 527–600.

39. E. Metchnikoff and E. Roux, 'Études expérimentales sur la syphilis', *Annales de l'Institut Pasteur*, 17 (1903), 809–21.

40. A. von Wassermann, A. Neisser, K. Bruck and A. Schucht, 'Weitere Mittelungen über den Nachweis spezifischer luetischer Substanzen durch Komplementbindung',

Zeitschrift für Hygiene und Infektionskrankheiten, 55 (1906), 451–70.

41. A. Fleming, 'A Simple Method of Serum Diagnosis of Syphilis', *Lancet*, 1 (1909), 1512–15.

42. W.D. Foster, *A Short History of Clinical Pathology* (1961), pp. 81–4.

43. H. Ericsson, *Glimpses from Forty Years of Clinical Bacteriology at Karolinska Hospital* (1981), p. 16. My thanks to Per Lundqvist of Ab Biodisk, Stockholm for drawing my attention to this reference.

44. H. Lee, *Lancet*, 2 (1856), 77.

45. Quétel, *History of Syphilis*, pp. 84–5, 116–17.

46. E. Baumler, *Paul Ehrlich: Scientist for Life* (1984); M. Marquardt, *Paul Ehrlich* (1949).

47. See P. Ehrlich, Nobel Lecture 'Partial Cells and Functions, Nobel Lecture, 11 December 1908', in *Nobel Lectures: Physiology or Medicine* (1967), pp. 304–20; C.-R. Prüll, 'Part of a Scientific Master Plan? Paul Ehrlich and the Origins of his Receptor Concept', *Medical History*, 47 (2003), 332–56.

48. Marquardt, *Paul Ehrlich*, pp. 89–91.

49. *Ibid.*, p. 93.

50. *Ibid.*, p. 115.

51. Paul Ehrlich Institut, PEI/S22, Paul Ehrlich's laboratory book of chemical preparations, 1906–11 January 1912.

52. M. Marquardt, *Paul Ehrlich*, pp. 142–4.

53. P. Ehrlich, *Einer Darstellung seines Wissenschaflichen Wirkens*

Festchrift zum 60 (1914), p. 418. Ehrlich's laboratory has been reconstructed in a small museum at the Georg Speyer Haus, Frankfurt-am-Main, although not in the original room.

54. Hydrochloride of dioxy-diamino-arseno-benzene.

55. Paul Ehrlich Institut, PEI/S69, laboratory book of Sahachiro Hata.

56. Georg Speyer Haus, notes from Ehrlich to Hata, 15 February 1909 and 26 June 1909.

57. Paul Ehrlich Institut, PEI/S22, Paul Ehrlich's laboratory book of chemical preparations, 1906–11 January 1912, p. 149, 7 September 1909; PEI/6S65, Paul Ehrlich's laboratory book of chemical preparations, 1910. Paul Ehrlich, *Beiträge zur Experimentellen Pathologie und Chemotherapie* (1909); 'Die Behandlung der Syphilis mit dem Ehrlischschen Präparat 606', *Sonderabdruck aus der Deutschen Medizinischen Wochenschrift*, 41 (1910).

58. P. Ehrlich and S. Hata, *Die Chemotherapie der Spirillosen* (1910), p. 149.

59. Georg Speyer Haus, instructions on injection technique written by Paul Ehrlich and given to Martha Marquardt, undated.

60. Paul Ehrlich Institut, PEI/B2, box of notes on, and photographs of, patients treated with salvarsan in New York, Sarajevo and in the Tropics, 1910–11; PEI/B6, box of photographs of bacterial action of salvarsan on spirochaetes and

album of photographs of patients in a tropical hospital, *c.* 1910; PEI/B10, photographs of plates showing the action of salvarsan on syphilis in patients in Sarajevo and New York.

61. Paul Ehrlich Institut, PEI/B10, case of J.W. Murphy, 13 November 1910–11 December 1910.

62. Paul Ehrlich Institut, PEI/B10, photographs 5–8, documenting case of 'L.B.', 23 November 1910–1 June 1911.

63. Paul Ehrlich Institut, PEI/B2, photograph 24, case of 'L.J.', 3 November 1910–12 June 1912.

64. See Georg Speyer Haus, advert for film on salvarsan shown in Hohenzollern Park, Berlin by the Institute for Medical and Scientific Cinematography, 1910.

65. Georg Speyer Haus, agreement with Hoechst and Casella for preparation and manufacture of sera, May 1907; see also J. Liebenau, 'Paul Ehrlich as a Commercial Scientist and Research Administrator', *Medical History*, 34 (1990), 65–78.

66. Copy of patent 224953 for manufacture of salvarsan, 10 June 1909 at Georg Speyer Haus.

67. Paul Ehrlich Institut, PEI/S59, laboratory book testing toxicity of salvarsan, 1909–10, Hoechst tests, pp. 72–4.

68. Copy of page from day book journal of Hoechst factory recording chemical work under Dr Bertheim, 30 June 1910, at Georg Speyer Haus.

69. Georg Speyer Haus, advert for salvarsan, 1910.

70. Marquardt, *Paul Ehrlich*, pp. 239–48.

71. W.H. Willcox and J. Webster, 'The Toxicology of Salvarsan: Dioxydiamido-Arseno-Benzol (Salvarsan or Kharsivan)', *British Medical Journal*, 1 April 1916, offprint in St Mary's Hospital Archives, DP42/15/20; P.A. Willcox, *The Detective Physician* (1970), pp. 83–4.

72. *Ibid.*, p. 176.

73. *The Times*, 10 April 1922.

74. St Mary's Hospital Archives, DP42/11/4, Sir William Willcox papers, press cuttings book 1909–22.

75. Willcox, *The Detective Physician*, p. 181.

76. Georg Speyer Haus, advert for salvarsan natrium, preparation 1206.

77. J. Wagner von Jauregg, 'The History of Malarial Treatment of Paretic Neurosyphilis', *American Journal of Psychiatry*, 102 (1946), 577–82.

78. J. Wagner vonn Jauregg, 'The Treatment of General Paresis by Inoculation of Malaria', *Journal of Nervous and Mental Diseases*, 55 (1922), 369–75.

79. G. Domagk, 'Ein Beitrag zur Chemotherapie der bacteriellen Infektionen', *Deutsche Medizinische Wochenshrift*, 61 (1935), 250–3; *Chemotherapie bakterieller Infektionen* (1944); 'Further Progress in Chemotherapy of Bacterial Infections: Nobel Lecture 12 December 1947', in *Nobel Lectures: Physiology or Medicine* (1965), pp. 490–529.

80. L. Colebrook, 'Gerhard Domagk, 1895–1964', *Biographical Memoirs of Fellows of the Royal Society* (1964), vol. 10, p. 39.

Chapter Five

1. Quétel, *History of Syphilis*, p. 158.
2. A.M. Brandt, *No Magic Bullet* (1987), p. 47.
3. E. Brieux, *Three Plays by Brieux* (1911).
4. G.R. Searle, *A New England?* (2004), p. 305.
5. See G.R. Searle, *Quest for National Efficiency* (1971).
6. Report of the Inter-Departmental Committee on Physical Deterioration, Cd. 2175, 1904.
7. W.J. Braithwaite, *Lloyd George's Ambulance Wagon* (1957), p. 116.
8. L.W. Harrison, 'Some Lessons Learnt in Fifty Years' Practice in Venereology', *British Journal of Venereal Diseases*, 30 (1954), 184–90.
9. R.W. Johnstone, *Report on Venereal Diseases* (1913).
10. M. Morris, *Lancet* (1913), 1810–11.
11. *Morning Post*, 22 July 1913.
12. *British Medical Journal* (1913), 230–1; *Lancet* (1913), 358.
13. E.B. Turner, 'The History of the Fight Against Venereal Disease', *Science Progress*, 21 (1916), 83–8.
14. C. Pankhurst, *The Great Scourge* (1913), pp. v–xi.
15. Final Report of the Royal Commission on Venereal Diseases, Cd. 8189, 1916, paras 10–11.
16. *Ibid.*, paras 127–32, 136.
17. Williams, *The London Lock*, p. 116.
18. Final Report of the Royal Commission on Venereal Diseases, Cd. 8189, 1916, para. 143.
19. *Ibid.*, para. 144; TNA: PRO MH 55/533, recommendations of Royal Commission on Venereal Diseases re Poor Law administration, 7 March 1916; *ibid.*, letter to Mr Symonds, 17 April 1916.
20. TNA: PRO MH 55/531, Local Government Board minutes, 26 April 1916.
21. Local Government Board, *Venereal Diseases Circular* (1916), pp. 6–7. In practice more patients preferred to attend VD clinics at hospital than consult their own general practitioners (London Borough of Redbridge Local Studies and Archives, *Report of Medical Officer of Health for Essex*, 1935, p. 20).
22. See St Mary's Hospital Archives, SM/AD 35/6/8, report of sub-committee to consider venereal diseases, 26 June 1916, where requests for information by Paddington Borough Council were met with the reply that 'the collection of information necessary to give statistics as to the venereal cases at the Hospital would entail so much labour that it is not possible with the disposal of the staff at the Hospital during the War'.
23. *Ibid.*, SM/AD 35/6/16, report of Medical Committee, 11 December 1916. The First World War was also marked by the further

extension of medical services paid from the public purse to the voluntary hospitals. At St Mary's Hospital, public money was first received from the London County Council in 1914 for the provision of medical services to elementary schoolchildren. By 1920, in addition to the Venereal Diseases Clinic, there was also a Tuberculosis Dispensary and medical services also provided for war pensioners, all receiving public funding. Maternity beds were later funded by the Borough of Paddington. The Venereal Diseases Clinic accounted for the major single share of the £10,789 received in 1920 from public sources. In 1917, when it first opened, the Clinic was in receipt of £1,500 but by 1920 this had risen to £2,700, over double the sum of £1,225 paid to the Tuberculosis Dispensary.

24. *British Medical Journal* (1916), 657.
25. TNA: PRO MH 55/530, note by Arthur Newsholme on the prohibition of advertising of false remedies, 1 November 1916.
26. *British Medical Journal* (1917), 557.
27. TNA: PRO MH 55/530, deputation from Asssociation of Municipal Councils to Lord Rhondda, statement of E.B. Turner, 24 January 1917.
28. *Ibid.*, Sir Hamar Greenwood.
29. B. Towers, 'Health Education Policy, 1916–26: Venereal Disease and the Prophylaxis Dilemma', *Medical History*, 24 (1980), 70–87; S.M. Tomkins, 'Palmitate or

Permanganate: The Venereal Prophylaxis Debate in Britain, 1916–1926', *Medical History*, 37 (1993), 382–98.
30. D. Evans, 'Tackling the "Hideous Scourge": The Creation of the Venereal Disease Treatment Centres in Early Twentieth Century Britain', *Social History of Medicine*, 5/3 (1992), 413–33.
31. *Lancet* (1917), 236–7.
32. St Mary's Hospital Archives, SM/AD 35/6/16, report of sub-committee into venereal diseases, 11 December 1916.
33. Evans, 'Tackling the "Hideous Scourge"', 430–1. The Medical Officer of Health for Essex cynically commented that 'at present the amount of money spent in attempting cures is not justified by the benefit which accrues there from', London Borough of Redbridge Local Studies and Archives, *Report of Medical Officer of Health for Essex*, 1918, p. 19.
34. Private information.
35. See M. Warboys, 'Unsexing Gonorrhoea: Bacteriologists, Gynaecologists and Suffragists in Britain, 1860–1920', *Social History of Medicine*, 17/1 (2004), 41–59.
36. E. Noeggerath, 'Latent Gonorrhoea, Especially with Regard to its Influence on Fertility in Women', *Transactions of the American Gynaecological Society*, 1 (1876), 268–300.
37. Final Report of the Royal Commission on Venereal Diseases, Cd. 8189, 1916, para. 83.

38. National Campaign for Combating Venereal Diseases, *Venereal Disease – Pamphlet* (1920).

39. W. MacPherson (ed.), *History of the Great War Based on Official Documents: Medical Services* (1923), vol. 2, p. 74.

40. Quétel, *History of Syphilis*, pp. 176–7.

41. A. Corbin, *Women for Hire: Prostitution and Sexuality in France after 1850* (1990), pp. 334–5.

42. G. Walker, *Venereal Disease in the American Expeditionary Forces* (1922), p. 85.

43. L.H.D. Sauerteig, 'Sex, Medicine and Morality During the First World War', in R. Cooter, M. Harrison and S. Sturdy (eds), *War, Medicine and Modernity* (1998), pp. 174–5.

44. Quoted, *ibid.*, p.176.

45. *Ibid.*, p. 172.

46. *Ibid.*, p. 177.

47. TNA: PRO CAB 24/45/GT(18)3932, memorandum of Lord Derby, 15 March 1918; CAB 23/5/WC366(18)13, War Cabinet, 18 March 1918.

48. TNA: PRO CAB 23/5/WC366(18)13, War Cabinet, 18 March 1918.

49. M. Harrison, 'The British Army and the Problem of Venereal Disease in France and Egypt during the First World War', *Medical History*, 39 (1995), 133–58. E.H. Beardsley, 'Allied against Sin: American and British Responses to Venereal Disease in World War I', *Medical History*, 20 (1976), 189–202.

50. National Archives, College Park, Maryland, Record Group 165, War Department and General Staff, box 433, syllabus accredited for use in official supplementary lectures on sex hygiene and venereal diseases, February 1918.

51. *Ibid.*, box 426, letter from Hilton Railey to Raymond B. Fosdick, 17 September 1917.

52. *Ibid.*, Record Group 90, Public Health Service, general records, newspaper cuttings collected by Venereal Diseases Division, box 245, 'Keeping Fit, VD Bulletin 1', October 1918.

53. *Ibid.*, 'Keeping Fit', pamphlet *c.* 1918.

54. R.B. Fosdick, 'The Program of the Commission on Training Camp Activities with Relation to the Problem of Venereal Disease', *Social Hygiene*, 4 (January 1918), 76.

55. National Archives, College Park, Maryland, Record Group 165, War Department and General Staff box 426, letter from Hilton Railey to Raymond B. Fosdick, 17 September 1917.

56. *Ibid.*, box 433, syllabus accredited for use in official supplementary lectures on sex hygiene and venereal diseases, February 1918.

57. *Ibid.*, Record Group 90, Public Health Service, general records, newspaper cuttings collected by Venereal Diseases Division, box 245, 'Fit to Fight, the Story of a Motion Picture Drama prepared by the Surgeon General', 1918.

58. Fosdick, 'The Program of the Commission on Training Camp Activities', 76.

59. Brandt, *No Magic Bullet*, pp. 101–3.
60. National Archives, College Park, Maryland, Record Group 120, American Expeditionary Forces, 1917–23, box 5259, 'Something to Think about for Men Going on Leave', 12 April 1919.
61. *Ibid.*, Record Group 90, Public Health Service, general records, newspaper cuttings collected by Venereal Diseases Division, box 245, 'On Guard', *c*. 1918–19.
62. W. MacPherson (ed.), *History of the Great War Based on Official Documents: Medical Services* (1923), vol. 2, p. 126.
63. Sauerteig, 'Sex, Medicine and Morality during the First World War', pp. 179.
64. Walker, *Venereal Disease in the American Expeditionary Forces*, p. 6.
65. TNA: PRO WO 32/11404, conference 10 May 1918, 11 July 1918.
66. J. Cassel, The Secret Plague (1987), pp. 122–3.
67. TNA: PRO WO32/5597, B.B. Cubitt, War Office, to General Officers Commanding in Commands at Home and Districts at Home, 18 March 1916.
68. TNA: PRO HO45/10893/359931, letter from 'chief petty officer on active service', 2 November 1918.
69. Walker, *Venereal Disease in the American Expeditionary Forces*, pp. 10–19.
70. TNA: PRO WO 32/5597, War Office decree, 18 March 1916.
71. Walker, *Venereal Disease in the American Expeditionary Forces*, p. 135.
72. R. Graves, *Goodbye to All That* (1979), p. 209.
73. J. Bourke, *Dismembering the Male* (1996), p. 85.
74. National Archives, College Park, Maryland, Record Group 165, War Department General and Special Staff, box 586, letter from J. Frank Chase to Raymond B. Fosdick, 13 October 1917.
75. Commission on Training Camp Activities, *Keeping Fit to Fight* (1918), p. 4.
76. A. Neilans, 'The Protection of Soldiers', *The Shield*, 1 (1916), 216–23.
77. TNA: PRO MH 55/530, deputation from Asssociation of Municipal Councils to Lord Rhondda, statement of Sir Hamar Greenwood, 24 January 1917.
78. P. Levine, *Prostitution, Race and Politics* (2003), pp. 162–3.
79. TNA: PRO HO 45/10802/307990/7, Defence of the Realm Act 13A, 1916.
80. TNA: PRO HO 45/10802/307990/15E, Defence of Realm Act 35C, 1917.
81. TNA: PRO HO 45/10893/359931, Order in Council, 22 March 1918.
82. *Ibid.*, evidence of National Council for Combating Venereal Disease, 1918.
83. *Ibid.*, letter from 'chief petty officer on active service', 2 November 1918.
84. *Ibid.*, letter from Women's Cooperative Guild, 28 October 1918.
85. *Ibid.*, letter from 'chief petty officer on active service', 2 November 1918.

86. *Ibid.*, letter from Women's Cooperative Guild, 28 October 1918.

87. *Ibid.*, committee of inquiry on Defence of Realm Act 40D, 1918.

88. TNA: PRO MEPO 2/3434, Metropolitan Police figures obtained from study of 2,312 social case sheets at Canadian Hospital, Etchinghill, Lyminge, 25 August 1918. A total of 584 cases of syphilis and 386 of gonorrhoea had been infected by prostitutes and 264 and 1,078 respectively by amateurs.

89. TNA: PRO WO 32/4745, extract from minutes of War Cabinet 465, 28 August 1918.

90. TNA: PRO WO 32/11403, letter from Sir Reginald Brade to May Ogilvie Gordon, president, National Union of Women Workers, 6 April 1918.

91. TNA: PRO WO 32/4745, War Cabinet memorandum prepared by Ian MacPherson, Deputy Secretary of State for War, 26 August 1918.

92. TNA: PRO WO 32/11402, Army Council instruction, April 1918.

93. L.W. Harrison, 'The Public Health Services and Venereal Diseases', *British Journal of Venereal Diseases*, 1 (1925), 12–22.

94. TNA: PRO MH 55/181, report of Committee of Inquiry into Venereal Diseases, 12 May 1923.

95. St Mary's Hospital Archives, SM/AD 2/10, 62, minutes of Board of Management, 25 February 1932; SM/AD 35/14/162, report of Medical Committee, 6 February 1933.

96. TNA: PRO MH 55/199, inspection of Dorchester VD Centre by Colonel Harrison, 24 December 1927.

97. TNA: PRO MH 55/196, note on interview with Mrs Rolfe of NCCVD, 3 July 1923.

98. *Ibid.*, letter from Dr G.D. Kettlewell, 15 August 1923.

99. M. Thomson, *The Problem of Mental Deficiency* (1998), p. 251.

100. PRO, MH 55/196, report on VD in children at Portsmouth, 27 June 1924.

101. *Ibid.*, report on inquiry into congenital syphilis, 1924.

102. PRO, MH 55/181, report of Committee of Inquiry into Venereal Diseases, 12 May 1923.

103. *Ibid.*

104. Lord Willoughby quoting Colonel Harrison in TNA: PRO MH 55/191, notes on deputation from Society for the Prevention of Venereal Diseases to Neville Chamberlain, Minister of Health, 26 July 1923.

105. TNA: PRO MEPO 2/2336, memorandum from Commissioner for Police, 2 May 1921.

106. TNA: PRO MH 55/191, notes on deputation from Society for the Prevention of Venereal Diseases to Neville Chamberlain, Minister of Health, 26 July 1923.

107. L.H.D. Sauerteig, '"The Fatherland is in Danger, Save the Fatherland": Venereal Disease, Sexuality and Gender in Imperial and Weimar Germany', in R. Davidson and L. Hall (eds), *Sex, Sin and Suffering: Venereal*

Disease and European Society since 1870 (2001), pp. 76–93.

108. P. Baldwin, *Contagion and the State in Europe, 1830–1930* (1999), pp. 400–18.
109. TNA: PRO MH 55/1322, note on contravention of 1917 Venereal Diseases Act, 3 April 1934.
110. G.L.M. McElligott, 'The Venereal History: Truth or Fiction', *British Journal of Venereal Diseases*, 8 (1932), 292.
111. 'British Society for Venereal Diseases meeting', *British Journal of Venereal Diseases*, 11 (1935), 40–1.
112. Personal information, Dr A.W. Frankland.
113. Obituary, 'Gerard Legh Malins McElligott', *St Mary's Hospital Gazette*, 78/8 (1972), 27–8.
114. Personal information, Michael Wolach.

Chapter Six

1. 'Remarks by the President in Apology for the Study Done in Tuskegee', Press Release, Office of the Press Secretary, the White House, Washington DC, 16 May 1997. See also *Washington Post*, 17 May 1997.
2. V.N. Gamble, 'Under the Shadow of Tuskegee: African Americans and Health Care', *American Journal of Public Health*, 87/11 (1997), 1773–8.
3. T. Parran, *Shadow on the Land* (1937).
4. National Archives, College Park, Maryland, Records Group 90,

Public Health Services, series 42, Venereal Diseases Division, decimal files 1918–36, Letter from O.C. Wenger to Walter Brunet, 3 April 1926.
5. Parran, *Shadow on the Land*, pp. 284–5.
6. Members included Thomas Parran, Harvard N. Cole of Western Reserve University, J.E. Moore of Johns Hopkins School of Medicine, Paul A. O'Leary of the Mayo Clinic and John H. Stokes of the University of Michigan, some of the leading venereologists of the 1930s. They had the support of the leading medical men of their times, including the venerable figure of William H. Welch of Johns Hopkins and Hans Zinsser of Harvard.
7. Parran, *Shadow on the Land*, p. 285.
8. National Archives, College Park, Maryland, Records Group 90, Public Health Services, series 42, Venereal Diseases Division, decimal files 1918–36, letter from H.S. Fisk to M.M. Davis, 19 July 1929.
9. R.E. Pomeroy, 'Michael M. Davis and the Development of the Health Movement, 1900–28', *Societas*, 2 (1972), 27–41.
10. O.C. Wenger and H.C. Ricks, 'The Public Health Aspect of Syphilis in the Negro Race in Certain Southern States', *Southern Medical Journal*, 24 (1931), 556–61.
11. Parran, *Shadow on the Land*, p. 161.
12. The counties studied were Albermarle County, Virginia; Pitt County, North Carolina; Bolivar

County, Mississippi; Tipton County, Tennessee; Glynn County Georgia; Macon County, Alabama.

13. National Archives, College Park, Maryland, Records Group 90, Public Health Services, series 42, Venereal Diseases Division, Taliaferro Clark files, letter from R.O. Wenger to Taliaferro Clark, 17 February 1931.

14. *Ibid.*, Taliaferro Clark files, Alabama file, 'report of Dr Clyde D. Frost concerning medical conditions in Macon County, Alabama, based on a personal visit during the Spring of 1931'.

15. *Ibid.*, 'report of Dr Clyde D. Frost'.

16. *Ibid.*, Taliaferro Clark files, proposal from Stuart Groves, State Health Officer, for syphilis control demonstration, 7 January 1930.

17. *Ibid.*, 'report of Dr Clyde D. Frost'.

18. Parran, *Shadow on the Land*, p. 167.

19. National Archives, College Park, Maryland, Records Group 90, Public Health Services, series 42, Venereal Diseases Division, Taliaferro Clark files, Alabama files, 'report of Dr Clyde D. Frost'.

20. Charles Johnson, *Shadow of the Plantation* (1934), p. 202.

21. Parran, *Shadow on the Land*, pp. 164–5.

22. National Archives, College Park, Maryland, Records Group 90, Public Health Services, series 42, Venereal Diseases Division, Taliaferro Clark files, Alabama files, 'report of Dr Clyde D. Frost'.

23. Johnson, *Shadow of the Plantation*, pp. 201–2.

24. J.H. Jones, *Bad Blood* (1993), pp. 71–4.

25. National Archives, College Park, Maryland, Records Group 90, Public Health Services, series 42, Venereal Diseases Division, Taliaferro Clark files, letter from Michael M. Davis to Clark, 13 November 1931.

26. *Ibid.*, letter from Clark to Parran, 17 May 1932.

27. *Ibid.*, letter from Clark to Paul A. O'Leary, 27 September 1932.

28. B. Luche, 'Tabes Dorsalis: A Pathological and Clinical Study of 250 Cases', *Journal of Nervous and Mental Disease*, 43 (1916), 395.

29. E. Bruusgaard, 'Über das Schicksal der nicht spezifisch behaldelten Luetiker', *Archive für Dermatologie und Syphilis*, 157 (1929), 309–32.

30. National Archives, College Park, Maryland, Records Group 90, Public Health Services, series 42, Venereal Diseases Division, Taliaferro Clark files, letter from Michael M. Davis to Clark, 13 November 1931.

31. National Archives, College Park, Maryland, Record Group 90, Public Health Services, series 42, Venereal Diseases Division, decimal files 1918–36, Macon County, letter from Dr D.G. Gill, Director of Bureau of Preventable Diseases, Alabama to O.C. Wenger, 10 October 1932.

32. *Ibid.*, letter from R.Á. Vondelehr to T. Clark, 20 October 1932.

33. *Ibid.*, letter from O.C. Wenger to T. Clark, 16 September 1932.

34. *Ibid.*, letter from H.S. Cumming to R.R. Moton, 20 September 1932.

35. *Ibid.*, letter from J.E. Moore to T. Clark, 28 September 1932.

36. *Ibid.*, notes by T. Clark on interview with Drs Moore and Keidel, 26 September 1932.

37. *Ibid.*, letter from J.E. Moore to T. Clark, 28 September 1932.

38. *Ibid.*, letter from T. Clark to Paul A. O'Leary, 6 October 1932.

39. *Ibid.*, letter from T. Clark to Paul A. O'Leary, 27 September 1932.

40. *Ibid.*, letter from O.C. Wenger to T. Clark, 3 October 1932.

41. *Ibid.*, letter from R.A. Vonderlehr to T. Clark, 20 October 1932.

42. *Ibid.*, letter from T. Clark to Michael M. Davis, 29 October 1932.

43. *Ibid.*, letter from R.A. Vonderlehr to T. Clark, 26 October 1932; letter from T. Clark to R.A. Vonderlehr, 31 October 1932.

44. *Ibid.*, letter from R.A. Vonderlehr to T. Clark, 2 November 1932.

45. *Ibid.*, letter from T. Clark to R.A. Vonderlehr, 25 January 1933.

46. *Ibid.*, letter from R.A. Vonderlehr to T. Clark, 7 January 1933.

47. *Ibid.*, letter from T. Clark to R.A. Vonderlehr, 10 December 1932.

48. *Ibid.*, letter from T. Clark to Paul A. O'Leary, 27 September 1932.

49. *Ibid.*, letter from O.C. Wenger to T. Clark, 25 December 1932.

50. *Ibid.*, letter from R.A. Vonderlehr to T. Clark, 17 December 1932.

51. *Ibid.*, letter from O.C. Wenger to T. Clark, 3 December 1932.

52. *Ibid.*, letter from T. Clarke to J.E. Moore, 25 March 1933.

53. *Ibid.* letter from O.C. Wenger to T. Clark, 25 December 1932.

54. *Ibid.*, letter from R.A. Vonderlehr to T. Clark, 12 January 1933.

55. *Ibid.*, notice from Macon County Health Department, 1933.

56. Jones, *Bad Blood*, pp. 127–9.

57. National Archives, College Park, Maryland, Record Group 90, Public Health Services, series 42, Venereal Diseases Division, decimal files 1918–36, Macon County, letter from R.A. Vonderlehr to T. Clark, 8 April 1933.

58. *Ibid.*, letter from T. Clark to R.A. Vonderlehr, 11 April 1933.

59. *Ibid.*, letter from R.A. Vonderlehr to O.C. Wenger, 18 July 1933.

60. *Ibid.*, letter from J.H. Ward, manager of Veterans' Administration Facility, Tuskegee, to T. Clark, 15 June 1933.

61. Jones, *Bad Blood*, p. 111.

62. National Archives, College Park, Maryland, Record Group 90, Public Health Services, series 42, Venereal Diseases Division, decimal files 1918–36, Macon County, letter from R.A. Vonderlehr to T. Clark, 7 January 1933.

63. *Ibid.*, letter from O.C. Wenger to R.A. Vonderlehr, 5 August 1933.

64. *Ibid.*, letter from R.A. Vonderlehr to Eugene H. Dibble, 28 July 1933; letter from E.H. Dibble to O.C. Wenger, 12 August 1933.

65. *Ibid.*, letter from R.A. Vonderlehr to O.C. Wenger, 24 July 1933.

66. *Ibid.*, letter from John R. Heller to R.A. Vonderlehr, 20 November 1933.

67. *Ibid.*, letter from R.A. Vonderlehr to E.H. Dibble, 17 May 1934.

68. *Ibid.*, letter from R.A. Vonderlehr to O.C. Wenger, 24 October 1933.

69. *Ibid.*, letter from R.A. Vonderlehr to J.E. Moore, 14 August 1933.

70. *Ibid.*, 'Narrative Report of Follow-up Work for October 1934' by Eunice V. Rivers.

71. Jones, *Bad Blood*, p. 187.

72. National Archives, College Park, Maryland, Record Group 90, Public Health Services, series 42, Venereal Diseases Division, decimal files 1918–36, Macon County, 'Narrative Report of Follow-up Work for October 1934' by Eunice V. Rivers.

73. E. Rivers, S.H. Schuman, L. Simpson and S. Olansky, 'The Twenty Years of Follow-up Experience in a Long-Range Medical Study', *Public Health Reports*, 68 (1953), 391–5.

74. Jones, *Bad Blood*, pp. 162–4.

75. *Ibid.*, pp. 177–8.

76. *Ibid.*, p. 164.

77. National Archive, South-East Region, Atlanta, Record Group 442, Records of Centers for Disease Control and Prevention, 1921–95, Tuskegee Syphilis Study Records, 1929–72, Ad-hoc committee to examine data from the Tuskegee Syphilis Study and offer advice on continuance of this study, 2 June 1969.

78. *Washington Star*, 25 July 1972.

79. Department of Health, Education and Welfare, *Final Report of the Tuskegee Syphilis Ad Hoc Advisory Panel* (1973).

80. Jones, *Bad Blood*, pp, 217–18.

81. A. Whitman, 'Obituary of Thomas Parran', *New York Times*, 17 February 1966.

82. T. Parran, 'The Next Plague to Go', *Survey Graphic*, 25 (July 1936), 411.

83. *Ibid.*

84. *Ibid.*, 405–11.

85. *Time*, 11 January 1937.

86. National Archives, College Park, Maryland, Record Group 90, Public Health Services, general classified records 1936–44, general VD and VD legislation, box 532, anonymous letter from 'a taxpayer', 25 December 1936.

87. US Congress, 75th Congress, 3rd Session, *Hearings on Investigation and Control of Venereal Diseases*, 12–14 April 1938, p. 55.

88. W.F. Snow, 'Syphilis and Federal Assistance to the States', *Journal of Social Hygiene*, 24 (1938), 417–21.

89. The project in Georgia was recorded in 1938 in a United States Public Health Service film entitled *Three Counties against Syphilis*, partly written by and featuring 31-year-old Leroy Burney, which shows the work of mainly white doctors and nurses with black patients (National Library of Medicine, National Institute of Health, Bethesda, Maryland, WC 160 VC no. 11 1938). The personable and highly presentable young Burney was also to be involved with a 1944 film on the dangers of syphilis entitled *To the People of the United States*.

90. 'Syphilis Tests', *Time*, 31 October 1938.

91. National Archives, College Park, Maryland, Record Group 90, Public Health Services, general

classified records, group 3, States 1936–44, box 120, file 0425, Chicago, Illinois, 'An Evaluation of the Chicago Syphilis Control Program after One Year' by O.C. Wenger, 15 April 1938.

92. *Ibid.*, proceedings of meeting called by the Hon. Edward J. Kelly, 18 January 1937.

93. *Ibid.*, 'An Evaluation of the Chicago Syphilis Control Program after One Year' by O.C. Wenger, 15 April 1938.

94. *Ibid.*

95. *Ibid.*, programme of *Spirochete* by Arnold Sundgaard, Blackstone Theatre, Chicago, 29 April 1938.

96. *Ibid.*, 'An Evaluation of the Chicago Syphilis Control Program after One Year' by O.C. Wenger, 15 April 1938.

97. *Ibid.*

98. S. Poirier, *Chicago's War on Syphilis* (1995), pp. 130–1.

99. National Archives, College Park, Maryland, Record Group 90, Public Health Services, general classified records, group 3, States 1936–44, box 120, file 0425, Chicago, Illinois, letter from R.A. Vondelerhr to David C. Elliott, 28 September 1937.

100. *Ibid.*, letter from R.A. Vonderlehr to O.C. Wenger, 18 January 1939.

101. *Ibid.*, memorandum from Surgeon Albert E. Russell to the surgeon general on his trip to Chicago, 20–25 March 1938.

102. *Ibid.*, 'An Evaluation of the Chicago Syphilis Control Program after One Year' by O.C. Wenger, 15 April 1938.

103. *Ibid.*, Chicago Syphilis Control Program, Annual Report, 1941.

104. *Ibid.*, letter from R.A. Vonderlehr to Clarence H. Payne, 21 March 1939.

105. *Ibid.*, letter from R.A. Vonderlehr to Clarence H. Payne, 5 April 1939.

106. *Ibid.*, 'An Evaluation of the Chicago Syphilis Control Program after One Year' by O.C. Wenger, 15 April 1938.

107. National Archives, College Park, Maryland, Record Group 90, Public Health Services, series 42, Venereal Diseases Division, decimal files 1918–36, box 239, file 417, 'Survey of the Venereal Diseases in the City of Baltimore' by Taliaferro Clark and Lida J. Usilton [1931].

108. National Archives, College Park, Maryland, Record Group 90, Public Health Services, general classified records 1936–44, group 9, general files, general VD and VD legislation, letter from Thomas Parran to Colonel Robert McCormick, 23 December 1937.

109. National Archives, College Park, Maryland, Record Group 90, Public Health Services, general classified records, group 3, States 1936–44, box 120, file 0425, Chicago, Illinois, letter from Mayor Kelly to Thomas Parran, 12 December 1941.

110. Poirier, *Chicago's War on Syphilis*, pp. 58–76.

111. National Archives, College Park, Maryland, Record Group 90, Public Health Services, general

classified records, group 3, States 1936–44, box 120, file 0425, Chicago, Illinois, letter from R.A. Vonderlehr to O.C. Wenger, 14 May 1938.

112. *Chicago Tribune*, 9 February 1938.
113. Parran, 'The Next Plague to Go', 410.

Chapter Seven

1. TNA: PRO HLG 7/756, Health and Local Government, circular letter from Arthur McNalty, Chief Medical Officer, 1 September 1939.
2. *Ibid.*, Ministry of Health Circular 1956, 26 January 1940.
3. *Ibid.*
4. J. Costello, *Love, Sex and War* (1986), p. 126.
5. P. Ziegler, *London at War* (1995), p. 53.
6. At the London Lock Hospital, the average annual number of new male patients was 2,000 throughout the war and rose to 3,408 only in 1946 on the return of demobilised troops. New cases of women rose from 218 in 1940 to 446 in 1943 and 594 in 1945. Williams, *The London Lock*, p. 132.
7. TNA: PRO MH 55/2317 notes of conference at Home Office, 16 April 1943.
8. Private information.
9. Costello, *Love, Sex and War*, p. 126.
10. *The Lancet*, 2 (1942), 18.
11. Wellcome Institute, RAMC 466/48, Royal Army Medical Corps collection, poster 'That's Phyllis, that was', anti-venereal disease campaign among troops in Italy, 1943–4.

12. TNA: PRO HLG 7/756, Health and Local Government, circular from Chief Medical Officer, 20 January 1943.
13. *Ibid.*, Health circular, 16 February 1943.
14. *Ibid.*, letter to W.W. Andrews, 16 February 1943.
15. *Ibid.*
16. *Ibid.*, brochure for *Social Enemy No. 1*, 27 January 1943.
17. TNA: PRO AIR 2/5995, report by Lord Amulree on the incidence of VD in areas visited with Air Chief Marshal Sir Philip Joubert, 16 September 1943.
18. TNA: PRO MH 55/2317, letter from Paul R. Hawley to John P. Douglas, 16 March 1943.
19. *Ibid.*, letter from Richard Law to Osbert Peak, 7 April 1943.
20. *Ibid.*, minutes of Joint Committee on Venereal Disease, 10 December 1943.
21. *Ibid.*, notes on meeting held at Home Office, 29 October 1942.
22. *Ibid.*, notes of conference at Home Office, 16 April 1943.
23. *Ibid.*, notes of meeting held at Home Office, 29 October 1942.
24. *Ibid.*, notes on conference held at Home Office, 16 April 1943.
25. TNA: PRO MH 55/1341, Statutory Rules and Orders, amendment by Order in Council of Defence (General) Regulations Act of 1939, 5 November 1942.
26. *Ibid.*, Ministry of Health circular, 8 January 1943.
27. TNA: PRO MH 55/2317, minutes of Joint Committee on Venereal Disease, 10 December 1943.

28. A.S. Wingfield, 'Twenty Seven Years of Uninterrupted Contact Tracing: The Tyneside Scheme', *British Journal of Venereal Diseases*, 48 (1972), 37–50.

29. J.E. Gordon, 'The Control of Veneral Disease: An Epidemiological Problem', *The Lancet*, 2 (1944), 711–15; Hilda M. Johns, 'Contact Tracing', *British Journal of Venereal Diseases*, 21 (1945), 15–17.

30. TNA: PRO MH 55/2317, minutes of Joint Committee on Venereal Disease, 10 December 1943.

31. Costello, *Love, Sex and War*, pp. 328–9.

32. National Archives, College Park, Maryland, Records Group 90, Public Health Services, classified records, group 3, States 1936–44, box 120, file 0425, Chicago, Illinois, letter from R.A. Vonderlehr to H.N. Bundesen, 25 May 1943.

33. *Ibid.*, general classified records, group 10, National Defence 1940–46, box 722, file 0425, VD 1940–44, letter from R.A. Vonderlehr to surgeon general, 7 December 1940.

34. *Ibid.*, memorandum from Raymond Vonderlehr supporting the May Act, 7 October 1941.

35. *Ibid.*, HR 2475, 'A Bill to Prohibit Prostitutes within such Reasonable Distance of Military and Naval Establishments as the Secretaries of War and/or the Navy Shall Determine to be Needful to the Efficiency, Health and Welfare of the Army and/or Navy', introduced January 1941, passed July 1941.

36. *Ibid.*, letter from Thomas Parran to Pat Cannon, 4 June 1941.

37. T. Parran and R. Vonderlehr, *Plain Words about Venereal Disease* (1941).

38. A.M. Brandt, *No Magic Bullet* (1987), pp. 162–3.

39. See illustrations between pp. 164 and 165 in *ibid*.

40. National Archives, College Park, Maryland, Records Group 90, Public Health Services general classified records, group 10, National Defence 1940–46, box 722, file 0425, VD 1940–44, memorandum from Judson Hardy to R.A. Vonderlehr on VD education in the army and air force medical corps, 3 October 1942.

41. J.T. Boone, 'The Sexual Aspects of Military Personnel', *Journal of Social Hygiene*, 27 (March 1941), 123.

42. National Archives, College Park, Maryland, Record Group 90, Public Health Services, general classified records, group 3, States 1936–44, box 120, file 0425, Chicago, Illinois, letter from R.A. Vonderlehr to Dr I.V. Sollins, 17 March 1942.

43. Costello, *Love, Sex and War*, p. 149.

44. National Archives, College Park, Maryland, Records Group 90, Public Health Services, general classified records, group 10, National Defence 1940–46, box 722, file 0425, VD 1940–44, letter from R.A. Vonderlehr to Dr Lee A. Stone, 3 July 1942.

45. E. Ness, 'Venereal Disease Control in Defense', *Annals of the American Academy* (March 1942), 89–93.

46. E. Ness, 'The New Offensive Along the Police Front, *Journal of Social Hygiene*, 28 (October 1942), 371.

47. TNA: PRO WO 222/1479, conference on VD held at GHQ, 9 December 1939.

48. Quétel, *History of Syphilis*, pp. 207–10.

49. *Ibid.*, pp. 244–5.

50. C. Paul, *Zwangs Prostitution: Staatlich Errichte Bordelle im Nationalsozialismus* (1994).

51. Adolf Hitler, *Mein Kampf* (1992), pp. 224–5.

52. For Nazi medicine and eugenics see Susan D. Bachrach (ed.), *Deadly Medicine: Creating the Master Race* (2005).

53. G.O. Watts and R.A. Wilson, 'A Study of Personality Factors among Venereal Disease Patients', *Canadian Medical Association Journal*, 53 (1945), 119–22; E.D. Witkower, 'The Psychological Aspects of Venereal Disease', *British Journal of Venereal Diseases*, 24 (1948), 59–67.

54. TNA: PRO WO 222/1302, Robert Lees, 'Method of Prevention of Venereal Disease', 14 April 1942.

55. TNA: PRO WO 204/6725, leaflet issued to soldiers, 1944.

56. T.A. Ratcliffe, 'Psychiatric and Allied Aspects of the Problem of Venereal Disease in the Army', *Journal of Royal Army Medical Corps*, 89 (1947), 122–31.

57. TNA: PRO AIR 2/5995, memorandum of Air Council Committee on morals and discipline, 28 September 1943.

58. Obituary, 'Gerard Legh Malins McElligott', *St Mary's Hospital Gazette*, 78/8 (1972), 27–8.

59. M. Harrison, 'Sex and the Citizen Soldier: Health, Morals and Discipline in the British Army during the Second World War', in Roger Cooter, Mark Harrison and Steve Sturdy (eds), *Medicine and Modern Warfare* (1999), p. 235.

60. TNA: PRO WO 222/1302, report of Robert Lees, consulting venereologist, 28 April 1941.

61. TNA: PRO WO 222/12, summary of action and policy 1939–43 by consulting venereologist, August 1943.

62. TNA: PRO WO 204/3015, report on VD in 15th Army by Gordon Cheyne, director of Public Health, 5 December 1943.

63. TNA: PRO WO 204/6725, letter from B.H. Robertson, 13 April 1944.

64. *Ibid.*, note by Robert Lees, 8 April 1944.

65. TNA: PRO WO 204/10571, note on VD from Office of Provost Marshal, Rome area, 13 January 1945.

66. B.P.F. Wanrooij, 'The Thorns of Love: Sexuality, Syphilis and Social Control in Modern Italy', in R. Davidson and L.A. Hall (eds), *Sex, Sin and Suffering* (2001), pp. 137–59.

67. TNA: PRO WO 204/6725, order from HQ 5 Area, 9 March 1944.

68. *Ibid.*, leaflet issued to soldiers, 1944.

69. *Ibid.*, note from Robert Lees, 8 April 1944.

70. Brandt, *No Magic Bullet*, p. 169.
71. TNA: PRO WO 204/6725, note from Robert Lees, 8 April 1944.
72. *Ibid.*, leaflet issued to soldiers, 1944.
73. TNA: PRO WO 222/1302, report of Robert Lees, 28 April 1944.
74. G.L.M. McElligott, 'The Prevention of Venereal Disease', in H.L. Tidy and J.M. Browne Kutschbach (eds), *Inter-Allied Conferences on War Medicine* (1947), p. 264.
75. TNA: PRO WO 222/12, summary of policy and action 1939–43 of consulting venereologist, August 1943.
76. TNA: PRO WO 204/6725, notes on prophylactic treatment, 1944.
77. S. Longden, *To the Victor the Spoils* (2004), p. 76.
78. W. Franklin Mellor (ed.), *Casualties and Medical Statistics* (1972), pp. 119, 192, 240, 242, 246, 264, 282, 334.
79. 'Sulphonamide Resistant Gonorrhoea' (editorial), *Journal of the Royal Army Medical Corps*, 82 (1944), 283–5; Herbert Bell, 'Gonorrhoea in Italy', *Journal of the Royal Army Medical Corps*, 84 (1945), 21–6.
80. H.W. Florey and H. Cairns, 'Penicillin in Warfare', *British Journal of Surgery*, 32 (1944), 110–24.
81. J. Howie, 'Gonorrhoea: A Question of Tactics', *British Medical Journal*, 2 (1979), 1631.
82. A. Fleming and L. Colebrook, 'On the Use of Salvarsan in the Treatment of Syphilis', *Lancet*, 1 (1911), 1631–4.
83. Biomedical Medical Sciences Research Centre Alexander Fleming, Vari, Greece, cartoon by Ronald Gray, *Private 606*, given to Almroth Wright and the Inoculation Department in 1936; K. Brown, *Penicillin Man* (2004), pp. 47–50.
84. *Ibid.*, pp. 63–4.
85. A. Fleming, W.H. Willcox, E. Holland and G.M.L. McElligott, 'Sulphanilamide: its Use and Misuse', *Transactions of the Medical Society of London*, 62 (1939), 19–33
86. A. Fleming, 'Penicillin in Venereal Diseases', *British Journal of Venereal Diseases*, 20 (1944), 133–6.
87. Brown, *Penicillin Man*; K. Brown, 'The History of Penicillin from Discovery to the Drive to Production', *Pharmaceutical Historian*, 34/3 (2004), 37–43.
88. A. Fleming, 'On the Antibacterial Action of Cultures of a Penicillium with Special Reference to their Use in the Isolation of *B. influenzae*', *British Journal of Experimental Pathology*, 10 (1929), 226–36.
89. Brown, *Penicillin Man*; G. Macfarlane, *Howard Florey* (1979); T.I. Williams, *Howard Florey* (1984).
90. National Archives, College Park, Maryland, Records Group 227, Office of Scientific Research and Development, Committee on Medical Research, memorandum on use of penicillin in syphilis by Chester Keefer, 27 October 1943.
91. *New York World Telegram*, 1 May 1946.

92. J.F. Mahoney, R.C. Arnold and A. Harris, 'Penicillin Treatment of Early Syphilis: a Preliminary Report', *Venereal Diseases Information*, 24 (1943), 355–7; J.F. Mahoney, R.C. Arnold, B.L. Sterner, A. Harris and M.R. Zwally, 'Penicillin Treatment of Early Syphilis', *Journal of the American Medical Association*, 126/2 (1944), 63–7.

93. J.E. Moore, J.F. Mahoney, W.H. Schwartz, T.H. Sternberg and W.B. Wood, 'The Treatment of Early Syphilis with Penicillin: A Preliminary Report of 1,418 Cases, *Journal of the American Medical Association*, 126/2 (1944), 67–73.

94. National Archives, College Park, Maryland, Records Group 90, Public Health Service, general classified records, group 9, box 531, file 0425, general venereal diseases, memorandum from W.S. Bean to R.C. Williams, 13 July 1944.

95. J.H. Stokes, T.H. Sternberg, W.H. Schwartz, J.F. Mahoney, J.E. Moore and W.B. Wood, 'The Action of Penicillin in Late Syphilis, Including Neurosyphilis, Benign Late Syphilis and Congenital Syphilis: Preliminary Report', *Journal of the American Medical Association*, 126/2 (1944), 73–8.

96. *Ibid.*, 73.

97. National Academy of Sciences, National Research Council Archives, Institute of Medicine, Committees on Military Medicine, correspondence, penicillin, file 2, letter from J.E. Moore, chairman of sub-committee on venereal diseases, to E.C. Andrus, 13 July 1943.

98. *Ibid.*, VD folder, *Venereal Diseases Bulletin*, minutes of a conference of the penicillin panel of the sub-committee on venereal diseases and committee on chemotherapeutics, 7 March 1944.

99. *Ibid.*, minutes of a conference of the penicillin panel, 14 April 1944.

100. National Archives, College Park, Maryland, Records Group 90, Public Health Service, general classified records, group 9, box 531, file 0425, general venereal diseases, letter from M.R. King, Medical Director of Bureau of Prisons to the surgeon general, 4 July 1944.

101. TNA: PRO WO 222/1300, report of Robert Lees, 13 April 1945.

102. *Ibid.*, report of Robert Lees, July–September 1944.

103. *British Medical Journal* (25 March 1944), 428–9.

104. National Academy of Sciences, National Research Council Archives, Institute of Medicine, Committees on Military Medicine, VD folder, *Venereal Diseases Bulletin*, minutes of a conference of the sub-committee on venereal diseases, 29 June 1944.

105. *Ibid.*, informal memorandum to medical officers in charge of US marine hospitals, second-class relief stations, quarantine and relief stations, 18 October 1944; Record Group 227, Office of Scientific Research and Development, series E-162, records of Executive Secretary, file

79–6, minutes of Committee on Medical Research, 23 September 1943.

106. National Academy of Sciences, National Research Council Archives, Institute of Medicine, Committees on Military Medicine, VD folder, *Venereal Diseases Bulletin*, minutes of a conference of Office of Scientific Research and Development investigators on penicillin in syphilis held at St Louis, Missouri, 18 November 1944.

107. G.L.M. McElligott, 'Venereal Diseases', in A. Fleming (ed.) *Penicillin* (1946), p. 283.

108. TNA: PRO MH, 96/1137, Ministry of Health circular, 24 March 1945; *ibid.*, 30 November 1945.

Chapter Eight

1. BL Add. MS 56222, George Joakimoglou.
2. Ministry of Health, *On the State of the Public Health* (1955).
3. Brandt, *No Magic Bullet*, p. 171.
4. *Ibid.*, p. 171.
5. Ministry of Health, *On the State of the Public Health* (1953).
6. E. Heineman, 'The Hour of the Woman: Memories of Germany's "Crisis Years" and West German National Identity', *American Historical Review*, 101 (1996), 354–95.
7. M. Freund, 'Women, Venereal Disease and the Control of Female Sexuality in Post-War Hamburg', in R. Davidson and L.A. Hall (eds),

Sex, Sin and Suffering: Venereal Disease and European Society Since 1870 (2001), pp. 205–19.

8. TNA: PRO FO 1014/470, conference on VD, 28 November 1947.

9. TNA: PRO FO 938/90, note by John Simpson, 14 January 1947.
10. Brandt, *No Magic Bullet*, p. 170.
11. Quétel, *History of Syphilis*, pp. 246–9.
12. Wanrooij, 'The Thorns of Love', pp. 146–9.
13. R. Castejón-Bolea, 'Doctors, Social Medicine and VD in Late-Nineteenth-Century and Early Twentieth-Century Spain', in R. Davidson and L.A. Hall (eds), *Sex, Sin and Suffering* (2001), p. 63.
14. E. Martinez Alonso, *The Adventures of a Doctor* (1962), p. 164.
15. Brandt, *No Magic Bullet*, p. 165.
16. Ministry of Health, *On the State of the Public Health* (1968).
17. F.J.G. Jefferiss, 'The Return of the Venereal Diseases', *British Medical Journal*, 1 (1962), 1751–3.
18. J.T. Patterson, *Grand Expectations: The United States, 1945–1974* (1996), p. 373.
19. *Ibid.*, p. 358.
20. R.R. Willcox, 'By No Means the Last Word', *St Mary's Hospital Gazette*, 77/7 (1971), 21.
21. B.P.W. Wells and C.B.S. Schofield, '"Target" Sites for Anti-VD Propaganda', *Health Bulletin*, 28/1 (1970), 76.
22. 'VD on TV' (editorial), *British Medical Journal*, 1 (1960), 1121–2.
23. F. McDonald, 'The Problem of the Homosexual with Venereal

Disease', *British Journal of Venereal Diseases*, 25 (1949), 13–15.

24. Ministry of Health, *On the State of the Public Health* (1958).

25. 'Profile: the Special Physicians', *St Mary's Hospital Gazette*, 72/3 (1966), 78–81.

26. M. Waugh, 'Studies on the Recent Early Epidemiology of Early Syphilis in West London', *British Journal of Venereal Diseases*, 48 (1972), 538.

27. Willcox, 'By No Means the Last Word', 21.

28. 'Profile: The Special Physicians', 78–81.

29. Willcox, 'By No Means the Last Word', 21.

30. A. Dalzell-Ward, C. Nichol and C. Haworth, 'Group Discussion with Male VD Patients', *British Journal of Venereal Diseases*, 36 (1960), 106–12.

31. 'The retirement of Dr F.J.G. Jefferiss', *St Mary's Hospital Gazette*, 81/6 (1975), 14–16.

32. R. Lees, 'VD – Some Reflections of a Venereologist', *British Journal of Venereal Diseases*, 26 (1950), 163.

33. R.R. Willcox, 'Immigration and Venereal Disease in England and Wales', *British Journal of Venereal Diseases*, 46 (1970), 412–21.

34. S. Rose, 'Girls and GIs: Sex and Diplomacy in Second World War Britain', *International History Review*, 46 (1997), 146–60.

35. J. Peel, 'The Manufacture and Retailing of Contraceptives in England', *Population Studies* (1963), 122.

36. T. Brown, 'Sheathed in History', *Nursing Standard*, 13/5 (1998), 26–7.

37. Willcox, 'By No Means the Last Word', 21.

38. R.S. Morton, *Sexual Freedom and Venereal Disease* (1971), pp. 190–1.

39. C.B.S. Schofield, *Sexually Transmitted Diseases* (1975), pp. 43–4.

40. W. Darrow, 'Changes in Sexual Behaviour and Venereal Disease', *Clinical Obstetrics and Gynaecology*, 18 (1975), 255–67; G.S. Berger, L. Keith and W. Moss, 'Prevalence of Gonorrhoea Among Women Using Various Methods of Contraception', *British Journal of Venereal Diseases*, 51 (1975), 307–9.

41. B.P.F. Wanrooij, 'The Thorns of Love', pp. 152–3.

42. 'VD on TV' (editorial), *British Medical Journal*, 1 (1960), 1121–2.

43. G.L.M. McElligott, 'Venereal Disease and the Public Health', *British Journal of Venereal Diseases*, 36 (1960), 211.

44. A. King, '"These Dying Diseases": Venereology in Decline?', *Lancet*, 1 (1958), 651–7.

45. A. King, 'Failure to Control Venereal Disease', *British Medical Journal*, 1 (1970), 451–7.

46. TNA: PRO BS 6/1001, evidence of Medical Society for the Study of Venereal Diseases to Royal Commission on STDs, 1976.

47. Willcox, 'By No Means the Last Word', 20–1.

48. R. Catterall, 'Education of Physicians in the Sexually

Transmitted Diseases in the United Kingdom', *British Journal of Venereal Diseases*, 52 (1976), 98.

49. Brandt, *No Magic Bullet*, pp. 176–8.
50. Patterson, *Grand Expectations*, p. 351.
51. Brandt, *No Magic Bullet*, p. 176.
52. 'VD on TV' (editorial), *British Medical Journal*, 1 (1960), 1121–2.
53. G. Rivett, *From Cradle to Grave* (1998), p. 305.
54. M.W. Adler and A. Mindel, 'Genital Herpes: Hype or Hope?' *British Medical Journal*, 286 (1986), 1207–8.
55. S. Turow, *The Burden of Proof* (1990).
56. M.D. Grmek, *History of AIDS* (1990), pp. 1–12.
57. *Ibid.*, pp. 34–6.
58. C. Norman, 'AIDS Virology: A Battle on Many Fronts', *Science*, 230 (1986), 518–21; 'Patent Dispute Divides AIDS Researchers', *Science*, 230 (1985), 640–3; 'AIDS Priority Fight Goes to Court', *Science*, 231 (1986), 11–12.
59. M.W. Adler and I.V.D. Weller, 'AIDS: Sense Not Fear', *British Medical Journal*, 288 (1984), 1177–8.
60. D.J. Jeffries, 'Doctors, Patients and HIV', *British Medical Journal*, 304 (1992), 1258–9.
61. Rivett, *From Cradle to Grave*, p. 392.
62. Brandt, *No Magic Bullet*, p. 189.
63. P. Farmer, 'Pestilence and Restraint: Haitians, Guantanamo, and the Logic of Quarantine', in C. Hannaway, V.A. Arden and J. Parascandola (eds), *AIDS and the Public Debate* (1995), pp. 139–52.

64. Rivett, *From Cradle to Grave*, p. 308.
65. K. Keersmaekers and A. Meheus, 'Epidemiology of Sexually Transmitted Infections and AIDS in Developing Countries', in O.P.A. Arya and C.A. Hart (eds), *Sexually Transmitted Infections and AIDS in the Tropics* (1998), pp. 3–30.
66. V. Berridge, *AIDS in the UK* (1996), pp. 27, 69–70.
67. D. Cohen, A.J. Pinching, A.J. Rees and D.K. Peters, 'Infection and Immunosuppression: A Study of the Infective Complications of 75 Patients with Immunologically-mediated Disease', *Quarterly Journal of Medicine*, 51 (1982), 1–15; A.J. Pinching, T.J. McManus, D.J. Jeffries, O. Moshtael, M. Donaghy, J.M. Parkin, P.E. Munday and J.R. Harris, 'Studies of Cellular Immunity in Male Homosexuals in London', *Lancet*, 2 (16 July 1983), 126–30; A.J. Pinching, J.N. Weber, L.A. Rogers, E.L. Berrie, D.J. Jeffries and J.R. Harris, 'Longitudinal Immunological Studies on a Cohort of Initially Symptom-free Homosexual Men in London with respect to HTLV-III Serology', *Advances in Experimental Medicine and Biology*, 187 (1985), 67–72.
68. D. Evans, 'Sexually Transmitted Disease Policy in the English National Health Service, 1948–2000: Continuity and Change', in R. Davidson and L.A. Hall (eds), *Sex, Sin and Suffering* (2001), pp. 237–52.

69. K. Fenton, A. Nicoll, and G. Kinghorn, 'Resurgence of Syphilis in England: Time for More Radical and Nationally Coordinated Approaches', *Sexually Transmitted Infections*, 77 (2001), 309–10; Public Health Laboratory Service, Department of Health, Social Services and Public Security, and the Scottish Information and Statistics Division, *Sexually Transmitted Infections in the UK: New Episodes Seen at Genitourinary Medicine Clinics, 1995–2000* (2001), p. 16.

70. Osler, *The Quotable Osler*, p. 146.

71. *Independent*, 21 March 2005; *Metro*, 21 March 2005; *Independent*, 25 November 2005. Dr Sarah Gill, associate specialist in sexually transmissible infections at St Mary's Hospital, confirms that complacency is one of the major factors in the resurgence of syphilis and other infections. Gay men are more confident of treatment for HIV and accordingly less concerned about safe sex. Similarly, there has been a rise among the heterosexual population as a result of ignoring the warnings about risky sex (discussion with author, December 2005).

72. *Independent on Sunday*, 13 February 2005. A warning about the dangers of an explosion of sexually transmitted infections as a result of casual attitudes to sex among the young compounded by the decline in government funding for genitourinary clinics was highlighted by the reporter Andy Davis in a BBC documentary, 'Love Hurts', on *Panorama*, broadcast on BBC1, 16 October 2005.

Bibliography

PRIMARY ARCHIVAL SOURCES

British Library, London

Collection of 231 advertisements, BL 551
Collection of 185 advertisements, BL C112
Alexander Fleming papers, BL Add. MSS 56106-225

Georg Speyer Haus, Frankfurt-am-Main (Germany)

Paul Ehrlich papers

Biomedical Medical Sciences Research Centre Alexander Fleming, Vari, Attika (Greece)

Alexander Fleming papers

National Academy of Sciences, National Research Council Archives, Institute of Medicine, Washington DC (USA)

Committee on Chemotherapeutic and Other Agents records
Committees on Military Medicine records
Venereal Diseases Bulletin

National Archives, Washington DC (USA)

Public Health Service records, RG 90
Office of the Surgeon General (Army) records, RG 112
American Expeditionary Forces, 1917-23, records, RG 120
War Department General and Special Staff records, RG 165
Office of Scientific Research and Development, RG 227

Bibliography

National Archives, South-East Region, Atlanta, Georgia (USA)

Centers for Disease Control and Prevention, RG 442

Paul Ehrlich Institut, Langen, Frankfurt-am-Main (Germany)

Paul Ehrlich papers

St Mary's Hospital Archives, London

St Mary's Hospital records, SM/AD
Papers of Sir William Willcox, DP 46

London Borough of Redbridge Local Studies and Archives

Reports of Medical Officer of Health for Essex, 1916–48

The National Archives: Public Records Office, London

TNA: PRO ADM: Admiralty records
TNA: PRO AIR: Air Ministry Records
TNA: PRO CAB: Cabinet papers
TNA: PRO CO: Colonial Office records
TNA: PRO HO: Home Office records
TNA: PRO HLG: Local Government Office records
TNA: PRO FD: Medical Research Council Archives
TNA: PRO MEPO: Metropolitan Police records
TNA: PRO MH: Ministry of Health records
TNA: PRO WO: War Office records

OFFICIAL PAPERS

Report of the Royal Commission on the Health of the Army, PP, 1857, 27
An Act for the Prevention of Contagious Diseases at Certain Naval and Military
    Stations, 29 July 1864, 27 & 28 Vic. c.85
An Act to Amend the Contagious Diseases Act 1866, 11 August 1869, 32 & 33 Vic. c.96
Report of the Royal Commission upon the Administration and Operation of the
    Contagious Diseases Act, C. 408 XIX, 1871
Report of the Inter-Departmental Committee on Physical Deterioration, Cd. 2175,
    1904

Final Report of the Commissioners, Royal Commission on Venereal Diseases, Cd. 8189, 1916

PRIMARY PUBLISHED SOURCES

Acton, William, 'Observations on Venereal Disease', *Lancet*, 2 (1846), 369

——, *Prostitution Considered in its Moral, Social and Sanitary Aspects*, London, Frank Cass, 1857

Adams, Joseph, 'Defence of Mr Hunter', *Medical and Physical Journal*, 8 (1802), 12–17

Adler, M.W. and Mindel, A., 'Genital Herpes: Hype or Hope?' *British Medical Journal*, 286 (1986), 1207–8

—— and Weller, I.V.D., 'AIDS: Sense Not Fear', *British Medical Journal*, 288 (1984), 1177–8

Andry, Nicolas, *De la génération des vers dans le corps de l'homme*, Paris, Laurent d'Houry, 1700

Astruc, Jean, *De morbis venereis*, Paris, P. du Mesnil for G. Cavalier, 1736

Auzias-Turenne, Joseph Alexandre, *La Syphilisation*, Paris, Ballière, 1878

Bacon, Francis, *Works*, ed. J. Spedding, R.L. Ellis and D.D. Heath, London, Longman, 1857–74

Balzac, Honoré de, *La Cousine Bette*, Paris, Livres de Poche, 1984

Barthez, Paul-Joseph, *Nouveaux eléments de la science de l'homme*, Paris, Jean Martel, 1778

Bell, Benjamin, *A Treatise on Gonorrhoea Virulenta and Lues Venerea*, Edinburgh, Watson and Mudie, 1797

Benedetti, Alessandro, *Diario de Bello Carolino*, Padua, M. Cerdonis, 1496

——, *Anatomice sive historia Corporis Humani*, Venice, J. and G. de Gregoriis, 1497

Benivieni, Antonio, *De Abditis Nonnulis ac Mirandis Morborum et Sanationum Causis*, Paris, C. Wechel, 1528

Berger, G.S., Keith, L. and Moss, W., 'Prevalence of Gonorrhoea among Women Using Various Methods of Contraception', *British Journal of Venereal Diseases*, 51 (1975), 307–9

Béthencourt, Jacques de, *Nova Penitentialsi Quadragesima, nec non Purgatorium in Morbum Gallicum sive Venereum*, Paris, Nicolai Savetier, 1527

Bloch, Iwan, *Der Ursprung der Syphilis*, Jena, G. Fisher, 1901–11

Boone, Joel T., 'The Sexual Aspects of Military Personnel', *Journal of Social Hygiene*, 27 (March 1941), 123

Booth, William, *In Darkest England and the Way Out*, London, Salvation Army, 1890

Boswell, James, *The Essential Boswell: Selections from the Writings of James Boswell*, ed. Peter Martin, London, Weidenfeld & Nicolson, 2003

Braithwaite, W.J., *Lloyd George's Ambulance Wagon: The Memoirs of W.J. Braithwaite*, ed. H.N. Bunbury, London, Methuen, 1957

Brand, Thomas, *Strictures in Vindication of Some of the Doctrines Misrepresented by Mr Foot in His Two Pamphlets Entitled, 'Observations Upon the New Opinions of John Hunter in His Late Treatise on the Venereal Disease'*, London, G. Nicol, 1787

Bretonne, Nicolas Restif de la, *Le Pornographe, ou Idées d'un honnete homme sur un projet de règlement pour les prostitutées*, London, J. Nourse, 1769

Brieux, Eugène, *Three Plays by Brieux*, tr. Charlotte Shaw, London, A.C. Fifield, 1911

Bruusgaard, E., 'Über das Schicksal der nicht spezifisch behaldelten Luetiker', *Archive für Dermatologie und Syphilis*, 157 (1929), 309–32

Buchan, William, *Observations Concerning the Prevention and Cure of the Venereal Disease*, London, T. Chapman, 1796

Bumm, Ernst von, *Der Mikro-Organismus der Gonorrhoischen Schleimhaut-Erkrankungen 'Gonococcus-Neisser': Nacht Untersuchungen beim Weibe und an der Conjunctiva der Neugeboren*, Wiesbaden, J. Bergmann, 1885

Caldwell, J.G., Price, E.V. and Schroeter, A.L., 'Aortic Regurgitation in the Tuskegee Study of Untreated Syphilis', *Journal of Chronic Diseases*, 26 (1973), 187–94

Calvin, John, *Opera omnia quae supersunt*, Braunschweig, C.A. Schwetchke, 1863

Casanova, Giacomo, *Histoire de ma vie*, Paris, Bouquins, 1993

Cattaneo, Jacopo, *Opus de Morbo Gallico*, Genoa, B. Silva, 1522

Catterall, R., 'Education of Physicians in the Sexually Transmitted Diseases in the United Kingdom', *British Journal of Venereal Diseases*, 52 (1976), 98

Cellini, Benevenuto, *Autobiography*, tr. George Bull, Harmondsworth, Penguin, 1998

Chesterfield, Lord, *Letters to his Son*, Oxford, Oxford University Press, 1992

Clowes, William, *A Brief and Necessary Treatise Touching the Cure of the Disease Now Usually Called* Lues Venerea, *by Unctions and Other Approved Ways of Curing*, 1596; reprinted, New York, Starnes and Leake, 1945

Clutterbuck, Henry D., *Remarks on Some of the Opinions of the Late Mr John Hunter Respecting the Venereal Disease*, London, T. Boosey, 1799.

Cohen, D., Pinching A.J., Rees, A.J. and Peters, D.K., 'Infection and Immunosuppression: A Study of the Infective Complications of 75 Patients with Immunologically-Mediated Disease', *Quarterly Journal of Medicine*, 51 (1982), 1–15

Columbus, Christopher, *The Four Voyages of Christopher Columbus*, ed. and tr. J.M. Cohen, Harmondsworth, Penguin, 1969

Commission on Training Camp Activities, *Keeping Fit to Fight*, Washington DC, Commission on Training Camp Activities, 1918

Conti da Foligno, Sigismondo dei, *Le Storie de' suoi Tempi dal 1475 al 1510*, Rome, G. Barbera, 1883

Corradi, A., 'Nuovi Documenti per la Storia delle Malattier Veneree in Italia della fine dell Quatrocento alla metà della Cinquecento', *Annali Universali di Medicina e Chirugia*, 269/808 (1884), 289–386

Dalzell-Ward, A., Nichol, C. and Haworth, C., 'Group Discussion with Male VD Patients', *British Journal of Venereal Diseases*, 36 (1960), 106–12

D'Argoty, Jacques Gautier, *Exposition anatomique des maux vénériens sur les parties de l'homme et les remèdes les plus usités*, Paris, J.B. Brunet and Demanville, 1773

Darrow, William, 'Changes in Sexual Behaviour and Venereal Disease', *Clinical Obstetrics and Gynaecology*, 18 (1975), 255–67

Daudet, Leon, *Devant la douleur*, Paris, Charpentier, 1915

Defoe, Daniel, *Roxana: The Fortunate Mistress*, Oxford, Oxford University Press, 1996

Deibert, A.V. and Bruyere, M.C., 'Untreated Syphilis in the Male Negro III: Evidence of Cardiovascular Abnormalities and Other Forms of Morbidity', *Journal of Venereal Disease Information*, 27 (1946), 301–14

Deidier, Antoine, *Dissertation médicinale sur les maladies vénériennes*, Paris, C.M. d'Houry, 1735

Department of Health, Education and Welfare, *Final Report of the Tuskegee Syphilis Ad Hoc Advisory Panel*, Washington DC, Department of Health, Education and Welfare, 1973

Diaz de Isla, Ruiz, *Tractado contra el mal serpentino*, Seville, D. De Robertis, 1539

Domagk, Gerhard, 'Ein Beitrag zur Chemotherapie der bacteriellen Infektionen', *Deutsche Medizinische Wochenshrift*, 61 (1935), 250–3

——, *Chemotherapie bakterieller Infektionen*, Leipzig, Hirzel, 1944

——, 'Further Progress in Chemotherapy of Bacterial Infections: Nobel Lecture 12 December 1947', in *Nobel Lectures: Physiology or Medicine*, 1965, pp. 490–529

Ehrlich, Paul, *Beiträge zur Experimentellen Pathologie und Chemotherapie*, Leipzig, Akademische Verlagsgesellschaft, 1909

——, 'Die Behandlung der Syphilis mit dem Ehrlischschen Präparat 606', *Sonderabdruck aus der Deutschen Medizinischen Wochenschrift*, 41 (1910)

——, *Einer Darstellung seines Wissenschaflichen Wirkens Festchrift zum 60*, Jena, Fischer, 1914

——, *Collected Papers of Paul Ehrlich*, ed. F. Himmelweit, London, Pergamon, 1956

——, and Hata, Sahachiro, *Die Chemotherapie der Spirillosen*, Berlin, Julius Springer, 1910

Ericsson, Hans, *Glimpses from Forty Years of Clinical Bacteriology at Karolinska Hospital*, Stockholm, Karolinska Institute, 1981

Falloppio, Gabriello, *De morbo gallico*, Padua, C. Gryphium, 1563

Fenton, K., Nicoll, A. and Kinghorn, G., 'Resurgence of Syphilis in England: Time for More Radical and Nationally Co-ordinated Approaches', *Sexually Transmitted Infections*, 77 (2001), 309–10

Fernel, Jean, *Universa Medicina*, Geneva, P. Chouet, 1643

Fleming, Alexander, 'A Simple Method of Serum Diagnosis of Syphilis', *Lancet*, 1 (1909), 1512–15

——, 'On the Antibacterial Action of Cultures of a Penicillium with Special Reference to their Use in the Isolation of *B. influenzae*', *British Journal of Experimental Pathology*, 10 (1929), 226–36

——, 'Penicillin in Venereal Diseases', *British Journal of Venereal Diseases*, 20 (1944), 133–6

——, (ed.), *Penicillin: Its Practical Application*, London, Butterworth, 1946

——, and Colebrook, Leonard, 'On the Use of Salvarsan in the Treatment of Syphilis', *Lancet*, 1 (1911), 1631–4

——, Willcox, W.H., Holland, E. and McElligott, G.M.L., 'Sulphanilamide: Its Use and Misuse', *Transactions of the Medical Society of London*, 62 (1939), 19–33

Florey, H.W. and Cairns, H., 'Penicillin in Warfare', *British Journal of Surgery*, 32 (1944), 110–24

Foot, Jesse, '[Review of] Observations on the New Opinions of John Hunter in his Late Treatise on Venereal Disease', *Monthly Review* (September 1788), 302–3

——, *The Life of John Hunter*, London, T. Becket, 1794

Fosdick, Raymond B., 'The Program of the Commission on Training Camp Activities with Relation to the Problem of Venereal Disease', *Social Hygiene*, 4 (January 1918), 76

Fournier, Alfred, *Leçons sur la syphilis tertiare*, Paris, Masson, 1875

——, *Syphilis et mariage*, Paris, Masson, 1880

——, *L'Hérédité syphilitique*, Paris, Masson, 1891

——, *Traité de la syphilis*, Paris, Masson, 2 vols., 1899 & 1901

——, *Prophylaxie de la syphilis*, Paris, Rueff, 1903

Fracastoro, Girolamo, *Syphilus sive morbus gallicus*, Verona, S. Nicolini da Sabbio, 1530

——, *De contagione et contagiosis morbis*, tr. and ed. W.C. Wright, New York, Putnam, 1930

——, *Syphilis*, ed. Geoffrey Eatough, Liverpool, Francis Cairns, 1984

Freud, Sigmund, *On Sexuality: Three Essays on the Theory of Sexuality and Other Works*, ed. Angela Richards, Harmondsworth, Penguin, 1991

——, *The Freud Reader*, ed. Peter Gay, London, Vintage, 1995

Galen, *Selected Works*, tr. P.N. Singer, Oxford, Oxford University Press, 1997

Gordon, J.E., 'The Control of Venereal Disease: An Epidemiological Problem', *The Lancet*, 2 (1944), 711–15

Grant, John, *Natural and Political Observations Made upon the Bills of Mortality*, London, Thomas Roycroft, 1662

Graves, Robert, *Goodbye to All That*, London, Guild Publishing, 1979

Gruner, Christian Gottfried (ed.), *Aphrodisiacus sive de Lue Venerea*, Jena, C.H. Cuno, 1789

Grünpeck, Joseph, *Tractus de Pestilentia Scorra sive mala de Franzos*, Augsburg, J. Schaur, 1496

Guicciardini, *The History of Italy* (1537), tr. Sidney Alexander, Princeton, Princeton University Press, 1984

Harrison, L.W., 'The Public Health Services and Venereal Diseases', *British Journal of Venereal Diseases*, 1 (1925), 12–22

——, 'Some Lessons Learnt in Fifty Years' Practice in Venereology', *British Journal of Venereal Diseases*, 30 (1954), 184–90

Health, Ministry of, *On the State of the Public Health*, London, HMSO, 1953

——, *On the State of the Public Health*, London, HMSO, 1955

——, *On the State of the Public Health*, London, HMSO, 1958

——, *On the State of the Public Health*, London, HMSO, 1968

Heller, J.R. and Bruyere, P.T., 'Untreated Syphilis in the Male Negro II: Mortality during 12 Years of Observation', *Venereal Diseases Information*, 27 (1946), 34–8

Hill, Berkeley, *Syphilis and Local Contagious Disorders*, London, James Walton, 1868

——, 'The Venereal Disease among Prostitutes in London', *British Medical Journal*, 2 (1868), 505–6

Hippocrates, *Hippocratic Writings*, tr. J. Chadwick and W.N. Mann, London, Penguin, 1978

Hitler, Adolf, *Mein Kampf*, London, Pimlico, 1992

Hunter, John, *A Treatise on the Venereal Disease*, London, J. Hunter, 1787

——, *The Works of John Hunter*, ed. James Palmer, London, Longman, 1835

——, *The Case Books of John Hunter*, ed. E. Allen, J.L. Turk and R. Murley, London, Royal Society of Medicine, 1993

Hutten, Ulrich von, *De Guaiaci Medicina et Morbo Gallico*, Mainz, J. Scheffer, 1519

——, *Of the Wood Called Guaiacum that Healeth the French Pockes and the Palsy, Lepree, Dropsy, Fallying Evil and other Diseases*, tr. T. Paynel, London, Thomas Berthelet, 1536

Ibsen, Henrik, *Ghosts*, in *Four Major Plays*, Oxford, Oxford University Press, 1981, pp. 89–164

James I & VI, *A Counterblast to Tobacco*, London, R.B., 1604

Jefferiss, F.J.G., 'The Return of the Venereal Diseases', *British Medical Journal*, 1 (1962), 1751–3

Jeffries, D.J., 'Doctors, Patients and HIV', *British Medical Journal*, 304 (1992), 1258–9

252

Johnson, Charles, *Shadow of the Plantation*, Chicago, Rosenwald Fund, 1934

Johnstone, R.W., *Report on Venereal Diseases*, London, Local Government Board, 1913

Johns, Hilda M., 'Contact Tracing', *British Journal of Venereal Diseases*, 21 (1945), 15–17

Joyce, James, *Ulysses*, Oxford, Oxford University Press, 1998

Keating, Peter (ed.), *Into Unknown England, 1866–1913: Selections from the Social Explorers*, London, Fontana, 1976

King, Ambrose, '"These Dying Diseases": Venereology in Decline?', *Lancet*, 1 (1958), 651–7

——, 'Failure to Control Venereal Disease', *British Medical Journal*, 1 (1970), 451–7

Koch, Robert, 'Die Aetiologie der Tuberkulose', *Mittheilungen aus dem Kaiserlichen Gesundheitsamte*, 2 (1884), 1–88

Labarthe, Paul, *Nos médecines contemporaines*, Paris, Lebigre-Duquesne, 1868

Landucci, Luca, *Diario fiorentino dal 1450 al 1516*, ed. I. del Badia, Florence, G.C. Sansoni, 1883

Larkin, J.F. and Hughes, P.L. (eds), *Tudor Royal Proclamations*, New Haven, Yale University Press, 1964–69

Lees, Robert, 'VD – Some Reflections of a Venereologist', *British Journal of Venereal Diseases*, 26 (1950), 163

Leroux, Gaston, *The Phantom of the Opera*, Ware, Wordsworth Editions, 1993

Leoniceno, Nicolo, *Libellus de Epidemia quam Vulgo Morbum Gallicum Vocant*, Venice, Aldus Manutius, 1497

Local Government Board, *Venereal Diseases Circular*, London, Local Government Board, 1916

Luche, Baldwin, 'Tabes Dorsalis: A Pathological and Clinical Study of 250 Cases', *Journal of Nervous and Mental Disease*, 43 (1916), 395

Luff, Arthur P., *Textbook of Forensic Medicine and Toxicology*, London, Longmans, 1895

McDonald, F., 'The Problem of the Homosexual with Venereal Disease', *British Journal of Venereal Diseases*, 25 (1949), 13–15

McElligott, G.L.M., 'The Venereal History: Truth or Fiction', *British Journal of Venereal Diseases*, 8 (1932), 292

——, 'Venereal Diseases', in Alexander Fleming (ed.), *Penicillin: Its Practical Application*, London, Butterworth, 1946, pp. 279–90

——, 'The Prevention of Venereal Disease', in Henry Letherby Tidy and J.M. Browne Kutschbach (eds), *Inter-Allied Conferences on War Medicine*, London, Staples Press, 1947, pp. 253–5

——, 'Venereal Disease and the Public Health', *British Journal of Venereal Diseases*, 36 (1960), 211

Mahon, Paul Augustin Olivier, *Important Researches Upon the Existence, Nature, and Communication of Venereal Infection in Pregnant Women, New-Born Infants and Nurses*, London, T. Becket, 1808

Mahoney, J.F., Arnold, R.C. and Harris, A., 'Penicillin Treatment of Early Syphilis: a Preliminary Report', *Venereal Diseases Information*, 24 (1943), 355–7

——, Arnold, R.C., Sterner, B.L., Harris, A. and Zwally, M.R., 'Penicillin Treatment of Early Syphilis', *Journal of the American Medical Association*, 126/2 (1944), 63–7

Marten, John, *A Treatise of all the Degrees and Symptoms of the Venereal Disease in Both Sexes*, London, Crouch, 1704

Martinez Alonso, E., *Adventures of a Doctor*, London, Hale, 1966

Massa, Niccolo, *Liber de Morbo Gallico*, Venice, S. Zilettus, 1532

Materrazo, Francesco, 'Cronaca della Città di Perugia da 1492 al 1503', in A. Fabretti (ed.), *Archivo Storico Italiano*, ser. 1, 16/2 (1851), 32–6

Maupassant, Guy de, *Boule de Suif*, Paris, Livres de Poche, 1984

Metchnikoff, Elie and Roux, Emile, 'Études expérimentales sur la syphilis', *Annales de l'Institut Pasteur*, 17 (1903), 809–21

Montaigne, Michel de, *Journal de voyage en Italie par la Suisse et l'Allemagne en 1580 et 1581*, ed. Maurice Rat, Paris, Garnier, 1942

Moore, J.E., Mahoney, J.F., Schwartz, W.H., Sternberg, T.H. and Wood, W.B., 'The Treatment of Early Syphilis with Penicillin: A Preliminary Report of 1,418 cases', *Journal of the American Medical Association*, 126/2 (1944), 67–73

Morgagni, Giambattista, *De Sedibus et Causis Morborum per Anatomen Indagatis*, Venice, Remondiniana, 1761

Morton, R.S., *Sexual Freedom and Venereal Disease*, London, Owen, 1971

Murray, Fanny, *Memoirs of the Celebrated Miss Fanny Murray*, London, J. Scott, 1759

National Campaign for Combating Venereal Diseases, *Venereal Disease – Pamphlet*, London, National Campaign for Combating Venereal Diseases, 1920

Neilans, A., 'The Protection of Soldiers', *The Shield*, 1 (1916), 216–23

Neisser, Albert, 'Über eine der Gonorrhoe eigentumliche Micrococcenform', *Centralblatt für die Medicinischen Wissenschaften*, 17 (1879), 497–800

Ness, Eliot, 'Venereal Disease Control in Defense', *Annals of the American Academy* (March 1942), 89–93

——, 'The New Offensive along the Police Front', *Journal of Social Hygiene*, 28 (October 1942), 371

Nobel Foundation, *Nobel Lectures: Medicine or Physiology 1922–41*, Amsterdam, Elsevier, 1965

——, *Nobel Lectures: Medicine or Physiology 1901–1921*, Amsterdam, Elsevier, 1967

Noeggerath, Emil, 'Latent Gonorrhoea, Especially with Regard to its Influence on Fertility in Women', *Transactions of the American Gynaecological Society*, 1 (1876), 268–300

Bibliography

Norman, Colin, 'AIDS Virology: A Battle on Many Fronts', *Science*, 230 (1985), 518–21

——, 'Patent Dispute Divides AIDS Researchers', *Science*, 230 (1985), 640–3

——, 'AIDS Priority Fight Goes to Court', *Science*, 231 (1986), 11–12

Olansky, S., Schuman, S.H., Peters, J.J., Smith, C.A. and Rambo, D.S., 'Untreated Syphilis in the Male Negro: 20 Years of Clinical Observation of Untreated Syphilitic and Presumably Nonsyphilitic Groups', *Journal of Chronic Diseases*, 4 (1956), 177–85

Olansky, S., Harrison, A., Cutler J.C. and Price, E.V., 'Untreated Syphilis in the Male Negro: 22 Years of Serological Study in a Selected Syphilis Study Group', *Archives of Dermatology*, 73 (1956), 516–22

Osler, William, *The Principles and Practice of Medicine*, 8th edn, New York, D. Appleton and Co., 1914

——, 'The Campaign against Syphilis', *Lancet* 1 (1917), 789

——, 'The Anti-Venereal Campaign', *Transactions of the Medical Society of London*, 11 (1917), 290–315

——, 'Internal Medicine as a Vocation', in *Aequanimitas: With Other Addresses to Medical Students, Nurses and Practitioners of Medicine*, 3rd edn, Philadelphia, P. Blakiston, 1932, pp. 131–46

——, *The Quotable Osler*, ed. Mark E. Silverman, T. Jock Murray and Charles S. Bryan, Philadelphia, American College of Physicians, 2003

Pankhurst, Christabel, *The Great Scourge and How to End It*, London, Emily Pankhurst, 1913

Paracelsus (von Hohenheim, Theophrastus), *Vom Ursprung und Herkommen der Franzosen sant der Recepten Heilung*, Nuremburg, F. Peypus, 1529

——, *Theophrast von Hohenheim gennant Paracelsus Sämtliche Werke*, ed. Karl Sudhoff and Wilhelm Matthiessen, Munich, R. Oldenbourg, 1922–33

Parent-Duchâtelet, Alexandre J.B., *De la prostitution dans la ville de Paris*, Paris, J.-B. Baillière, 1836

Parran, Thomas, 'The Next Plague to Go', *Survey Graphic*, 25 (July 1936), 405–11

——, *Shadow on the Land: Syphilis*, New York, Reynal and Hitchcock, 1937

—— and Vonderlehr, Raymond, *Plain Words about Venereal Disease*, New York, Reynal and Hitchcock, 1941

Patterson, Alexander, 'Statistics of Glasgow Lock Hospital since its Foundation in 1805, with Remarks on the Contagious Diseases Acts and on Syphilis', *Glasgow Medical Journal*, 18 (1882), 414–15

Peake, John '[Review of] a Candid Review of Jesse Foot's Observations on the New Opinions of John Hunter, in His Late Treatise on the Venereal Disease, Ending with the Subject of Gonorrhoea', *Analytical Review*, 2 (1788), 60

Pepys, Samuel, *The Shorter Pepys*, ed. Robert Latham, London, Bell and Hyman, 1985

Pesare, P.J., Bauer T.J. and Gleeson, G.A., 'Untreated Syphilis in the Male Negro: Observation of Abnormalities over 16 Years', *Journal of Syphilis, Gonorrhoea and Venereal Diseases*, 34 (1950), 201–13

Peters, J.J., Peers, J.H., Olansky, S., Cutler, J.C. and Gleeson, G.A., 'Untreated Syphilis in the Male Negro: Findings in Syphilitic and Nonsyphilitic Patients', *Journal of Chronic Diseases*, 1 (1955), 127–48

Pico della Mirandola, Giovanni, *Disputationes adversus Astrologiam Divinatricem* (1496), ed. E. Garin, Florence, 1946–52

Pinching, A.J., McManus, T.J., Jeffries, D.J., Moshtael, O., Donaghy, M., Parkin, J.M., Munday, P.E. and Harris, J.R., 'Studies of Cellular Immunity in Male Homosexuals in London', *Lancet*, 2 (16 July 1983), 126–30

——, Weber, J.N., Rogers, L.A., Berrie, E.L., Jeffries, D.J. and Harris, J.R., 'Longitudinal Immunological Studies on a Cohort of Initially Symptom-free Homosexual Men in London with respect to HTLV-III Serology', *Advances in Experimental Medicine and Biology*, 187 (1985), 67–72

Pintor, Petrus, *Tractatus de Morbo Foedo et Occulto his Temporibus Affligente*, Rome, Eucharius Silber, 1500

Pliny the Elder (Gaius Plinius Secundus), *Natural History: A Selection*, tr. John F. Healy, Harmondsworth, Penguin, 1991

Pope, Alexander, *Alexander Pope: A Critical Edition of the Major Works*, ed. P. Rogers, Oxford, Oxford University Press, 1993

Portoveneri, Giovanni, 'Memoriale di Giovanni Portoveneri dall' anno 1494 sino al 1502', ed. F. Bonaini, in *Archivo storico italiano*, ser. 1, 6/12 (1845), 337–8

Public Health Laboratory Service, Department of Health, Social Services and Public Security, and the Scottish Information and Statistics Division, *Sexually Transmitted Infections in the UK: New Episodes Seen at Genitourinary Medicine Clinics, 1995–2000*, London, Public Health Laboratory Service, 2001

Rabelais, François, *The Histories of Gargantua and Pantagruel*, tr. J.M. Cohen, Harmondsworth, Penguin, 1955

Ratcliffe, T.A., 'Psychiatric and Allied Aspects of the Problem of Venereal Disease in the Army', *Journal of Royal Army Medical Corps*, 89 (1947), 122–31

Ricord, Philippe, *Traité pratique des maladies veneriennes*, Paris, De Just Rouvier, 1838

——, *Lettres sur la Syphilis: Adressées à M. Le Redacteur en Chef de l'Union Médicale*, Paris, Bureau del'Union Médicale, 1851

Rivers, Eunice, Schuman, Stanley H., Simpson, Lloyd and Olansky, Stanley, 'The Twenty Years of Follow-up Experience in a Long-Range Medical Study', *Public Health Reports*, 68 (1953), 391–5

Rockwell, D.H., Yobs, A.R. and Moore, M.B., 'The Tuskegee Study of Untreated Syphilis: The 30th Year of Observation', *Archives of Internal Medicine*, 114 (1961), 792–8

Rogers, Blair O., 'A Chronological History of Cosmetic Surgery', *Bulletin of the New York Academy of Medicine*, 47 (1971), 265–302

Rollet, Joseph, 'Études cliniques sur la chancre produit par la contagion de syphilis secondaire, et spécialement sur la chancre de mamelon et de la bouche', *Archives générales de médecine*, 13 (1859), 129–44, 306–22, 397–417

Rousseau, Jean-Jacques, *Émile*, tr. Barbara Foxley, London, J.M. Dent, 1911

Sanudo, Marin, *I Diarii*, ed. R. Fulin, Venice, F. Visentino, 1879–1902

Schaudinn, Fritz R. and Hoffmann, Paul Erich, 'Vorläufiger Bericht über das Verkommen von Spirochaeten in Syphilischen Krankheitsprodukten und bei Papillomen', *Arbeiten aus dem Kaiserlichen Gesundheitsamte*, 22/2 (1905), 527–600

Schellig, Karl, *In Pustulas Malus Morbum quem Malum de Francia Vulgus Appelat que sunt de Genere Fornicarum*, Heidelberg, Friedrich Misch, 1495–6

Schofield, C.B.S., *Sexually Transmitted Diseases*, Edinburgh, Churchill Livingstone, 1975

Schuman, S., Olansky, S., Rivers, E., Smith, C.A. and Rambo, D.S., 'Untreated Syphilis in the Male Negro: Background and Current Status of Patients in the Tuskegee Study', *Journal of Chronic Diseases*, 1 (1955), 543–58

Shafer, J.K., Usilton, L.J. and Gleeson, G.A., 'Untreated Syphilis in the Male Negro: A Prospective Study of the Effect on Life Expectancy', *Public Health Reports*, 69 (1954), 691–7

Silvestro, Tommaso di, 'Diario di Ser Tommaso di Silvestro', ed. L. Fumi, in *Rerum Italicarum Scriptores*, Bologna, Città di Castello e Bologna, 15/5 (1925)

Snow, William F., 'Syphilis and Federal Assistance to the States', *Journal of Social Hygiene*, 24 (1938), 417–21

Stokes, J.H., Sternberg, T.H., Schwartz, W.H., Mahoney, J.F., Moore, J.E. and Wood, W.B., 'The Action of Penicillin in Late Syphilis, Including Neurosyphilis, Benign Late Syphilis and Congenital Syphilis: Preliminary Report', *Journal of the American Medical Association*, 126/2 (1944), 73–8

Stoker, Bram, *Dracula*, Ware, Wordsworth Editions, 1993

Sydenham, Thomas, *The Whole Works of that Most Excellent Practical Physician Dr Thomas Sydenham*, 9th edn, tr. John Pechey, London, J. Darby, 1729

Tissot, S.A.A.D., *Onanism or A Treatise upon the Disorders Produced by Masturbation*, London, J. Pridden, 1756

Torella, Gaspar, *Tractatus cum Consiliis contra Pudendagram seu Morbum Gallicum*, Rome, Petrus de Turre, 1497

——, *Dialogus de Dolore cum Tractatu de Ulceribus in Pudendagra Evenire Solitis*, Rome, Giovanni Besicken and Martino d'Amsterdam, 1500

Trye, Charles Brandon, *A Review of Jesse Foote's Observations on the New Opinions of John Hunter, in His Late Treatise on the Venereal Disease*, London, John Murray, 1787

Turner, Daniel, *Syphilis: A Practical Dissertation on the Venereal Disease*, London, J. Walthoe, 1727

Turner, E.B., 'The History of the Fight against Venereal Disease', *Science Progress*, 21 (1916), 83–8

Turow, Scott, *The Burden of Proof*, London, Bloomsbury Publishing, 1990

Vasari, Giorgio, *Lives of the Painters, Sculptors and Architects*, London, Everyman, 1996

Villalobos, Francisco Lopez de, *Summario de la Medicina en Romance Trovado Con Un Tratado Sobre Las Pestiferas Bubas*, Salamanca, Antonio Barreda, 1498

Voltaire, François Marie Arouet de, *Candide*, Oxford, Oxford University Press, 1968

Vonderlehr, R.A., Clark, T., Wenger, O.C. and Heller, J.R., 'Untreated Syphilis in the Male Negro: A Comparative Study of Treated and Untreated Cases', *Journal of American Medical Association*, 107 (1936), 856–60

——, Clark, T., Wenger, O.C. and Heller, J.R., 'Untreated Syphilis in the Male Negro: A Comparative Study of Treated and Untreated Cases', *Venereal Disease Information*, 17 (1936), 260–5

Wagner vonn Jauregg, Julius, 'The Treatment of General Paresis by Inoculation of Malaria', *Journal of Nervous and Mental Diseases*, 55 (1922), 369–75

——, 'The History of Malarial Treatment of Paretic Neurosyphilis', *American Journal of Psychiatry*, 102 (1946), 577–82

Walker, George, *Venereal Disease in the American Expeditionary Forces*, Baltimore, Medical Standard Books, 1922

Wassermann, August von, Neisser, Albert, Bruck, Karl and Schucht, A., 'Weitere Mittelungen über den Nachweis spezifischer luetischer Substanzen durch Komplementbindung', *Zeitschrift für Hygiene und Infektionskrankheiten*, 55 (1906), 451–70

Watts, G.O. and Wilson, R.A., 'A Study of Personality Factors among Venereal Disease Patients', *Canadian Medical Association Journal*, 53 (1945), 119–22

Waugh, M., 'Studies on the Recent Early Epidemiology of Early Syphilis in West London', *British Journal of Venereal Diseases*, 48 (1972), 538

Wells, B.P.W. and Schofield, C.B.S., '"Target" Sites for Anti-VD Propaganda', *Health Bulletin*, 28/1 (1970), 76

Wenger, O.C. and Ricks, H.C., 'The Public Health Aspect of Syphilis in the Negro Race in Certain Southern States', *Southern Medical Journal*, 24 (1931), 556–61

Willcox, R.R., 'Immigration and Venereal Disease in England and Wales', *British Journal of Venereal Diseases*, 46 (1970), 412–21

——, 'By No Means the Last Word', *St Mary's Hospital Gazette*, 77/7 (1971), 20–1

Wilcox, W.H. and Webster, J., 'The Toxicology of Salvarsan: Dioxydiamido-Arseno-Benzol (Salvarsan or Kharsivan)', *British Medical Journal*, 1 April 1916, offprint in St Mary's Hospital Archives, DP 42/15/20

Wilde, Oscar, *The Picture of Dorian Gray*, in *Complete Works of Oscar Wilde*, London, Collins, 1966, pp. 17–167

Wingfield, A.S., 'Twenty Seven Years of Uninterrupted Contact Tracing: The Tyneside Scheme', *British Journal of Venereal Diseases*, 48 (1972), 37–50

Witkower, E.D., 'The Psychological Aspects of Venereal Disease', *British Journal of Venereal Diseases*, 24 (1948), 59–67

Wycherley, William, *The Country Wife*, in Robert G. Lawrence, ed., *Restoration Plays*, London, J.M. Dent, 1992, pp. 11–104

Zambotti, Bernardino, 'Diario Ferrase dall' anno 1476 sino al 1504', ed. G. Pardi, in *Rerum Italicarum Scriptores*, Bologna, Città di Castello e Bologna, 24/7, 1934–7

SECONDARY PUBLISHED SOURCES

Adler, M.W., 'The Terrible Peril: A Historical Perspective on the Venereal Diseases', *British Medical Journal*, 281 (1980), 206–11

Allen, Peter Lewis, *The Wages of Sin: Sex and Disease, Past and Present*, Chicago, University of Chicago Press, 2000

Arber, A., *Herbals, their Origin and Evolution: A Chapter in the History of Botany*, Cambridge, Cambridge University Press, 1953

Arrizabalaga, Jon, Henderson, John and French, Roger, *The Great Pox: The French Disease in Renaissance Europe*, New Haven, Yale University Press, 1997

Arya, O.P.A. and Hart, C.A. (eds), *Sexually Transmitted Infections and AIDS in the Tropics*, New York, CAB Publishing, 1998

Bachrach, Susan D. (ed.), *Deadly Medicine: Creating the Master Race*, Washington DC, United States National Holocaust Museum, 2004

Baldwin, Peter, *Contagion and the State in Europe, 1830–1930*, Cambridge, Cambridge University Press, 1999

Barlow, D., '*Neisseria gonorrhoea*' in J.G.G. Ledingham and David A. Warrell (eds), *Oxford Concise Textbook of Medicine*, Oxford, Oxford University Press, 2000, pp. 1599–602

Baumler, Ernst, *Paul Ehrlich: Scientist for Life*, New York, Holmes and Meier, 1984

Beardsley, Edward H., 'Allied against Sin: American and British Responses to Venereal Disease in World War I', *Medical History*, 20 (1976), 189–202

Bell, Herbert, 'Gonorrhoea in Italy', *Journal of the Royal Army Medical Corps*, 84 (1945), 21–6

Berridge, Virginia, *AIDS in the UK: The Making of Policy, 1981–1994*, Oxford, Oxford University Press, 1996

Bettley, J., 'Post Voluptatem Misericordia: The Rise and Fall of the London Lock Hospitals', *London Journal*, 10/2 (1984), 167–75

Black, Jeremy, *Italy and the Grand Tour*, New Haven, Yale University Press, 2003

Bolton, Roy, *A Brief History of Painting, 2000 BC to AD 2000*, London, Robinson, 2004

Bourke, Joanna, *Dismembering the Male: Men's Bodies, Britain and the Great War*, London, Reaktion Books, 1996

Brandt, Allan M., *No Magic Bullet: A Social History of Venereal Disease in the United States since 1880*, Oxford, Oxford University Press, 1987

Brock, Thomas D. (ed.), *Milestones in Microbiology, 1546–1940*, Washington DC, American Society for Microbiology, 1999

Brown, Kevin, *Penicillin Man: Alexander Fleming and the Antibiotic Revolution*, Stroud, Sutton, 2004

——, 'The History of Penicillin from Discovery to the Drive to Production', *Pharmaceutical Historian*, 34/3 (2004), 37–43

Brown, Ted, 'Sheathed in History', *Nursing Standard*, 13/5 (1998), 26–7

Burckhardt, Jacob, *Civilization of the Renaissance in Italy*, tr. S.G.C. Middlemore, Harmondsworth, Penguin, 1990

Carmichael, A.G., 'Syphilis and the Columban Exchange: Was the New Disease really New?', in M.G. Maques and J. Cules (eds), *The Great Maritime Discoveries and World Health*, Lisbon International Congress on the Great Maritime Discoveries and World Health, 1991, 187–90

Cartwright, Frederick, *A Social History of Medicine*, Harlow, Longman, 1977

—— and Biddiss, Michael, *Disease and History*, 2nd edition, Stroud, Sutton, 2004

Cassel, Jay, *Secret Plague: Venereal Disease in Canada, 1838–1939*, Toronto, University of Toronto Press, 1987

Castejón-Bolea, Ramón, 'Doctors, Social Medicine and VD in Late-Nineteenth-Century and Early Twentieth-Century Spain', in Roger Davidson and Lesley A. Hall (eds), *Sex, Sin and Suffering: Venereal Disease and European Society Since 1870*, London, Routledge, 2001, pp. 61–75

Clarke-Kennedy, A.E., *London Pride: The Story of a Voluntary Hospital*, London, Hutchinson Benham, 1979

Colebrook, Leonard, 'Gerhard Domagk, 1895–1964', *Biographical Memoirs of Fellows of the Royal Society*, London, Royal Society, 1964, vol. 10, p. 39

Comrie, J.D., *History of Scottish Medicine*, London, Wellcome Historical Museum, 1932

Conway, J.F., 'Syphilis and Bronzino's London Allegory', *Journal of the Warburg and Courtauld Institutes*, 45 (1986), 250–5

Cooter, Roger, Harrison, Mark and Sturdy, Steve (eds), *War, Medicine and Modernity*, Stroud, Sutton Publishing, 1998

—— —— ——, *Medicine and Modern Warfare*, Amsterdam, Rodopi Press, 1999

Corbin, Alain, *Women for Hire: Prostitution and Sexuality in France after 1850*, Cambridge, Mass., Harvard University Press, 1990

Costello, John, *Love, Sex and War, 1939–1945*, London, Pan, 1986

Couzens, Tim, *Hand of Fate: The History of the Longs, Wellesleys and Draycott Estate in Wiltshire*, Bradford on Avon, ELSP, 2001

Crosby, A.W., *The Columban Exchange: Biological and Cultural Consequences of 1492*, Westport, Conn., Greenwood Press, 1972

Cummins, J.S., 'Pox and Paranoia in Renaissance Europe', *History Today*, 38 (August 1988), 28–35

Darby, Robert, 'Where Doctors Differ: The Debate on Circumcision as a Protection against Syphilis, 1855–1914', *Social History of Medicine*, 16/1 (2003), 57–78

Davidson, Roger, '"A Scourge to be Firmly Gripped": the Campaign for VD Controls in Interwar Scotland', *Social History of Medicine*, 6/2 (1993), 213–35

——, '"Searching for Mary, Glasgow": Contact Tracing for Sexually Transmitted Diseases in Twentieth-Century Scotland', *Social History of Medicine*, 9/2 (1996), 195–214

——, *Dangerous Liaisons: A Social History of Venereal Disease in Scotland*, Amsterdam and Atlanta, Rodopi, 2000

—— and Hall, Lesley (eds), *Sex, Sin and Suffering: Venereal Disease and European Society since 1870*, London, Routledge, 2001

Debus, A.G., *The Chemical Philosophy: Paracelsian Science and Medicine in the Sixteenth and Seventeenth Centuries*, New York, 1977

Del Negro, Piero (ed.), *The University of Padua: Eight Centuries of History*, Padua, Signum Padova Editrice, 2001

Dracobly, Alex, 'Ethics and Experimentation on Human Subjects in Mid-Nineteenth-Century France: the Story of the 1859 Syphilis Experiments', *Bulletin of the History of Medicine*, 77/2 (2003), 332–66

Düring, Monika von, Didi-Huberman, Georges and Poggessi, Marta, *Encyclopaedia Anatomica: A Complete Collection of Anatomical Waxes*, Cologne, Taschen, 2004

Edwards, Tim, *Men in the Mirror: Men's Fashion, Masculinity and Consumer Society*, London, Cassell, 1997

Evans, David, 'Tackling the "Hideous Scourge": The Creation of the Venereal Disease Treatment Centres in Early Twentieth Century Britain', *Social History of Medicine*, 5/3 (1992), 413–33

——, 'Sexually Transmitted Disease Policy in the English National Health Service, 1948–2000: Continuity and Change' in Roger Davidson and Lesley A. Hall (eds), *Sex, Sin and Suffering: Venereal Disease and European Society Since 1870*, London, Routledge, 2001, pp. 237–52

Fabricius, Johannes, *Syphilis in Shakespeare's England*, London, Jessica Kingsley Publishers, 1994

Farmer, Paul, 'Pestilence and Restraint: Haitians, Guantanamo, and the Logic of Quarantine', in C. Hannaway, V.A. Arden and J. Parascandola (eds), *AIDS and the Public Debate: Historical and Contemporary Perspectives*, Amsterdam, IOS Press, 1995, pp. 139–52

Fisher, Trevor, *Prostitution and the Victorians*, Stroud, Sutton Publishing, 1997

Flem, Lydia, *Casanova or the Art of Happiness*, tr. Catherine Temerson, Harmondsworth, Allen Lane, 1998

Foster, R.F., *Lord Randolph Churchill: A Political Life*, Oxford, Oxford University Press, 1981

Foster, W.D., *A Short History of Clinical Pathology*, Edinburgh, Livingstone, 1961

Freund, Michaela, 'Women, Venereal Disease and the Control of Female Sexuality in Post-War Hamburg', in Roger Davidson and Lesley Hall (eds), *Sex, Sin and Suffering: Venereal Disease and European Society Since 1870*, London, Routledge, 2001, pp. 205–19

Gamble, Vanessa Northington, 'Under the Shadow of Tuskegee: African Americans and Health Care', *American Journal of Public Health*, 87/11 (1997), 1773–8

Gentilcore, David, *Healers and Healing in Early Modern Italy*, Manchester, Manchester University Press, 1998

Gilman, Sander L., *Health and Illness: Images of Difference*, London, Reaktion Books, 1995

Gittings, Robert, *John Keats*, London, Heinemann, 1968

Goldsworthy, Cephas, *The Satyr: An Account of the Life and Work, Death and Salvation of John Wilmot, Second Earl of Rochester*, London, Weidenfeld & Nicolson, 2001

Grmek, Mirko D., *History of AIDS: Emergence and Origin of a Modern Pandemic*, Princeton, Princeton University Press, 1990

Guerra, Francisco, 'Maya Medicine', *Medical History*, 8/1 (1964), 31–43

——, 'Aztec Medicine', *Medical History*, 10/4 (1966), 315–38

Hackett, C.J., 'On the Origin of the Human Treponematosis', *Bulletin of the World Health Organisation*, 29 (1963), 7–41

Hale, John, *Civilization of Europe in the Renaissance*, London, HarperCollins, 1993

Halioua, Bruno and Ziskind, Bernard, *Medicine in the Days of the Pharaohs*, Cambridge, Mass., Belknap Press, 2005

Hall, Lesley, *Hidden Anxieties: Male Sexuality 1900–1950*, Cambridge, Polity Press, 1991

——, 'War Always Brings It On: War, STDs and the Civilian Population in Britain 1850–1950', in Roger Cooter, Mark Harrison and Steve Sturdy (eds), *Medicine and Modern Warfare*, Amsterdam, Rodopi Press, 1999, pp. 205–23

Hannaway, C., Arden, V.A. and Parascandola, J. (eds), *AIDS and the Public Debate: Historical and Contemporary Perspectives*, Amsterdam, IOS Press, 1995

Harrison, Mark, 'The British Army and the Problem of Venereal Disease in France and Egypt during the First World War', *Medical History*, 39 (1995), 133–58

——, 'Sex and the Citizen Soldier: Health, Morals and Discipline in the British Army during the Second World War', in Roger Cooter, Mark Harrison and Steve Sturdy (eds), *Medicine and Modern Warfare*, Amsterdam, Rodopi Press, 1999, pp. 225–50

——, *Disease and the Modern World*, Cambridge, Polity Press, 2004

——, *Medicine and Victory: British Military Medicine in the Second World War*, Oxford, Oxford University Press, 2005

Harvey, John, *Men in Black*, London, Reaktion Books, 1995

Hatcher, John, *Founders of Medical Laboratory Science*, London, Institute of Laboratory Medical Sciences, 1978

Hayden, Deborah, *Pox: Genius, Madness and the Mysteries of Syphilis*, New York, Basic Books, 2003

Heineman, Elizabeth, 'The Hour of the Woman: Memories of Germany's "Crisis Years" and West German National Identity', *American Historical Review*, 101 (1996), 354–95

Hill, C.R. and Drey, R.E.A., *Drug Jars*, Oxford, Museum of the History of Science, 1980

Hobby, Gladys L., *Penicillin: Meeting the Challenge*, New Haven, Yale University Press, 1985

Hollingsworth, Mary, *The Cardinal's Hat*, London, Profile, 2004

Honeybourne, M.B., 'The Leper Hospitals of the London area', *Transactions of the London and Middlesex Archaeological Society*, 21/1 (1963), 3–61

Howie, J., 'Gonorrhoea: A Question of Tactics', *British Medical Journal*, 2 (1979), 1631

Hudson, E.H., *Non-Venereal Syphilis*, Edinburgh, Livingstone, 1958

Hughes, Kathryn, *The Short Life and Long Times of Mrs Beeton*, London, Fourth Estate, 2005

Hunter, Irvine J., 'Syphilis in the Illness of John Hunter', *Journal of the History of Medicine and Allied Sciences*, 8 (1953), 249–62

Hutcheon, Linda and Michael, *Opera: Desire, Disease, Death*, Lincoln, University of Nebraska Press, 1996

Jones, James H., *Bad Blood: The Tuskegee Syphilis Experiment*, 2nd. edn, New York, Free Press, 1993

Jütte, R., 'Syphilis and Confinement in Early Modern German Hospitals for Syphilitics', in N. Finizsch and R. Jütte (eds), *The Prerogative of Confinement*, Cambridge, Cambridge University Press, 1995

Keersmaekers, K. and Meheus, A., 'Epidemiology of Sexually Transmitted Infections and AIDS in Developing Countries', in O.P.A. Arya and C.A. Hart (eds), *Sexually Transmitted Infections and AIDS in the Tropics*, New York, CAB Publishing, 1998, pp. 3–30

Kelly, Michael, 'Swediaur: The Vicious Anti-Hunterian Rheumatovenerologist', *Medical History*, 11 (1967), 170–4

Kidwell, Carol, *Pietro Bembo: Lover, Linguist, Cardinal*, Montreal and Kingston, McGill-Queen's University Press, 2004

Kipple, Kenneth F., *The Cambridge Historical Dictionary of Disease*, Cambridge, Cambridge University Press, 2003

Lamont-Brown, Raymond, *Royal Poxes and Potions: the Lives of Court Physicians, Surgeons and Apothecaries*, Stroud, Sutton, 2001

Lanza, Benedetto, Pucetti, Maria Luisa, Poggessi, Marta and Martelli, Antonio, *Le Cere Anatomiche della Specola*, Firenze, Arnaud, 1997

Ledingham, J.G.G. and Warrell, David A. (eds),*Oxford Concise Textbook of Medicine*, Oxford, Oxford University Press, 2000

Levine, Philippa, 'Venereal Disease, Prostitution and the Politics of Empire: the Case of British India', *Journal of the History of Sexuality*, 4 (1994), 579–602

Levine, Philippa, *Prostitution, Race and Politics: Policing Venereal Disease in the British Empire*, New York and London, Routledge, 2003

Liebenau, Jonathan, 'Paul Ehrlich as a Commercial Scientist and Research Administrator', *Medical History*, 34 (1990), 65–78

Liggins, Emma, 'Writing against the "Husband-Fiend": Syphilis and Male Sexual Vice in the New Woman Novel', *Women's Writing*, 7/2 (2000), 175–95

Lindemann, Mary, *Medicine and Society in Early Modern Europe*, Cambridge, Cambridge University Press, 1999

Longden, Sean, *To the Victor the Spoils: D-Day to VE Day, the Reality behind the Heroism*, Moreton-in-Marsh, Arris Books, 2004

Lord, Alexandra M., '"Naturally Clean and Wholesome": Women, Sex Education and the United States Public Health Service, 1918–1928', *Social History of Medicine*, 17/3 (2004), 423–41

MacCarthy, Fiona, *Byron: Life and Legend*, London, John Murray, 2002

MacCulloch, Diarmid, *Reformation: Europe's House Divided, 1490–1700*, Harmondsworth, Penguin, 2003

MacFarlane, Gwyn, *Howard Florey: The Making of a Great Scientist*, Oxford, Oxford University Press, 1979

McHugh, Paul, *Prostitution and Victorian Social Reform*, London, Croom Helm, 1980

McNalty, A.S., *Henry VIII, a Difficult Patient*, London, C. Johnson, 1952

MacPherson, William (ed.), *History of the Great War Based on Official Documents: Medical Services*, vol. 2, London, HMSO, 1923

Maehle, Andreas-Holger, 'Protecting Patient Privacy or Serving Public Interests? Challenges to Medical Confidentiality in Imperial Germany', *Social History of Medicine*, 16/3 (2003), 383–401

Manchester, Keith, *The Archaeology of Disease*, Bradford, Bradford University Press, 1982

Marquardt, Martha, *Paul Ehrlich*, London, Heinemann, 1949

Marques, M.G. and Cules, J. (eds), *The Great Maritime Discoveries and World Health*, Lisbon, 1991

Martin, Peter, *Life of James Boswell*, London, Weidenfeld & Nicolson, 1999

Mazumdar, Pauline M.H., '"In the Silence of the Laboratory": The League of Nations Standardizes Syphilis Tests', *Social History of Medicine*, 16/3 (2003), 437–59

Mellor, W. Franklin (ed.), *Casualties and Medical Statistics: History of the Second World War: United Kingdom Medical Services*, London, HMSO, 1972

Merians, Linda E., *The Secret Malady: Venereal Diseases in Eighteenth-Century Britain and France*, Lexington, University of Kentucky Press, 1996

Miller, Hugh, *Secrets of the Dead*, London, Macmillan, 2000

Mörgeli, Christoph, *The Museum of the History of Medicine of the University of Zurich*, Zurich, Institute of the History of Medicine, 1994

Bibliography

Moore, Lucy (ed.), *Con Men and Cutpurses: Scenes from the Hogarthian Underworld*, London, Penguin, 2001

Moore, Wendy, *The Knife Man: The Extraordinary Life and Times of John Hunter, Father of Modern Surgery*, London, Bantam Press, 2005

Moroni, Paolo, 'Origins and Development of Bologna's Dermatological School', *Acta Dermatovenerologica Alpina, Pannonica et Edriatica*, 10/2 (2001), 1–7

Morton, R.S., 'Some Early Aspects of Syphilis in Scotland', *British Journal of Venereal Diseases*, 38 (1962), 175–80

——, *Venereal Diseases*, Harmondsworth, Penguin, 1974

—— and Raschid, S., 'The Syphilis Enigma: The Riddle Resolved?', *Sexually Transmitted Infections*, 77 (2001), 322–4

Munger, Robert S., 'Guaiacum, the Holy Tree from the New World', *Journal of the History of Medicine*, 4 (1949), 202

Murat, Laure, *La Maison du Docteur Blanche*, Paris, J.C. Lattès, 2001

Neushul, Peter, 'Fighting Research: Army Participation in the Clinical Testing and Mass Production of Penicillin during the Second World War', in Roger Cooter, Mark Harrison and Steve Sturdy (eds), *War, Medicine and Modernity*, Stroud, Sutton Publishing, 1998, pp. 203–24

Ongaro, Giuseppe, 'Medicine', in Piero Del Negro (ed.), *The University of Padua: Eight Centuries of History*, Padua, Signum Padova Editrice, 2001, pp. 162–3

Opie, Iona and Peter (eds), *The Oxford Dictionary of Nursery Rhymes*, Oxford, Oxford University Press, 1997

Orme, N., 'The Reformation and the Red Light', *History Today*, 37 (March 1987), 36–41

Pagnel, Walter, *Paracelsus: An Introduction to Philosophical Medicine in the Era of the Renaissance*, Basle, S. Karger, 1958

Parascandola, John, 'VD at the Movies: PHS Films of the 1930s and 1940s', *Public Health Reports*, 111/2 (1996), 173–5

——, 'John Mahoney and the Introduction of Penicillin to Treat Syphilis', *Pharmacy in History*, 43/1 (2001), 3–13

Patterson, James T., *Grand Expectations: The United States, 1945–1974*, New York, Oxford University Press, 1996

Paul, Christa, *Zwangs Prostitution: Staatlich Errichte Bordelle im Nationalsozialismus*, Berlin, Hentrich, 1994

Peakman, Julie, *Lascivious Bodies: A Sexual History of the Eighteenth Century*, London, Atlantic Books, 2004

Peel, J., 'The Manufacture and Retailing of Contraceptives in England', *Population Studies* (1963), 122

Pelling, Margaret, 'Appearance and Reality: Barber-Surgeons, the Body and Venereal Disease in Early Modern London', in A.L. Beier and R. Finlay (eds), *The Making of the Modern Metropolis: London 1500–1700*, London, Longman, 1986, pp. 82–112

Bibliography

Perine, P.L., 'Non-Venereal Endemic Treponematoses: Yaws, Endemic Syphilis (Bejel) and Pinta', in J.G.G. Ledingham and David A. Warrell (eds), *Oxford Concise Textbook of Medicine*, Oxford, Oxford University Press, 2000, pp. 1677–80.

Pichois, Claude and Ziegler, Jean, *Baudelaire*, London, Vintage, 1991

Platts, Margaret M., 'Some Medical Syndromes Encountered in Nineteenth-Century French Literature', *Journal of Medical Ethics*, 27 (2001), 82–8

Poirier, Suzanne, *Chicago's War on Syphilis 1937–1940: The Times, the Trib and the Clap Doctor*, Chicago, University of Illinois Press, 1995

Pomata, Gianna, *Contracting a Cure: Patients, Healers and the Law in Early Modern Bologna*, Baltimore, Johns Hopkins University Press, 1998

Pomeroy, Ralph E., 'Michael M. Davis and the Development of the Health Movement, 1900–28', *Societas*, 2 (1972), 27–41

Porter, Roy, *The Greatest Benefit to Mankind: A Medical History of Humanity from Antiquity to the Present*, London, Harper Collins, 1997

——, *Bodies Politic, Disease, Death and Doctors in Britain, 1650–1900*, London, Reaktion Books, 2001

——, *Quacks: Fakers and Charlatans in Medicine*, Stroud, Tempus, 2003

—— and Hall, Lesley, *The Facts of Life: The Creation of Sexual Knowledge in Britain, 1650–1950*, New Haven, Yale University Press, 1995

Post, J.B., 'A Foreign Office Survey of Venereal Disease and Prostitution Control, 1869–70', *Medical History*, 22 (1978), 327–34

Pötzsch, Regine (ed.), *The Pharmacy: Windows on History*, Basel, Editiones Roche, 1996

Pressel, David M., 'Nuremberg and Tuskegee: Lessons for Contemporary American Medicine', *Journal of the National Medical Association*, 95/12 (2003), 1216–25

Prideaux, Sue, *Edvard Munch: Behind the Scream*, New Haven, Yale University Press, 2005

Prüll, Cay-Rüdiger, 'Part of a Scientific Master Plan? Paul Ehrlich and the Origins of his Receptor Concept', *Medical History*, 47 (2003), 332–56

Purdie, D.W. and Gow, N., 'The Maladies of James Boswell, Advocate', *Journal of the Royal College of Physicians of Edinburgh*, 32 (2002), 197–202

Qualtiere, Louis F. and Slights, William W.E., 'Contagion and Blame in Early Modern England: The Case of the French Pox', *Literature and Medicine*, 22/1 (2003), 1–24

Quétel, Claude, *History of Syphilis*, tr. Judith Braddock and Brian Pike, London, Polity Press, 1990

Qvist, George, 'John Hunter's Alleged Syphilis', *Annals of The Royal College of Surgeons of England*, 59 (1977), 205–9

Redford, Bruce, *Venice and the Grand Tour*, New Haven, Yale University Press, 1996

Reverby, Susan M., *Tuskegee's Truths: Rethinking the Tuskegee Syphilis Study*, Chapel Hill, University of North Carolina Press, 2000

Bibliography

Richardson, Harriet (ed.), *English Hospitals 1660–1948: A Survey of their Architecture and Design*, Swindon, Royal Commission on the Historical Monuments of England, 1998

Rivett, Geoffrey, *From Cradle to Grave: Fifty Years of the NHS*, London, King's Fund, 1998

Roberts, Charlotte and Cox, Margaret, *Health and Disease in Britain from Prehistory to the Present Day*, Stroud, Sutton Publishing, 2003

Rose, S., 'Girls and GIs: Sex and Diplomacy in Second World War Britain', *International History Review*, 46 (1997), 146–60

Russell, P.A., 'Syphilis: God's Scourge or Nature's Vengeance? The German Printed Response to a Public Problem in the Early Sixteenth-Century', *Archive for Reformation History*, 80 (1989), 286–307

Sauerteig, Lutz H.D., 'Sex, Medicine and Morality during the First World War', in Cooter Roger, Mark Harrison and Steve Sturdy (eds), *War, Medicine and Modernity*, Stroud, Sutton Publishing, 1998, pp. 167–88

——, '"The Fatherland is in Danger, Save the Fatherland": Venereal Disease, Sexuality and Gender in Imperial and Weimar Germany', in Roger Davidson and Lesley Hall (eds), *Sex, Sin and Suffering: Venereal Disease and European Society Since 1870*, London, Routledge, 2001, pp. 76–93

Scarisbrick, J.J., *Henry VIII*, London, Eyre and Spottiswoode, 1968

Schain, Richard, *The Legend of Nietzsche's Syphilis*, Westport, Conn., Greenwood Press, 2001

Scott, H.H., 'The Influence of the Slave Trade in the Spread of Tropical Diseases', *Transcripts of Royal Society of Tropical Medicine and Hygiene*, 38 (1943), 169

Searle, G.R., *The Quest for National Efficiency*, Oxford, Oxford University Press, 1971

——, *A New England? Peace and War, 1886–1918*, Oxford, Oxford University Press, 2004

Seiler-Baldinger, Annemarie, 'The Pharmacy of the Rain Forests', in Regine Pötzsch (ed.), *The Pharmacy: Windows on History*, Basel, Editiones Roche, 1996, pp. 45–59

Smith, F.B., 'Ethics and Disease in the Late-Nineteenth Century: The Contagious Diseases Acts', *Historical Studies*, 15 (1971), 118–35

——, *The People's Health, 1830–1910*, London, Weidenfeld & Nicolson, 1979

——, 'The Contagious Diseases Acts Reconsidered', *Social History of Medicine*, 3/2 (1990), 197–215

Smythe, Donald, 'Venereal Disease: The AEF's experience', *Prologue: Quarterly of the National Archives* (Summer 1993), 119–31

Stone, Lawrence, *The Family, Sex and Marriage in England, 1500–1800*, abridged edn, Harmondsworth, Penguin, 1978

Swarzenski, Georg, 'Un Quadro di Luca Giordano in Francoforte sul Meno', *Bolletino d'Arte* (July 1922), 17–21

Thomas, Hugh, *Rivers of Gold: The Rise of the Spanish Empire*, London, Phoenix, 2004

Thomson, Matthew, *The Problem of Mental Deficiency: Eugenics, Democracy and Social Policy in Britain, c. 1870–1959*, Oxford, Oxford University Press, 1998

Thomson, Richard, Cate, Philip Dennis and Chaplin, Mary Weaver, *Toulouse-Lautrec and Montmartre*, Washington, National Gallery of Art, 2005

Tomalin, Claire, *Samuel Pepys: The Unequalled Self*, London, Penguin, 2003

Tomkins, S.M., 'Palmitate or Permanganate: The Venereal Prophylaxis Debate in Britain, 1916–1926', *Medical History*, 37 (1993), 382–98

Tosti, A., *Storie all' Ombra del Malfrancese*, Palermo, 1992

Towers, Bridget, 'Health Education Policy, 1916–26: Venereal Disease and the Prophylaxis Dilemma', *Medical History*, 24 (1980), 70–87

Turner, E.B., 'The History of the Fight against Venereal Disease', *Science Progress*, 11 (1917), 83–8

Walkowitz, Judith R., *Prostitution and Victorian Society: Women, Class and the State*, Cambridge, Cambridge University Press, 1980

——, 'The Making of an Outcast Group: Prostitutes and Working Women in Nineteenth-Century Plymouth and Southampton', in Martha Vicinus (ed.), *A Widening Sphere: Changing Roles of Victorian Women*, London, Methuen, 1980, pp. 72–93

Walther, Ingo F., *Gauguin*, Cologne, Taschen, 2004

Wanrooij, Bruno P.F., 'The Thorns of Love: Sexuality, Syphilis and Social Control in Modern Italy', in Roger Davidson and Lesley Hall (eds), *Sex, Sin and Suffering: Venereal Disease and European Society Since 1870*, London, Routledge, 2001, pp. 137–59

Warboys, Michael, 'Unsexing Gonorrhoea: Bacteriologists, Gynaecologists and Suffragists in Britain, 1860–1920', *Social History of Medicine*, 17/1 (2004), 41–59

Watts, Sheldon, *Epidemics and History: Disease, Power and Imperialism*, New Haven, Yale University Press, 1997

Webster, Charles, 'Alchemical and Paracelsian Medicine', in Charles Webster (ed.), *Health, Medicine and Mortality*, Cambridge, Cambridge University Press, 1979, pp. 301–34

Weimerskirch, P.J., and Richter, G.W., 'Hunter and Venereal Disease', *The Lancet*, 1 (1979), 503–4

White, Robert M., 'Unravelling the Tuskegee Study of Untreated Syphilis', *Archives of Internal Medicine*, 160/5 (2000), 585–98

Willcox, Philip A., *The Detective Physician: The Life and Work of Sir William Willcox*, London, Heinemann, 1970

Williams, David Innes, *The London Lock: A Charitable Hospital for Venereal Disease 1746–1952*, London, Royal Society of Medicine Press, 1999

Williams, Trevor Illtyd, *Howard Florey: Penicillin and After*, Oxford, Oxford University Press, 1984

Wrebenwein, Renate, 'Luca Giordano: Kampf der Tugend gegen das Laster', in *Entdecklungen in Hessener Museen*, Frankfurt, Insel, 1985, pp. 218–21

Wright, D.J.M., 'John Hunter and Venereal Disease', *Annals of the Royal College of Surgeons of England*, 63 (1981), 198–202

—— and Conska, G.W., 'Syphilis', in J.G.G. Ledingham and David A. Warrell (eds), *Oxford Concise Textbook of Medicine*, Oxford, Oxford University Press, 2000, pp. 1680–6

Wyke, T.J., 'The Manchester and Salford Lock Hospital, 1818–1917', *Medical History*, 19 (1975), 73–86

Yanov, A., *The Origins of Autocracy: Ivan the Terrible in Russian History*, Berkeley, University of California Press, 1981

Zeldin, Theodore, *France 1848–1945: Ambition and Love*, Oxford, Oxford University Press, 1979

——, *France 1848–1945: Taste and Corruption*, Oxford, Oxford University Press, 1980

Ziegler, Philip, *King William IV*, London, Fontana, 1971

——, *London at War, 1939–1945*, London, Sinclair-Stevenson, 1995

Zimmermann, E.L., 'Was Fracastoro the First to Describe Alopecia Syphilitica?', *Janus*, 39 (1935), 105–26

Zivanovic, Srboljub, *Ancient Disease: The Elements of Palaeopathology*, tr. L.F. Edwards, London, Methuen, 1982

Index

button scurvy, 7
Buxtun, Peter, 159
Byron, Lord, 80–1

Cairns, Hugh, 185
calomel, 99, 129
Calvin, John, 11
Cambridge, Duke of, 64
Capone, Al, 166, 178
Capucin monks, 16
Caroline, Queen of
England, 51
Casanova, Giacomo, 50–1
Casella, 103, 106
Catherine of Aragon,
Queen of England, 32
Cattaneo, Jacopo, 11
Catullus, 27–8
Cavour, Camillo, 183
Cellini, Benvenuto, 23
Celtic humours, 51
Celtis, 12
Center for Disease Control,
Atlanta, 159
Chain, Ernst, 188
Chamberlain, Joseph, 74
Chamberlain, Neville, 168
Charles II, King of
England, 38–9
Charles V, Holy Roman
Emperor, 23, 28
Charles VIII, King of
France, 1–2, 9
Charles, John, 174, 192–3
chaud pisse, see
gonorrhoea
chemical affinity theory,
101–2
chemical prophylaxis,
129–30, 137
Chénier, André, 63
Cheselden, William, 86
Chesterfield, Lord, 46–7
Chicago Board of Health,
164
Chicago Daily News, 164
Chicago Laundry
Association, 164
Chicago Syphilis Control
Program, 162–6
Chicago Tribune, 163, 165
Chicago, University of, 164

Childers, H.C.E., 73
China smilax, *see* Root of
China
chlamydia, 204
Christ's Hospital, London,
18
Christian Disease, 10
Churchill, Randolph, 83
Churchill, Winston, 185–6,
188
cinchona bark, 35
City Match, 59
clap, *see* gonorrhoea
Clap, Mother, 49
clap clinics, 121–2, 135–6,
139–40
Clark, Taliaferro, 148–54,
165
Cleland, John, 48
Clement VII, pope, 23
Clinton, Bill, 141
Clinton, Henry Pelham, 47
Clowes, William, 17, 20–1
Colebrook, Leonard, 186
colonialism, 76–7
Columban exchange, 6–7,
21
Columbus, Christopher,
5–6, 7, 27, 55
Commission on Training
Camp Activities,
126–7
Company of Divine Love
(Genoa), 16
complement fixation test,
97
compound 606, *see*
salvarsan
condom, 36–7, 50, 51–2,
120, 177, 184,
199–201, 206–7
contacts tracing, 174–5
contagion, theory of, 25,
96
Contagious Diseases Acts,
64–75, 115, 117
Conti da Foligno,
Sigismondo, 9, 10
contraception, 199–201
Cook, James, 10
Cooperative Clinical
Group, 143, 151

Copernicus, 28
Cornaro family, 47
Costa, Lorenzo, 30
Cotta, Giovanni, 27–8
Country Wife, 39–40
Credé, Karl Sigmund, 97
Cumano, Marcello, 2
Cumming, Hugh S., 143,
150
Curry, Edwina, 206

Damaged Goods, 112–13
Darnley, Lord, 34
Darwin, Charles, 114
Daudet, Leon, 78
Davis, Michael M., 143
Dean, G., 53
Defence of Realm Act
(Regulation 33B),
173–4
Defence of Realm Act
(Regulation 40D),
132–5, 175
Defoe, Daniel, 48
Deidier, Antoine, 43
dermatology, 83, 139
Diaz de Isla, Ruy, 5
Dibble, Eugene H., 150,
154, 155
Dickens, Charles, 80
diet for syphilitics, 20–1
disinfection stations,
128–30, 175, 184
Dr Ehrlich's Magic Bullet,
170–1
Dr Kildare, 203
Domagk, Gerhard,
110–11
Donizetti, Gaetano, 81
Dorchester Venereal
Diseases Clinic, 136
Dracula, 77
Dreadnoughts, 199
Duncan, Andrew, 89
Dürer, Albrecht, 13
Durex, 199–200

Eagle, Harry, 188
Ebers papyrus, 8
Ecce Homo, 79
Edward VI, King of
England, 32

271